TINKERS AND GENIUS

BOOKS BY EDMUND FULLER

NOVELS	BROTHERS DIVIDED
	A STAR POINTED NORTH
NON-FICTION	TINKERS AND GENIUS, *the Story of the Yankee Inventors*
	VERMONT, A HISTORY *of the Green Mountain State*
	GEORGE BERNARD SHAW, *Critic of Western Morale*
	JOHN MILTON
	A PAGEANT OF THE THEATRE
COMPILATIONS	THESAURUS OF BOOK DIGESTS *(with Hiram Haydn)*
	MUTINY!

*

*

*

AMERICAN PROCESSION SERIES

*

HENRY G. ALSBERG

GENERAL EDITOR

*

*

*

*

TINKERS

AND GENIUS

THE STORY OF THE YANKEE INVENTORS

BY

EDMUND FULLER

HASTINGS HOUSE, PUBLISHERS, NEW YORK

ACKNOWLEDGMENTS

I wish to thank the Yale University Library for permission to quote at some length from the Eli Whitney Papers, in their manuscript collection, and for other facilities of that great library, and aid from its staff. I am indebted also to the New York Public Library. Thanks are due to the Kent School Library, and to its Librarian, Mr. John Park, for many helpful courtesies extended to me. I thank Mr. Charles K. Davis, and a number of museums and galleries, for permission to reproduce pictures as specifically acknowledged where they appear.

E. F.

Published simultaneously in Canada
by S. J. Reginald Saunders, Publishers,
Toronto 1

Library of Congress Catalog Card Number: 55–10952

Printed in the United States of America

DEDICATED TO

KENT SCHOOL,

IN THE FIFTIETH

YEAR OF ITS

SERVICE.

CONTENTS

PREFACE

EVERYBODY is prepared to swear that the Yankees were inventive—even fabulously so. Josh Billings said of them: "They are natural mechanics; the history of man's necessities is the history of their inventions." Emerson tells of a sea captain who contrasted the Yankee methods of ship-loading with the "main strength and ignorance" which were the stock-in-trade of European dockmen, saying, "Four truckmen and four stevedores at Long Wharf [Boston] will load my brig quicker than a hundred men at any port in the Mediterranean."

Mark Twain's Connecticut Yankee bragged the classic brag: "I could make anything a body wanted—anything in the world, it didn't make any difference what; and if there wasn't any quick new-fangled way to make a thing, I could invent one . . ."

All this verbal smoke rose from a genuine fire. Something special (though I won't quite say unique), something intensive, in the creative realm, with regional characteristics of its own, occurred with New England as its focus, in the latter part of the 18th and the first part of the 19th centuries.

The purpose of this book is to tell the story of this burgeoning of Yankee inventiveness, to tell it in terms of patterns of human action and experience. I have not forced the story into any rigid blueprint or thesis. It is *not* a history of invention, accepting the obligations that would be proper for such a work. I have included only what seemed to me sufficiently interesting and significant to represent the basic patterns without repeating the vast number of parallel cases that could be adduced for almost everything that is contained here. It is the tale of some inventive Yankees, especially but by no means exclusively, those of Connecticut. The Nutmeg State, with its particularly rich traditions, serves me as home base—not as a boundary.

The things these New Englanders did in mechanics, the things they invented and made, their own ways that they carried out with them in their migrations into the rest of the land, profoundly affected American history. I'm interested in why and how they did what they did. I have some notions about it, but won't claim much more than that. If a full set of answers exists—which I doubt—at any rate I haven't got it.

My attitude as to what inventions or inventors may be, is quite liberal. I take them as found. All the same, pursuit of definitions, and some theoretical considerations about invention, have a proper place here. I have stored such matters away as conclusions in the last chapter, to be read by all who are willing to bear with me into a relatively more abstract evaluation of the story told.

A student once asked me, "Why was Abraham Lincoln the kind of man he was?" I replied, "Happily, I can't answer that, nor can anybody else." Why happily? Because there are preserved here the twin mysteries of personality and creativity. While these remain mysteries—and I believe in the mercy of God they always will, in spite of the strivings of various determinists—man never can wholly regiment and remake man at his own whim, or control or limit his potential. What makes a Franklin, or a Whitney, or any such inventor, the man he is? Influences and factors galore will be seen and noted here, but the vital core of that question remains a gratifying mystery.

Edmund Fuller

Kent, Connecticut
March, 1955

CHAPTER 1

CAPTAIN NEMO IN CONNECTICUT

The ingenuity of these people is
singular in their secret modes of
mischief.
      —BRITISH NAVAL OFFICER

IN AUGUST of 1776, little more than a month after the
Declaration of Independence was signed, the British Fleet
lay in New York harbor. The city itself was still in possession of the Continentals, but Long Island had just been lost
and the enemy peered at the Battery from Governor's Island. General Washington had his headquarters in the
Kennedy house, at No. 1, Broadway, though he was not to
sleep there long, or tranquilly.

Under the protective darkness of an August night, off
Whitehall stairs at the tip of Manhattan Island, not far
from the General's Headquarters, a man named Ezra Lee,
a sergeant, embarked on a short, perilous voyage in one of
the strangest craft that had ever been seen.

Standing by were Generals Washington and Putnam,
some lesser officers, and the young Yale man, David Bushnell, who had conceived, designed, and built the contrivance, and named it the *American Turtle*. It was so-called
because its general shape was much like two turtle cara-
paces fastened together upright in a roughly ovoid form.
Sergeant Lee, departing from the other impressions, called
it a "clam." It was six feet from keel to top and about seven

1

and a half in length, counting the projections of propeller and rudder, but it was very narrow. Only one man could ride in it, having to lower himself gingerly through an opening in what today we would call its conning tower. The body was made of oak, iron-hooped and tar coated.

Once inside, Sergeant Lee was perched upon a little seat, surrounded by an array of controls. His craft lay awash, when in normal floating position, with just the glass-paned brass dome immediately over his head barely visible above the surface of the water. This lid screwed tight and was like a many-faceted bug's eye. Two panes of thick glass were in front of him, two on each side, one in the rear, and one directly overhead. The pilot could see out reasonably well, considering his low angle and the splash of water, and by daylight could get a dim, interior light even at quite a depth.

Lead ballast gave the vessel floating stability. If Lee wished to submerge, there was ready at his hand a lever which would admit added water ballast into a chamber beneath his feet, and another handle to pump out the water when he wished to rise. Coming up from behind, accessible to his left hand, was the stick of the rudder. Before him, for his right hand, was a crank, its shaft projecting out forward, through watertight packing, to the first screw propeller ever used. It was turned manually to pull, not push, the boat.

This was not the familiar two or three bladed propeller of modern usage, and there are some contradictions in the accounts of just what it was. Most versions, and the pictures, say it was a helix, a continuous screw-thread making three full turns around its axis at a sharp pitch. If so, it was an adaptation, to produce motion, of the spiral tube, or screw, devised by Archimedes to lift water. But Lee, reminiscing in old age, said the propellers consisted of paddles like the vanes of a windmill. Another such propeller pointed directly upward, beside the dome, to aid in submerging and rising, together with the manipulation of ballast.

On the *Turtle's* back was a kind of hump, clinging like a leech. It has often been described as an egg, made of wood and hooped with iron. Inside was a formidable charge of powder. The aim was for Sergeant Lee to maneuver the *Turtle* under the hull of one of the British warships, which lay near Staten Island. With an auger that rose beside the vertical propeller, he was to make a hole in the timbers. The auger had a detachable bit, or spike, to remain in the hull, with a cord leading to the bomb. The weapon could be released from within the *Turtle*. It would be anchored to the ship by its cord and automatically, upon being released, a twenty-minute time clock began to tick off seconds until the moment when a musket firing mechanism was set off, to explode the charge.

The intrepid Lee had a compass before his eyes, to help in navigation. But by dark of night in his little floating coffin there was no light. So a small bit of "foxwood" was fastened on the needle of the compass, and also on the gauge of the crude barometer which gave him his depth readings. This was the traditional "foxfire" of the forests, a luminescent wood fungus giving off a dim but steady glow. Bushnell had anticipated the luminous clock dial. Other than this faint aid, all operations had to depend on touch. It was a claustrophobe's nightmare.

For the pilot's breathing, the *Turtle* had primitive snorkel tubes curving up and over from its dome, and these were equipped with automatic float valves to seal them up at any time that they were under water.

What the brave sergeant was attempting, what General Washington and his fellow officers, and the anxious inventor were witnessing, was the beginning of the first attempt at submarine warfare. It was about eleven o'clock when the *Turtle*, with only its low dome faintly visible, began its wobbling course out into the black waters of the harbor, in tow to the rowboat that was to take it part way toward the fleet. There was nothing the spectators could do except to go away to await daylight and the hoped for events.

Now let us see what befell Sergeant Lee, after being cast off by his tow boat, which dared not accompany him too far. He did not enter the craft until just before his escort left him. As he got under way on his own, bad luck struck. A strong ebb-tide carried him far past the fleet. It took him two and a half hours of strenuous cranking to get back to the British ships near Staten Island. Still awash, in the dim pre-dawn light that was creeping upon the scene, he could see the forms of men on decks and hear their voices.

Using all his water screws and ballast controls, he worked his submarine beneath the hull of no less a target than the fleet's flagship, the mighty *Eagle,* of sixty-four guns, carrying Admiral Lord Howe, himself. What a chapter in history might have been written there, but for one of the classic frustrations that dog the inventive.

With all things going as planned, Lee began to fumble against the vast hull with his auger. He tried again and again, shifting position, re-attacking, but the auger would not take hold. He believed that the hull of the *Eagle* was copper sheathed, but the auger still should have been able to pierce it. The trouble was a matter of relative weight. The *Turtle* wasn't heavy enough. The pressure on the auger, instead of penetrating the hull, shoved the submarine away from the ship.

Lee made many anxious, fumbling efforts. He was aft on the *Eagle* and as he tried to work forward beneath her, groping for a more vulnerable spot, he miscalculated his ballast and slid up along the curve of the hull, popping out of the water like a cork.

To his dismay, it was now quite light, and he was a sitting duck. He had to give up the job and head for the Battery, submerged to avoid detection. His goal was four miles away but at least the tide, which had given him trouble before, had turned and was helping now.

But his troubles weren't over. Near Governor's Island his compass stuck. He had to surface, to see his way home. Hessians on the shores of Governor's Island caught sight of the strange, glass-paned, pipe-embellished dome bobbing past on its erratic course. They put out in a barge, thinking to investigate and perhaps harpoon this odd fish.

Lee saw them coming. The *Turtle* was like a fish in a

barrel, defensively. The sergeant did the only thing he could think of and released his time bomb, even though it would take twenty-minutes to go off. By Lee's account, he expected the *Turtle* to be taken, along with the torpedo, so that all would be blown up together, Kamikazelike. No military secret would escape. The Hessians saw the "egg," did not care for the looks of it, fearing a "Yankee trick" Lee said, and prudently went back to their island. The sergeant cranked along his weary way.

Currents carried the floating infernal machine into the mouth of the East River. General Putnam, looking on from Manhattan, and watchers on Governor's Island, alike, saw it explode with an impressive geyser. Lee was lucky that it had not drifted along with him.

When the *Turtle* was near enough to be sighted from Whitehall stairs, a skiff put out and towed him in. The inventor and General Washington again were present. Congratulations were in order, in spite of the failure. The Commander-in-Chief, who had helped to finance the craft, said to Jefferson, in later years, "I then thought and still think it was an effort of genius."

Indeed it was. History must agree. In the contexts both of the inventor's life and background, and of the prior state of experiments of such nature, it was an extraordinary plunge of spontaneous creativity.

Out of such creative ventures arose the well-grounded tradition of the inventive Yankee, the tinkerer, the mechanical wizard, the creator of "notions" across the whole scale from the pipe-dream of perpetual motion, to submarines, to wooden nutmegs. Bushnell is a Yankee of Yankees, he fits the pattern to perfection.

Many reasons are advanced as to why so many Yankees were inventive. Most of them are quite persuasive, and are sound so far as they go. The trouble is, if you add them all up, you still face an element of mystery about the why and whence of this inventive upsurge.

The land was stony and only in relatively rare places

was it ideal for farming. Farm implements had to be mended
often. Better ones had to be made to meet the needs. There
were long, isolated winters to be spent pondering and tinkering over such problems.

There were restrictive economic policies that the mother
country had imposed upon the colonies. These helped to
inspire the Yankee to use his own wits to meet his own
needs in defiance of England, in the realm of *things* as
much as in the realm of politics.

There was the fact that a good many of these Yankees—
though by no means all of them—were in New England
because they wanted to be—were there in pursuit of an
idea. Nothing stimulates the wit and creativity so much as
dedication to a guiding idea.

There are periodic springs of creativity in human history.
The Yankees experienced one of them. Necessity didn't
cause it, but it gave impetus and direction to it. History
shows us long periods of urgent necessity in human experience which no invention or creative idea arose to meet. It
also exhibits many cases of ideas or mechanical inventions
that lay still-born because there was no context of necessity
to welcome them. These had to be re-invented at some fit-
ting time.

The young patriot Bushnell was trying to meet a necessity—some means of coping with the overwhelming balance of sea power held by England. The colonists could
send no adequate ships of war against British fleets in the
harbors of Boston or New York. But how might it be, if
by cunning they could strike the proud ships mysteriously
from the depths of the very waters in which they floated
complacently? This was Bushnell's inspiration—the origin
of the *Turtle,* and the other ingenious mechanisms which
we shall see in a few moments, in resuming Bushnell's
story.

His invention was an answer to a challenge. It was, so to
speak, "a new way to pay old debts." In terms of precisely
what it was meant to do, it failed to work. But it filled the
British with a sense of insecurity on their strong ships. It

worked as a weapon of nerves. And his less spectacular floating mines wrought more tangible results.

More important, the *Turtle* was a great stride toward the submarine and the screw propeller. Robert Fulton took up where Bushnell left off. Under the first spell of seeing Napoleon as a new force for liberty against a decayed monarchy, Fulton built a remarkable submarine, his *Nautilus,* hoping to give France the means to balance British naval power. That, too, was abortive, but was yet another step forward. Americans never ceased trying. In the Civil War, a nine-man Confederate submarine sank the *Housatonic* which was blockading Charleston, but the sub itself was lost in the action. John P. Holland and Simon Lake, late in the century, were the chief designers of the modern submarine in this country.

But Bushnell is worth attention for more than the *Turtle* and his mines. His background, the interest taken by many others in his work, and even the enigmatic eclipse of his career, all are representative of that special and tangible quality that can be singled out as Yankee inventiveness. Let's pursue him farther.

David Bushnell conceived and designed the *American Turtle,* and began to supervise its construction at Saybrook, on the Connecticut River, while still an undergraduate at Yale. He was a farm lad, born in Westbrook, Connecticut, with nothing in his heritage or environment to make us anticipate his brilliant college activities in the mechanic arts.

He was almost thirty when he entered college. Apparently this was the satisfaction of a long desire, for it followed upon his father's death, when David sold his inheritance to make his education possible. At Yale he doubted some of the "facts" imparted to him. One point that aroused his interest was the assertion that gunpowder would not explode under water. He promptly set about to disprove this.

Rigging a two-pound charge of powder, well-compressed, under a hogshead laden with stones and reinforced at the bottom with two-inch oak planks, he set off the charge under water with spectacular results, in a fountain of water, stones, and shattered timber. He perceived quickly the formidable compressing effect of water on an explosion.

The Revolution began during Bushnell's college years. His inventions were meant to be his contribution toward meeting the great threat of British sea power. One of the earliest records of his activity is contained in a note in curious Latin* from a Tutor to Ezra Stiles, who was not yet President of the College. It is preserved in Stiles' diary, entry of August 15, 1775:

> Last Eveng. I rec^d a letter from Mr Tutor Lewis of Yale College. Speaking of Mr Bushnel, a student there he says—[Translation] "This man is the inventor of a machine which is now built and nearly completed, which could destroy the ships in Boston harbor by the explosion of gunpowder. The machine is so shaped that it may move along quickly twenty or more feet under water and is able to carry 2,000 lbs. of gunpowder and to attach it to the keel of a ship. Thereupon in ten minutes or one half hour, as the operator wishes, the clockwork will fire the charge." &c—

The *Turtle,* by the way, never was used in Boston harbor. Dr. Benjamin Gale, a physician of Killingworth, Connecticut, and incidentally one of the first men to make statistical studies, wrote to Silas Deane, the Connecticut Delegate to the Continental Congress, on November 9, 1775.

---

* Tutor Lewis' Latin, presumably used for security reasons, may be of interest to some.

> Hic Homo est Machinae Inventor, quae ad Naves Bostoniae portu Pulveris pyrii Explosione destruendas, nunc est fabricata & fere perfecta. Machina ita est formata, ut 20 aut amplius pedes sub undas celeriter transeat, & Pulveris pyrii 2000^{lb} portare et Navis Carinae infigere possit. Statim vel post Minuta decem vel Semi-horam, secundum Operatoris Voluntatem, Horologium totam Massam inflammabit.

The letter was largely about Bushnell's enterprises, describing the *Turtle* in detail and adding:

"He has made such a trial of the explosion of gunpowder under water, since Dr. Franklin did me the honor to call upon me, as has exceeded his most sanguine expectations, and is now convinced his magazine will contain three times so much powder as is necessary to destroy the largest ship in the navy. . . . I do insist upon it, that I believe the inspiration of the Almighty has given him understanding for this very purpose and design."

Much official interest was taken in Bushnell's activities by the college, the state, and the military. The inventor came at the invitation of Governor Trumbull and the Council of Connecticut to describe his plans, and was urged to proceed. As the work went ahead, he became security-conscious about it, so that Gale later reports that Bushnell "makes all his affairs a secret even to his best friends."

Dr. Gale continued to keep Silas Deane posted. On November 22, in '75, he said that the *Turtle* was being tested in the Connecticut River, but that there had been delays because the "forcing pump" (obviously for the action of submerging and rising), made by a Mr. Doolittle, had not been according to specifications. (The whole problem of specifications in those hand-tinkered days would be enough to drive a modern engineer out of his mind. A sheet of metal might be described as "about the thickness of a worn shilling." How worn is a shilling?)

A letter of the 7th of December mentions a two months delay due to money (official encouragement and some financial help did not keep most of the cost from coming out of Bushnell's pocket). But the same letter says that frost destroyed the luminescence of the foxwood on the compass and barometer. Dr. Gale asks Deane "to inquire of Dr. Franklin whether he knows of any kind of phosphorescence which will give light in the dark and not consume the air. Otherwise the execution must be omitted until next Spring, after the frosts are past."

This curious, and to our age truly primitive, problem re-

mains unsolved as of February 1, 1776, when Gale again
asks: "If the Philosopher's Lanthorn may be attained, and
will give a better light than what is proposed, should be
glad you would get what knowledge you can from Dr.
Franklin respecting it." It is not so much needed, he explains, to find the target, as to make possible a quick get-
away, so the pilot may know "what point to steer, and to
know whether he rises or sinks deeper, for the personal
safety of the operator." He adds, "I have lately seen the
man and conversed freely with him. He is no enthusiast; a
perfect philosopher and by no means doubtful of succeeding."

Events show that no substitute for the foxfire was brought
forward by that wellspring of lore, Franklin, toward whom
so many such queries were automatically turned. Night
use of the *Turtle* was impossible until warm weather.

During the summer prior to the attempt on the *Eagle,*
the *Turtle* was brought to New York. In secure coves, up
Long Island Sound, Bushnell trained a number of men in
its operation. Report says that he was not personally strong
enough for the exhausting manual job of cranking through
the water. He is said to have had a brother who was to be
the pilot, but that the brother falling ill made it necessary
for another of the trainees, our Ezra Lee, to step into the
task.

After New York was evacuated, later in the same season,
Sergeant Lee made another try on a frigate farther up the
Hudson. He was unsuccessful in getting next to his target.

The failure of this elaborate attempt to torpedo enemy
ships did not deter Bushnell from other efforts, relatively
more successful. He tried to sink the frigate *Cerberus* in
Long Island Sound, near New London. From a small boat,
he set afloat a bomb at the end of an immensely long
tether, attempting to maneuver it into contact with the frigate from a safe distance. Sailors from a nearby schooner
intercepted it and took it aboard. The bomb went off, destroying the schooner. This bomb had an automatic firing
mechanism, initially actuated by a wheel with sharp points

on the rim, like the rowel of a spur. When the device was hauled up along the side of a ship, or even floated against it, the turning of this wheel set the firing mechanism to work, bringing an explosion in a few minutes.

In December of '76, Bushnell launched the famous "battle of the kegs," at Philadelphia, where units of the British fleet lay in the Delaware. Apparently he sent down-current, from above the fleet, as many as two or three hundred contact mines, encased in kegs. Some of them may have been hitched up in tandem. At any rate, the concentration of them was important to the scheme, for one of the circumstances that thwarted it was the scattering of the kegs by floating ice, which apparently set some of them off with inspiring effect, and some small craft are said to have been destroyed.

Some writers have become mixed up as to the result and thought that this venture brought ridicule on Bushnell. On the contrary, there was a certain success. The British became so jumpy that sailors would fire at any floating object. The fleet upped-anchor and withdrew down the river. It was the British who suffered ridicule. They became a laughingstock and one of the local wits of Philadelphia, Francis Hopkinson, wrote the long and slightly tedious ditty (to be sung to "filthy tunes" as Falstaff said) called "The Battle of the Kegs."

In fragments of it, a frightened lookout who has seen the menacing objects, warns his Captain:

> These kegs, I'm told, the rebels hold,
>   Pack'd up like pickled herring;
> And they've come down t'attack the town,
>   In this new way of ferry'ng.

> The motley crew, in vessels new,
>   With Satan for their guide, sir,
> Pack'd up in bags, or wooden kegs,
>   Come driving down the tide, sir.

After the fleet has rallied, with confusion and cannon fire, the ballad concludes:

> Such feats did they perform that day,
>   Against these wicked kegs, sir,
> That years to come, if they get home,
> They'll make their boasts and brags, sir.

"The ingenuity of these people is singular in their secret modes of mischief," a British commodore bemoaned to his superiors at home.

The reputation of Bushnell as a mysterious threat to the British spread widely. The Continental Army took pains to keep him a mystery man, for it was feared attempts might be made to abduct him. If he wasn't destroying the enemy navy he was certainly waging a valuable war of nerves, and who could tell what he would do next? In 1779, by a fluke of chance, he was captured with some others near Norwalk, Connecticut, but he was not identified and being a civilian of no apparent significance, he was exchanged after a few days. Later that year, he was commissioned a Captain in the Corps of Sappers and Miners, and was generally on hand when anything out-of-the-way was to be tried.

The course of Bushnell's life after the Revolution is truly perplexing. Here was a man of undoubted genius, whose talents were known to those in the highest places in his country. Yet he disappeared, by choice, into absolute obscurity.

Was he embittered? He hadn't failed. Apparently he pretty thoroughly exhausted his own means in his experiments and got back none of it, but his life did not come to financial ruin. It has been suggested on inconclusive evidence that he went to France to seek backers for his submarine and was embittered, or at least discouraged, by rejection there. We have no French confirmation of this. He is supposed to have met Fulton there, as a possible explanation of Fulton's extensive borrowings from Bushnell's devices. But Fulton's greatest friend was Joel Barlow, who had been at Yale with

Bushnell and quite probably was well acquainted with the *American Turtle*. So we cannot presume any Bushnell-Fulton meetings. His disappearance was so thorough that he was presumed by many who had known him, and even his relatives, to have gone to France and been killed in the Revolution. At any event, it was a case of, "Whatever became of Bushnell?"

Certainly he never invented anything else, or even tried to. What he did do was discovered only years later and was as improbable as the engines he had created. In 1795 or '96, a new teacher turned up in a school in Columbia County, Georgia. After a few years, having studied medicine, he settled in Warrenton, Georgia, as a "practitioner of physic," known as Dr. Bush. Not until he died, in his eighties, some thirty years later, and his will was probated, did the secret come out that old Dr. Bush was none other than the long-vanished David Bushnell.

Timothy Dwight was a tutor at Yale in Bushnell's days there. The young man's exploits so greatly impressed him that he incorporated them in his poem *Greenfield Hill,* written eighteen years later just before Dwight became President of Bushnell's *alma mater.* The poet in Dwight, a struggling thing at best, was moved to such hyperbole as to suggest a veritable Captain Nemo.

> See Bushnell's strong, creative genius, fraught
> With all th' assembled powers of skilful thought,
> His mystic vessel plunge beneath the waves,
> And glide thro' dark retreats, and coral caves!

CHAPTER 2

WATER AND WHEELS—SAWS AND STONES

So much downright work was perhaps never wrought on the earth's
surface in the same space of time
as during the first forty years after
the settlement.

—JAMES RUSSELL LOWELL

IF WE LOOK at Bushnell as a Yankee inventor, it brings
the question before us—where did the Yankee come from?
We talk quite freely of Yankees, from Yankee-Doodle time
on. When we speak of the earliest settlers, we talk about
Pilgrim Fathers and Puritans. We tend to slur over the
transition from the one to the other.

So, since we're going to go on, in due time, from Bushnell to look at a good many other Yankee inventors con-
centrated mainly in some fifty years more or less from the
prelude of the War for Independence, we must turn back
for a couple of chapters to trace the paths by which they
got there. Those Pilgrim Fathers and Puritans were a busy
and active people in far more than theology. They started
the industries that bred the Yankee skills. Let's have a look
at some of them.

In 1670, at Saugus, Massachusetts, a vigorous man of
middle years, named Joseph Jenks, Jr., was working in the

iron forge of his father. Old Jenks, for that day and age, was well stricken in years, approaching seventy but still hearty. He was to last until eighty-one, constantly active. If you lived to such an age in that era, you were no weakling. Old Jenks had been the first great artisan in iron to practice on these shores—a teacher of many that came after him.

The younger Joseph had followed his father from England. For a long time he had worked with the old man, but now the itch to move was upon him. He was minded to marry with Esther Ballard, of nearby Lynn, and be off to an opportunity that was beckoning.

The name of Jenks, father and son, was known widely in the colonies. Only that of Leonard was its rival in the iron crafts. Now certain letters had come to young Joseph from men in another plantation, from a place on the Bay of the Narragansetts, the settlement called Providence. A man named Roger Williams had separated in his thought and religious practice from the Bay Colony Puritans and been expelled. In what was now known as Rhode Island— though it was only part island with a good balance of mainland—with Providence as his seat, Williams and his followers called themselves Baptists, and among their attitudes was that repugnant one called toleration.

Some of the men of Providence represented to young Jenks that about four miles north of their settlement, on a river variously known as the Blackstone (from Rhode Island's first actual settler), the Pawtucket, or the Seekonk, there was a handsome fall of water. This was a tempting lure to any ambitious, restless artisan. The men of Providence would greatly like to have an iron forge and perhaps a sawmill, and other mills, adjacent to them. None among them was equipped for such work. Although the land around the falls was owned already, arrangements could be made if the right man would come to exploit the resources there.

This was what Joseph Jenks was looking for. He married his Esther, said goodbye to the old man, and was off to the Pawtucket, which meant "the falling of the waters." In

1671 he was on the spot. From one of the men of Providence he purchased sixty acres of land. His house he built to overlook the river and falls. At the foot of the falls, on the west side, he built his forge, and as fast as he could accomplish the work, he established a sawmill.

The potential power of this river was better even than he had hoped. The central falls was a drop of some fifty feet, but the falls were channelled and divided with much irregularity that meant a diversity of possible power sites. What was more, the further reaches of this river, upstream, had additional falls or precipitate rapids filled with the promises of power.

Immediately below the main falls, near the forge, the river was shallow and filled with tumbled boulders. Here from immemorial time Indian paths had converged to cross the river. Yet not much farther below, the channel deepened again, to form a head of navigation leading down the four miles to Providence and the Bay. Joseph Jenks knew it at once to be a building place with a future.

He could not do all his work alone. As the Providence men had anticipated, others followed Joseph Jenks into the tiny settlement of Pawtucket. Soon there would be grist mills to join the sawmill, and who could foresee all the useful work to which the waters would be put?

Jenks had been there only a few years, diligently working, when the tides of Indian-white warfare swept over the land in the bloody King Philip's War. In 1765, raiding Indians swooped over the Rhode Island settlements. Notwithstanding the high personal regard in which the red men held Roger Williams, he could not dissuade them from war. Providence itself was attacked. As for Jenks at Pawtucket, his forge was burnt in a swift attack and he counted himself lucky to get away to Providence with his family alive. There could be no going back until peace was accomplished.

Canonchet, great sachem of the Narragansetts, who waited to watch developments before committing his people to join with the warring Wampanoags of Philip, had really a more formidable force than his ally. Massachusetts men fought the battle of the great swamp with the Narragansetts in central Rhode Island and won a costly victory. Canonchet still had a dangerous striking force left. As the white men whittled it down, he withdrew and made a final stand near the burnt-out forge of Joseph Jenks. There, at the foot of the falls, on the rocks of the old Indian crossing, the proud Canonchet lost his gun in the water and was taken alive—to be later delivered over to the Mohicans for slaughter.

Back to this scene, in 1677, came Jenks with his family and his neighbors. The forge was rebuilt. The settlement of Pawtucket grew steadily from that time forward. The hardworking Joseph had a hardworking wife. Esther bore him four sons and six daughters. One of these sons, yet another Joseph, became Governor of Rhode Island.

In those early days, the west side of the river, where Jenks had located, was Rhode Island land, but the east side was Massachusetts. Yet the town of Pawtucket was developing on both sides of the stream. Soon urgent need was felt for a bridge across the tumbling falls. Three generations of Jenkses were involved in the building of a succession of bridges that connected the states, ultimately made a unit of the divided town, and formed a vital link for the Boston-Providence post road. In 1862 the east side of the river was ceded to Rhode Island.

Later we shall see how the destiny of Pawtucket was bound up with a firm called Almy and Brown, and a man named Samuel Slater, and another iron-working family named Wilkinson. The purpose of this brief glimpse of Joseph Jenks, Jr., and the founding of Pawtucket, has been to show one specific example of the genesis of a New England town at the head of navigation and the first falls. In this case, it was power that drew the settler there. The church, the school, and the village green followed the forge and the mill.

New England was stony, mountainous, and wooded. In the days of settlement it might have been described as a coastline, a fall line, and a backwoods. In that order it was settled and developed—the coast, the fall line, and the forest lands. The hilly and sometimes downright rugged terrain was such that the first falls, in most instances, were remarkably close to tidewater, and the best rivers seemed to descend in endless steps of falls and rapids from their sources. Starting with the primitive saw and grist mill an industrial destiny was certain for such land, and such a destiny would attract and breed inventive, mechanical skills. New England grouped itself about those falls of the waters, and though hydro-electric power or various fuels may have supplanted the local "white coal" in many places today, all the same New England industry remains in the basic fall-line pattern around which it took form, and all the important heads of water are very much in use. Springfield and Windsor, Vermont; Nashua and Manchester, New Hampshire; Hartford, Connecticut; Lowell, Massachusetts, and old Pawtucket are still the testimony.

The process of development differed somewhat in every case, of course, but let's try to generalize it as much as we can, to see how New England life gathered itself around the waters, to see how the mill and forge came along, with the artisans, side by side with the preacher and teacher and statesman who tend to get top billing in the histories. By looking into this we will find out something of the heritage of that semifabulous creature who followed—the Yankee.

A modest river flows through the New England countryside, nearing one of the great bays or coves of the sea toward which it has worked patiently, perhaps for hundreds of miles from some small lake or nest of mountain springs. This is before the white man came. The river shares the land with the Indians. In its course it has gathered in an assortment of lesser streams. Whatever its windings and ramblings, there is one constant in its direction—*down*. Down it must go, sometimes placidly through a level valley, sometimes torrentially in white-water rapids, sometimes thunderously over a precipitous drop.

Men number the features of a river from its end, not its beginning. A short way inland on this typical small New England river, a group of English settlers comes to what they call its first falls—not spectacular, but a drop of several feet. It is enough to be a magnet for settlement. Indeed, the streams of water themselves, falling or not, mark out the force lines of the magnetic field of first settlements in new lands. Water is the destiny of these settlers. It has brought them to these coasts, led them deeper into the land, caused them to stop and plant the seed of a town, after which it will minister to their needs and industries as long as the water flows, for as long as it flows, there is power.

The settler must use these rich forests around him, for fuel, for building, for tanbark. He is counting on that tumbling water to help him. Probably he will use it first to saw his wood. Then he, or some neighboring settler, will use it to turn the stones and grind his grain. If you think it should be the other way round, remember that this settler may have had wood to cut for some time before he had grain to grind. As time goes on, another will use the water to break his flax, another to run his fulling mill, his triphammer or some similar pounding or stamping process, another to card his wool and cotton, another to spin it, another to run his lathes and make his clocks or guns, and there will come a day on some of the river when the mill races and sluices have become great penstocks of steel; the millwheels, turbines. From the river, now, in the latter day, flows the subtle, protean current of electricity. Years and generations have passed, the use has changed, but two things about the river have remained constant: it still flows down, and it is still power, transmit it as you will, transform it as you will, employ it as you will.

At the falls of the river many a New England town had its genesis. The white frame church, or one of brick or stone, appeared on the green, and the white frame houses, and those of brick or stone, rose up around the common and radiated outward along the often eccentric pattern of the roads that became streets. Sometimes the village

growth was arrested here, and the flow of the water that
had been the start became a minor factor in the town's life
or yielded its value from the realm of the practical to the
esthetic.

It would be a mistake, though, to envision the growth of
a New England town as a spontaneous springing up of the
loveliness that evolved later. The stately elm took a long
time to grow on village streets and greens. Mud, stumps,
and raw wood had to be the beginning. The New Haven
Green, when Eli Whitney went to Yale College, as late as
1790 still was bleakly barren of trees, uneven in terrain,
and ornamented with nothing more appealing than scattered tombstones.

Where there were great falls, as at or near the places that
became known as Lowell, and Nashua, and Manchester,
and New Haven, and Pawtucket, and Hartford—where the
stream flowed strongly, unaffected by the clearing of land
that dried up many small creeks—where it did not freeze
tight in the winter but rushed on even beneath its ice—in
these places the towns changed. Houses that had arisen
close to mills and factories were driven back by them, in
time. The mill neighborhood became different—the factory-
town had arrived, and the frame, brick, stone churches and
houses tended to draw farther and farther aloof from the
whirling wheels and clattering machines; even, in time,
from the great stores and shops, and public buildings, that
had come in where once the homes were. This is one of the
ways a city grows.

The mills of the early settlements were the first expression of Yankee ingenuity, before the Yankee had even invented himself. Little of the knowledge that went into them
was original discovery, but Yankee inventors, known and
anonymous alike, made the mills better in ways large or
small, and the mills bred more inventors. The mills were
the earliest power users, and power is foremost of the inventor's problems. The building of the mills—even simple
ones—was in itself a large order, requiring wheelwright,

carpenter and mason, probably blacksmith—often as not most of them combined in the ingenuity and vigor of one man.

The water mill is ancient, going well back before the Christian era. Its first use may have been for the simple raising of the water itself—a water-driven wheel turning a chain of buckets. All the basic ways of applying the force of water to a wheel seem to be pre-Christian in their antiquity and all of these, applied variously through many centuries, were part of the knowledge fund of the New England settler. He invented none of them, but he had the multiple problems of rigging them, making them work a little better, and making the applications and transmissions of power more versatile.

A water wheel is simply a large, double wheel, the rims of which are connected by paddle vanes, or pockets, against which moving water thrusts to turn the wheel. If the water supplies the motion, you have a mill, for whatever use you may choose. If you put such a wheel on a boat and turn the wheel by mechanical power, you have a paddle-wheel boat; you have reversed the respective roles of the water and the wheel.

The most efficient water wheel is the type called overshot. The water is led by a sluice to the top of the wheel and falls down upon it. Pockets, rather than simple vanes, are generally used for this type of wheel. Its high efficiency is due to the fact that not just the velocity but also the weight of the water contribute to the power. Early New England prints show us many mills with the water brought to the top of the wheel in sluices of wood supported by spindly pole trestles, or sometimes in elaborate arched stone ducts.

If you have a good, strong, swift current, either in the stream itself or in the sluice, you can use the undershot type of wheel. The water runs below the wheel, moving it solely by the force of the water against the vanes. There were many of these in the New England colonies because there was plenty of swift water, and such wheels were rela-

tively cheaper and easier to build than the overshot type.
The water for either can be conveyed a considerable way, if
necessary, so long as there is enough of it and the source of
water is higher than the mill, to ensure velocity.

The simple wheel turns a horizontal axle. For such use
as a grist mill, where a vertical axle is needed for the re-
volving grinding stones, a set of gears was necessary to
transmit the power from the horizontal to the vertical axle.
Occasionally a grist mill might be found with a more primitive horizontal wheel, turning sideways in the current, with
its vertical axle extending upward to turn the millstone by
direct application of power.

An almost forgotten type of mill important in the life of
the early settlers living on the coast was the tide mill. It
was especially adapted to deep coves and inlets where the
water was relatively calm yet the tidal rise and fall were
substantial. The basic principle involved a large, enclosed
millpond with a water gate raised to admit the high tide.
The gate was then lowered and the impounded water released through sluices to turn undershot wheels.

Long Island had a number of tide mills, Massachusetts
had some at Boston as well as others. A tide mill at Boston around 1643 has been called a "startling invention,"
which is hardly the case unless within a local context, for
such mills date from at least the 11th century in Venice
and I know of no indication that they were first invented
there.

One or more Boston tide mills used as sluice or race a
canal known as Mill Creek, which in the earliest days of the
town separated the north from the central section. A cove
toward the north near to the later Hanover Square formed
a tidal millpond. In after years it was reclaimed by fill from
Beacon Hill and now the North Station stands about on its
site.

That tide mills played their part for something close to
two hundred years in early American life is shown in the
circumstance that in 1773 the legislature of Connecticut,
at a time of drought that stopped the wheels on many

streams, issued to one John Shipman a patent for an improved tide mill, giving him a forty-year monopoly for the town of Saybrook and twenty miles west from the Connecticut River. The Yankee did not try, like Canute, to command the tides, but he harnessed them.

I should note that while water mills were the major factor in New England, nevertheless there, as elsewhere in the colonies, wind- and steed-mills (horses or oxen) were used for grinding or sawing. The Dutch, having special skills with the windmill, used it extensively in New Netherlands.

The sawmill and the grist mill came into the colonies at about the same time, but there are some respects in which the sawmill is the more significant. Again it is no primary American invention. The natural creation of a land of forests—and equally natural to be brought into such a land —the sawmill had its major development in Germany and Scandinavia. It was known in England, but partly because of the furious resistance of the English hand laborer to the introduction of such machines, sawmills were erected in this country, in Maine and Massachusetts, around 1633 and '34, whereas 1663 is a date sometimes given as approximately that of the first sawmill in England. There the transition from clay-floored to timber-floored dwellings for people of relatively modest rank accompanied the establishment of the sawmill.

In early New England there was no log cabin stage— that type of structure being a Scandinavian invention that was brought to Delaware by the Swedes. It was adopted and spread rapidly because it was appropriate to heavily timbered frontiers in America as it was to the forested north regions that engendered it. But in New England the early rise of the power sawmill helps to account for the rather rapid transition of the Puritans from their temporary first shelters of branches, woven into wattles and sealed with clay. These original dwellings were either roughly conical or, in some reconstructions, suggest a crude quonset hut shape. Yet in a remarkably short span of time, all over New England, the settlers were replacing these with houses of

sawed timbers, essentially medieval in their architecture—
gradually taking on indigenous characteristics as building
went on through the generations. As for the later mill
towns, Charles Dickens gave a graphic description of the
blend of primeval mud and new lumber in Lowell when
that rather rare community was only relatively new,
in 1842.

As a digression from timber, the opening of kilns for
brick and tile and the quarrying of stone and slate were
developed with remarkable rapidity. Not only were there
well-built frame houses in early Boston town, but in 1657,
only twenty-seven years from the original settling of the
Bay Colony, a contemporary letter speaks of "large and spacious houses, some fairly set forth with brick, tile, slate,
and stone, and orderly placed, whose continual enlargement
presageth some sumptuous city."

It's odd that the earliest written reference to a saw
worked by water power is by the fourth-century Roman
writer Ausonius, who speaks of a saw for cutting marble.
(This was a technique to which Vermont inventors made
major contributions.) Sawmills first appeared in Germany
at about the time of Ausonius. All these early mills, including those of New England, used a reciprocating motion
(that is, backward and forward, or up and down) and most
of them suspended the blade vertically. (I've encountered
no early mention of horizontal blades in this country.) The
gang saw, of multiple, parallel blades, was well known by
colonial times. The circular saw was a novelty, at least in
this country, at the time of Eli Terry, maker of wooden
clocks, around 1816.

So many early references to machinery are vague that it
is helpful to have a description from an English tract of
1650, of a sawmill intended for construction in America.
There were doubtless many variations but I think that from
this we get a reasonably representative picture of a 17th-
century sawmill:

> This heer is not altogether like those of Norway, for
> they make the piece of Timber approach the sawes

on certaine wheels with teeth; but because of repara-
tions which these tooth'd wheels are often subject
unto, I will omit that use, and in stead thereof put
two waits about two or three hundred pounds weight
apiece . . . The chords wherewith the said weights
doe hange, to be fastened at the end of the 2 peeces
of moving wood, which slide on two other peeces
of fixed wood, by the meanes of certaine small
pulleys, which should always draw the sayd peeces
of moving wood, which advancing always toward
the sawes rising and falling, shall quickly be cut into
4, 5 or 6 peeces, as you shall please to put on sawes
. . . the ingenious Artist, may easily convert the
same to an instrument of threshing wheat, breaking
of hemp or flax, and *other as profitable uses*.

But I want to turn aside, now, in my thread of story, to
talk awhile of certain men, who will bring us back, in time,
to streams and wheels.

There was no better liked and admired man in the early
New England colonies than John Winthrop, Jr. Son of the
great Puritan Governor of Massachusetts, he was himself a
Puritan of deep persuasion, yet of less ferocity than his father. In matters relating to the persecution of Quakers,
the younger Winthrop, as Governor of Connecticut, acted
with such moderation, staying within laws that he was
bound to administer yet holding bigots in firm check, that
his close friend Roger Williams was moved to write to him:
"You have always bene noted for tendernes toward mens
soules, especially for conscience sake to God."
The Governorship of Massachusetts could have been his,
as successor to his father. He chose, instead, to accept that
of Connecticut, of which Colony he had been a founder on
behalf of Lord Say and Sele and Lord Brook. New London
later became his permanent home. Massachusetts, Rhode
Island, even New Netherlands and also the English, back
home, all desired that this man should live and do his work

among them. The retirement to private life which he greatly craved was denied him by popular insistence—he was still Governor at his death.

An old portrait of Winthrop bears a certain resemblance to the Droushout Shakespeare, except that dark page-boy bangs in the Puritan cover what is a domed and balding forehead in the playwright. The similarity is in the contours of the face, in large, nearly circular and gently melancholy eyes, a notably long nose, and a mustache.

In Roger Williams' warm encomium there were other qualities noted than his tolerance. One of these: "You have bene noted for tendernes toward the bodies and infirmities of poor mortalls." Winthrop was a practicing physician throughout his career. The elder Oliver Wendell Holmes analyzed the pharmacopoeia of Winthrop in a well known lecture. But the Governor was a man of interest and acumen in yet other fields of science. He was abreast of the advanced thought of his times in mathematics, astronomy, mineralogy, chemistry, alchemy (which had not yet lost its respectability), and occult phenomena. He claimed to have discovered the fifth satellite of Jupiter—official recognition of its existence did not occur until more than two hundred years later. His library, much of which is preserved, ranged across all the fields of learning, from classical reading through philosophy and theology, but with a heavy proportion in the sciences. He was the close friend of Robert Boyle, the chemist, knew Isaac Newton and Christopher Wren, and was intimate with the diplomat-adventurer-philosopher-physician, Kenelm Digby, notwithstanding that the latter was a Roman Catholic. Winthrop was one of the founders of the Royal Society, in 1660, and contributed articles to its *Transactions*. Shipbuilding in the colonies, and brewing, were the subjects of some of his papers. In the one on brewing he was interested in the possibilities of beer from Indian maize.

Volume Forty of the *Transactions* discloses that only the conclusion of the Civil Wars throttled a plan by which the Society, with Boyle and other notables, "would have left

England, and, out of esteem for the most excellent and valuable Governor, John Winthrop the Younger, would have retired to his new-born Colony. . . ."

His personal prospecting and his encouragement of such searches vastly aided in unfolding New England's mineral endowments. Iron, tin, copper, antimony (much used medicinally by him and other physicians of his time), black lead, alum, vitriol, rock salt and salt springs were among the substances for which, said the Assembly of Connecticut, grants would be made to Winthrop in consideration of any find.

In the colonies—as is true wherever men have made new settlements—salt was an urgent necessity. To depend upon the vagaries of shipping for its importation was impossible, however helpful every shipload might be. We overlook, in modern days, the crucial role of salt in civilization, even though we are taught that the salt in our blood is our bond with a former state of life in the sea. From Greek days when the phrase arose about a bad slave being "not worth his salt," through Roman days when salt taxes and government monopolies affected the political destinies of nations, down to the famous salt march of Gandhi in modern India, the little cubic crystals of sodium chloride and their chemical relatives have influenced our lives.

It wasn't that the New England colonies simply needed salt for their diet. The providing of such a demand would not have been difficult. The life and wealth of the early colonies were the fisheries—which maintained their importance even after trade and industry and agriculture developed, too. The fisheries required salt, in great quantity, for in that day before the deep freeze, salting was the method of preserving fish whether for home use or export. It was also the method of preserving meats. The Indians' method with both fish and meats was to smoke them, but this could not meet the needs of the fisheries.

Bradford describes the unhappy experience the Plymouth Plantation had with a pretender sent from England to establish salt works. After great expenditures of time, mate-

rials, and labor—a "chargeable business" Bradford called it
—the salt master stood exposed as "an ignorante, foolish,
self-willed fellow."

In addition to quantity, the quality of salt was important.
Dirty or chemically impure salts could have disastrous effects. Salt was welcomed from almost anywhere, yet in 1670
the Massachusetts Legislature had to stipulate that salt from
the Tortudas [Tortugas] could not be used: "fishing being
advantageous and likely to be impaired by using Tortudas
Salt, which leaves spots on fish by reason of shells and trash
in it . . . no fish salted with Tortudas Salt, and thereby
spotted, shall be accounted merchantable fish."

I have not wandered away from John Winthrop, Jr. Of
his many contributions to colonial industry, improved methods of salt production were among the most important. Unhappily I cannot find any concrete evidence about the nature of his procedures, other than that they involved solar
evaporation from pans or shallow pools. His friend Robert
Boyle—*The Sceptical Chymist*—was much preoccupied
with studying the properties of sea water—a circumstance
quite probably bearing upon Winthrop's salt interests.

The clue to his work is that the Massachusetts General
Court, in March of 1648, took the following steps about
his proposals:

> . . . upon treaty with Mr. Winthrop, touching the
> making of salt out of meer salt water, for the use of
> the country, it is apprehended and assented by both
> parties, that for incouragment of the said worke, be-
> ing of so general concernment, it is enacted by au-
> thority of this Court, that for so many families or
> households as are resident within this jurisdiction,
> Mr. Winthrop shall be paid after the next harvest,
> so many bushels of wheate or of other corne and
> wheate to the value of wheate, yet so as the one half
> of it be in wheate certaine upon the delivery of so
> many bushels of good white salt at Boston, Charles
> Towne, Salem, Ipswich, and Salsbury, to be re-
> ceived and paid for by the Commissioners for public

rates upon two months' notice given by Mr. Winthrop—the constables shall have power to levy it.
The second year the commission shall receive and
pay for two bushels of salt for each family, at the
price of 3s. a bushel, and for other two years, the
commission shall take of, and make payment for
two hundred tons of salt at 2s. per bushel, at such
Salt worke as said Mr. Winthrop shall appoint, and
he shall have leave to erect works in any place or
places in the jurisdiction not appropriated. . . .

He was granted, also, 3,000 acres of land on characteristic
terms so familiar in the stipulations by which townships
and legislatures encouraged and invited mills and industries
throughout all the growth of New England. The substantial
grant of land would be cancelled, "provided that he set not
up a considerable salte worke, we meane to make one hundred tun per annum of salt between the Capes of Massachusetts Bay, within three years next coming."
The only evidence as to how this all worked out is in the
circumstance, fairly suggestive of success it seems to me,
that eight years later, in 1656, Winthrop's works were apparently still producing, for the Court extends his privileges
for another twenty-one years (which happened to be just
one year over the span of life remaining to him). There is
no sign that his active personal participation—or even the
venture itself—continued for any such length of time. Also
the time between the early and later grants may have been
more fruitful in experimental promise than in yield.
Edward Burt, in 1652, also received Massachusetts
concessions for salt works. More than a century later, around
1777, John Sears and others established an elaborate evaporation works at Dennis, on Cape Cod. In due time he introduced windmills to pump the sea water into the evapo-
rating pans. This general procedure became so important a
mode of salt manufacture that the Cape and other parts of
the New England coast were long marked by batteries of
windmills at points along the beaches.

Prices for salt varied widely at the different stages of its accessibility and manufacture. The elder Winthrop wrote to his son, from Massachusetts, in 1646, that a Dutch ship had arrived with 250 tons, "so as salt was abated in a few hours from thirty-six to sixteen a hogshead" (shillings, presumably). As with textiles and other manufactures, the coming of the Revolution imparted the strain and impetus of necessity to colonial salt manufacture. A curious aspect of the weighing and packing of the commodity turns up in frontier Pennsylvania after the war. Salt was commonly sold there in barter for cattle, by the bushel. The salt was measured out by hand, gingerly. Not only was it not packed down in the bushel, but not even a heavy footstep was permitted on the floor (like a housewife with a cake in the oven).

Unlike less fortunate parts of the world, the United States is richly endowed with natural salts in their various forms. When settlements had pushed well inland, such great deposits of high grade rock salt and natural brines were found as to supply the needs of the whole country. The first major finds in salt were in the area of Syracuse, New York. Subsequent important salt locations were found in Pennsylvania, Ohio, Michigan, Kansas, Texas, New Mexico, Louisiana, Idaho, Wyoming, Oklahoma, Nevada—and of course the most spectacular of all, The Great Salt Lake of Utah and its adjacent salt flats.

To get back to our friend Winthrop, another of his important industrial interests was iron, an industry of widespread and major concern throughout the colonies. The role of the iron furnaces from the shores of Lake Champlain, to the Hudson Valley, and in Western Connecticut, and Massachusetts was vital when the time came that the New England colonies threw themselves into the determined struggle for independence.

At Saugus, in Massachusetts, was a swampy region of ponds abounding in limonite, a clay-like ore commonly called bog-iron (or meadow-iron). England had a good deal of iron in this form, so the English knew how to use it.

The ore was obtained either by draining, where possible, or by dragging the ponds and swamps with scoops, as in oyster dredging. John Winthrop was one of the prime movers in an enterprising group who, in 1643, organized the Company of Undertakers for the Iron-works, of Saugus. Another member was high-tempered, independent Thomas Dexter, maternal great-great-grandfather of Paul Revere. This was the time of the great depression in the colonies, the lessening of trade with England, the falling-off of emigrations from England, and even the return of many people to the mother country—all circumstances attendant upon the political climate changing in England as Parliament gained the upper hand in the long struggle with King Charles.

It was at this time, too, that the several "plantations" of Plymouth, Massachusetts, Connecticut, and New Haven, all as yet independent of one another, took the earliest, prophetic move toward federation by setting up for mutual protection as The United Colonies of New England. A few years earlier the Pequot War (1637) had made Connecticut relatively safe, but other trials and threats of every sort lay before them which they saw might best be met in unity than in separateness.

The far-seeing men of the colonies were not content to leave themselves prey to distant events after such fashion. It was a precarious time, but all the same a time when capital must be risked to develop industries and resources of all kinds at home. So both public bodies and private venturers worked together to exploit the natural wealth about them and the ingenuity and enterprise within them. Also, as an adequate flow of trade was not then possible with England, the shipowners of the colonies began to fare forth in new and destiny-laden directions. The rapid increase in trade with the West Indies spread more and more to all the Atlantic coasts, on both sides of the water, into the Mediterranean, and in due time these trade lines were to extend themselves around the Horn to the Pacific coasts, then westward further (or else around the Cape of Good Hope to

Madagascar and north) so that ultimately all the coasts and islands of Asia and its seas, and of the Austral regions, and the whaling waters of the Pacific became goals of the Yankee.

The Yankee went to exotic lands, brought back exotic products, made enormous fortunes and indeed generated from the depression that first forced him farther out into the trade winds the capital that made the mills and factories at home hum and expand. Both the culture and the industry of New England were profoundly influenced by her seafaring destiny.

Rum was prominent among the cargoes that a sober people shipped. And there were those who sent their ships to African coasts and brought back human cargoes. New Englanders (not all—but some) traded in slaves. A New Englander invented the cotton gin that made a waning slave economy flourish and expand, and New Englanders were the spearheads of the abolition movement that helped precipitate a war to end an evil New England had helped to make.

Winthrop happened to be in England at the time of the forming of the Saugus iron company. So was his great friend, Roger Williams, seeking a charter for his liberal settlement of Rhode Island. This was also the year of the murder of Anne Hutchinson, whose religious dissents had led the Massachusetts Colony to expel her. She and her family were massacred by Indians in what is now Westchester County, near the New Amsterdam which she had felt would be a place of refuge. The younger Winthrop came back to Massachusetts in this same year (1643), bringing with him a band of experienced iron workers from the town of Hammersmith. These were taken to the works (on the banks of the Saugus, but then called Lynn) where they made themselves a settlement and named it Hammersmith, in time-honored tradition.

The General Court had been asked for support. It granted no funds, but offered many privileges, prerogatives, and tax exemptions, provided a goodly supply of iron was forthcoming within two years. The Saugus settlers were given lands and a twenty-one year monopoly of iron work in the area, with the promise of six more sites in the future if all were fulfilled. The home needs must have priority, but assuming these to be satisfied, the company was authorized to export iron where they wished except—with a familiar ring for the modern world—to enemies.

It has to be confessed that the iron works were not a thumping success. The company had tough luck in the management of the bogs and ponds, for their activities led to the flooding of some adjacent lands and resulting lawsuits. Franklin once observed that, "There are croakers in every country, always boding its ruin." Local croakers, in this case, professed alarm that the land would be utterly denuded of its wood by the insatiable needs of the iron furnaces.

At least there was some basis for this worry (contrasted to the blithe indifference with which American woods generally were cut off). Pine commonly grew in the bog-iron terrain and it made the most satisfactory charcoal for smelting. Roughly 120 bushels of charcoal were needed to smelt one ton of iron. One acre of good, dense woods yielded about 1,600 bushels of charcoal—producing about thirteen tons of iron. No large iron industry, in the modern sense, could have developed until coke, or gas, were available as fuels.

Finally as Hubbard, a contemporary, reported the enterprise at Saugus: "Instead of drawing out bars of iron for the country's use, there was hammered out nothing but contention and lawsuits, which was but a bad return for the undertakers."

But it was not a bad return for the country. The general interest in iron works had been stimulated and other sites, as well as other and more valuable types of ore, were being found. More important, skills had been developed and knowledge spread in the crafts involved. The men imported from Hammersmith in England to the new Hammersmith in Massachusetts were decidedly a good return.

Attention turns, now, from the great John Winthrop, Jr., to one of the workmen he had brought over with him, in 1643, a Welshman named Joseph Jenks (variously spelt Jencks and Jenckes, in those days). The first outstandingly gifted iron worker to come to these shores, he well earned the name "the Tubal-cain of New England," after that ancient, dim figure in Genesis, Tubal-cain, "an instructer of every artificer in brass and iron." (His brother Jubal, incidentally, "was the father of all such as handle the harp and organ.")

Like Longfellow's smith, Jenks was "a mighty man," though we know little of his person. A contemporary, in speaking of the Saugus iron venture, remarks caustically on the disappointments attending some of the theories on which it had been based: " . . . yet experience hath outstript learning here, and the most quick-sighted in the Theory of things have been forced to pay pretty roundly to Lady Experience for filling their heads with a little of her active after-wit. . . ."

Without too grievously violating context, I venture that Jenks embodied the experience that out-stript learning. He was the master spirit among the imported workmen. The very tools, vessels, and models needed were built by his hands or on his instruction, and he cast the first iron in the colonies. By tradition, the earliest article is supposed to have been an iron pot, of one-quart capacity.

Jenks was quick to go into business for himself. Though remaining with the company, he purchased from them the right to build and operate his own forge on their premises for private enterprise. In the Spring of 1646, the Assembly granted him a fourteen year patent "for the making of engines for mills, to go by water, for the more speedy despatch of work than formerly, and for the making of scythes and other edged tools with a new-invented sawmill, that things may be afforded cheaper than formerly."

Nine years later, in 1655, he received a patent for a new style of scythe, "for the more speedy cutting of grass." The scythe then in use, centuries old, was rather short, stubby, thick-bladed—actually it was very like the short, heavy "brush hook" blade which I have wielded lustily in my time against the sumac and like scourges. What Jenks did was to lengthen and thin out the blade. To give it strength other than at the expense of its fine edge, he welded an iron strip to the back of the blade. It was a basic change in the instrument, and what is most to its credit, there has been no other such basic change in the scythe since his day. New England's Tubal-cain is still represented by every hand mower.

This patent of Jenks' was one of the earliest of any kind in the country. In fact, it was not what we now consider a patent but a monopoly in the direct gift of the General Court. A provision of the Massachusetts "Body of Liberties" (1641) said there "should be no monopolies but of such new inventions as were profitable to the country, and that for a short time only." The term of such a "patent" was solely in the discretion of the Court and could vary from one case to another.

There is a legend that Jenks cut the dies for the first coins minted in America, the famous "pine tree shillings" (and oak and willow trees), and even that his daughter-in-law made the pine tree design. I call this a legend because it has been doubted by some very capable doubters on persuasive arguments, but I report the story because it persists and it could have been true.

That early Massachusetts coinage (which was illegal and at which diplomatic colonials besought Charles II to wink by representing the oak on one of the coins to be the Royal Oak which once sheltered the exiled king) was struck because the Colony was desperately in need of a usable currency. Trade with England had become too sporadic and was too one-sided to maintain an adequate currency circulation in the colonies since remittances home had to be made in British coin. A bewildering array of coins from Spain and Portugal, Russia, France and Holland, and Heaven knows where else, circulated in New England's ports. Their value was hard to establish by any reliable standard. Clipping, counterfeiting and such deplorable practices could flourish under this condition. The Bay Colony coinage was not an act of revolutionary defiance—it was rather a somewhat bold usurpation of a right to which the colony sought to win at least a grudging consent.

Whoever may have cut the dies, the Massachusetts coins were minted by the firm of Hull and Sanderson, the leading partner being the remarkable John Hull, first of America's great silversmiths, first to learn his craft on these shores. Hull is a story in himself, but not for this book. The chronicles of his family are more than ordinarily well preserved. Not only did he keep journals and a neat letter book, but wedded his daughter to Samuel Sewall, later judge, and the great diarist of colonial America. (Slanderous gossip said he gave as dower her weight in silver from his profits at minting.) Hull, in his youth, had early gained such status as to marry into the prominent Quincy family, with John Winthrop, Sr., performing the marriage.

I cannot tarry with Hull, but at the same time cannot resist throwing in the final admonition he gave, in his late years, to the captain of one of his several trading ships, it so reflects the authentic mood of that remarkable brood of Puritan merchants, pious capitalists.

> . . . I know you will be carefull to see to the worship of God every day on the vessell and to the sanctification of the lords day and suppression of all prophaines that the lord may delight to be with you and his blessing upon you which is the hearty prayer of your frend and owner
>
> JOHN HULL

Whatever doubt there may be as to whether Joseph Jenks cut the dies with which John Hull minted pine tree shillings, there is no doubt that the town of Boston commissioned the ingenious ironmaster to make America's first "Ingine" to carry and pump water in case of fire. It was one of the earliest of such anywhere.

Boston, curiously, whether through greater inflammability than most towns or for other reasons, was particularly rich in fire engine inventors. It might have been attributed to a hot-box if the early town could have anticipated the later city's time of exaltation as "hub of the universe." In 1765, David Wheeler, blacksmith, invented a fire engine and set up to manufacture them. The same Wheeler was an early commercial exploiter of Franklin's lightning rod. The trades adapted well, for if his rods failed his fire engines could be used. A few years later, Benjamin Dearborn, of Boston, inventor of a scale and other notions, also patented improved pumps for a fire engine.

Jenks wanted to start large scale wire drawing, but failed to get support for this venture. He died in 1683, at the age of 81, at Saugus, where the iron company staggered along in its declining operations until about 1688.

Jenks had a son, Joseph, Jr., who followed him from England after a few years and pursued the same trade. Subsequently, as we have seen, he became the founder of Pawtucket, Rhode Island, drawn there by its fine waterpower. That same great liquid asset, so plentiful in New England, caused Pawtucket to become the seat of power spinning in America, after the Revolution, when the remarkable Samuel Slater came from England with the secrets of complex machinery locked in his mind. In turn, yet a third Joseph Jenks, grandson of the first, became Governor of Rhode Island from 1727 to 1732. A Stephen Jenks, of this remarkable line, was making muskets for Revolutionary soldiers, at North Providence, when the War for Independence came.

Perhaps it was one of the Jenks who began the process of one of pioneer America's anonymous, folk inventions— the American felling axe.

The English settlers brought with them the "trade axe," which came to be so-called because of the eagerness with which the Indians bartered for it. The short-handled, smaller headed hatchet form of this axe, was invented by some unknown American smith and became the famous Indian tomahawk, which was not an Indian, but a white man's creation, ironically, considering the number of white heads it cracked open.

The axe brought from England had virtually no poll (the hammer part, on the opposite side of the handle from the blade), or at least the blade side was always larger and heavier than the poll. This was the case with the tomahawk, too. The true American axe, which slowly emerged from the forges and anvils of unknown ironworkers, not only was a poll-axe, but also the poll became substantially heavier than the tapering, sharpened blade side. This gave it much more steadiness, balance, and bite than any English or European axe ever had. And this was the instrument, evolved on these shores, which for both good and bad, cut off the great primeval forests of America. The American woodsman was much slower to accept the now familiar double-edged felling axe. He called it a "back wounder." The ancient Cretans knew the double-edged axe and called it the *labrys*. It was the royal symbol of Minos, and gave us the word "labyrinth," which was the name of his vast palace at Knossos, more bewildering than the Pentagon.

Among the first Joseph Jenks' patents, or monopolies, was one for improvements in "Engines for mills to goe with water." This brings us back to where we started—the relationship between water power and settlements and the measures by which early communities wooed millers and artisans of various sorts to settle and practice among them.

The town agreements with those who ran the mills in 17th-century colonial times are revealing of values, community relationships, and communal philosophies. Any mill was regarded as something in which the town had a large stake. A source of water power, a good mill site, did not seem to our early fathers matters about which private rights or wishes could carry the day against the general need. If it was not a kind of socialism, it was at least an early recognition of the principle of eminent domain, which after all *is* a form of socialism, bringing us full circle. The point is that *laissez-faire* and rugged individualism in basic

economic matters were far from the minds of our founding
fathers who were much more concerned in matters of a
common stake. Thus, to step out of New England, in the
1670's, to the banks of the Schuylkill, we find a Court
opinion that:

> . . . it being very necessary that a mill be built on
> the Schuylkill, and there being no fitter place than
> the falls called Captain Hans Moonson's Falls, the
> Court are of opinion that Mr. Hans Moonson *ought*
> to build a mill there (as he says he will), or else
> suffer another to build for the convenience of all
> parts.

No dog-in-the-manger camping on a useful mill site was to
be tolerated. All the same, the General Court of Massachusetts was known to remand a question involving a property
right from its own jurisdiction to that of the town itself,
the higher Court being reluctant "to meddle with any man's
proprietie." Whereas the Assembly seldom gave a direct
financial aid it did sometimes give a man a reassuring promise of help in a publicly valuable but risky enterprise, "if
he doe laye out his estate in such a manner about this
publique worke, and that God shall cross him therein so
that he be impoverished thereby . . ."

When Timothy Hatherly, the founder of Scituate, and
his partner Joseph Tilden built a sawmill there, in 1656,
the town defined precisely the terms under which sawing
was to be done, including price controls:

> . . . in case any of the townsmen do bring any
> timber into the mill to be sawed, the owners of the
> mill shall saw it, whether it be for boards or plank,
> before they saw any of their own timber; and they
> are to have the one half for sawing the other half.
> And in case any man of the Town that doth bring
> any timber to the mill to be sawed shall want any
> boards for his particular use, the owners of the
> mill shall sell him boards for his own use so many
> as he shall need, for the country pay at 3*s*. 6*d*. an

hundred inch sawn; but in case the men of the town
do not supply the mill with timber to keep it at work,
the owners of the mill shall have liberty to make use
of any timber upon the Common to saw for their
benefit.

This particular mill was one of the many that were destroyed by Indians in 1676 in the fury of King Philip's
War, in which Scituate suffered heavily. Which reminds me
that the first sawmill in French Canada is said to have been
built near Montreal, around 1704, by a Massachusetts man,
appropriately named Sawyer, who had been carried off to
Canada on one of the Indian raids from the north, that
scourged Massachusetts; a threat that grew worse as the
wars with France drew on. Canada had had no one with
the necessary skills and knowledge, previously. Sawyer did
the job to ransom himself and his son from the French.

A mill agreement similar to that of Scituate was made
for one on Stony Brook, at Groton, Connecticut. John
Prescott set up a grist mill and his son Jonas, a sawmill,
around 1686. It was stipulated for Jonas that he must
"accommodate the town with merchantable boards at six-
pence a hundred feet cheaper than they were sold at any
other Saw-mills, and for town pay, and that town be
supplied before any other persons, provided, always, the
Saw-mill do not hinder the grist mill."

In 1650, a town meeting in New London, Connecticut,
agreed to cooperate with our old acquaintance, John Winthrop, Jr., for setting up a corn mill, and the town under-
took to provide the labor of building the dam and the
heavy work of the mill. "Further it was agreed, that no
person, or persons, shall set up any other milne to grind
corne, for the town of Pequett [Pequot], within the limits
of the town, either for the present, or for the future, so long
as Mr. Winthrop, or his heirs, do uphold the milne to grind
the town corn."

Winthrop leased out this mill and his lessee aggrieved
the town by his poor fulfilment of his obligations, causing

the townspeople to complain of being "much damnified."

The rallying of the town to meet the mill's need, in construction or emergency, is seen in Buchanan Read's rambling verses in a "New Pastoral," which sings of

> The ceaseless jar and whirr of rumbling stones,
> And clattering hoppers, garrulous with grain . . .

When the freshet bursts the dam

> The stream has fallen; and at the miller's dam,
> The neighbors, by good master Ethan called,
> Collecting come with crow-bar, pick, and spade,
> And in the breach begin the swift repair.

These matters of mills and millers, scythe inventors and iron workers, and even of statesmen-scientist-physicians such as Winthrop, are the background of daily growth and work behind the colonial events that get top billing in the history books. In the first few years at Plymouth what mill was needed? What was there to grind? The very first water mill at Plymouth was simply a pounding mill for samp, the crude crushed corn. Those were days when famine ruled the winter, when Governor Bradford had honored guests and recorded: "the best dish we could present them with is a lobster or piece of fish, without bread or any thing else but a cup of fair spring water . . ." and when Elder Brewster dined solely on a dish of clams and offered thanks for the divine favor "to suck of the abundance of the sea, and of treasures hid in the sand."

While political events in England influenced the traffic back and forth from the plantations, while Puritans, Brownists, and various factions quarrelled with Baptists and Quakers, while Morton's group danced about poles at Merrymount to Puritan horror, while Roger Williams and Anne Hutchinson were expelled from Massachusetts and Rhode Island was founded, while Harvard College had its start, while first the Pequot War and then the fearful

slaughter and destruction of King Philip's War largely
ended the active Indian threat in New England—during
all these trains of events, from day to day ingenuity and
inventiveness were combining with labor and vision. Sites
were sought, mills built, industries begun, grains planted
and harvested.

So it was that from the hungers of Plymouth, from early
and desperate dependency upon ships from home, those of
the new world so wrought, by "Sion's Wonder-Working
Providence," that when the political and economic tensions
grew large between colonies and mother country, Edmund
Burke, on the eve of Revolution, cautioned his countrymen
in florid periods:

> For some time past, the Old World has been fed
> from the New. The scarcity you have felt would have
> been a desolating famine, if this child of your old
> age, with a true filial piety, with a Roman charity,
> had not put the full breast of its youthful exuberance
> to the mouth of its exhausted parent.

CHAPTER 3

IRON AND INDIANS—SILVER AND BELLS

The carpenters gave nine cheers,
which was answered by the seamen
and calkers, because they had in
fourteen days completed coppering
the ship with copper made in the
United States.

—LOG OF U.S.S. *Constitution*,
JUNE 26, 1803

DURING THE height of excitement, in King Philip's War, a young worker in iron named Uriah Leonard found himself in almost as hot a battle spot as that in which King David had put his namesake, the Hittite. He was riding from Taunton, Massachusetts, to his family's iron forge in nearby Raynham when a fusillade of musketballs surprised him. He snatched off his hat and whacked the horse with it, plunging into a gallop. Bullets punched through the brandished hat and creased the horse's neck. Uriah was lucky; none touched him and he eluded the ambush, arriving safely at the forge though blood ran freely down both the legs of his horse.

He was the first and only one of the Leonards to encounter such trouble. Though it was a time of massacre, and though houses and mills were burned in great number, no attack was made on the Leonard forge. It stood not

43

far from Fowling Pond, which was the source of its bog ore. The rebellious young chieftain whom the white man called King Philip, but whose name was Metacom, was a Wampanoag, one of the two sons of the white man's friend, Massasoit. His brother, whom the whites had called Alexander, died somewhat mysteriously and revenge for suspected murder plus a general resentment of the steady encroachments of the white man sparked one of the great periodic Indian attempts to expel the English. But according to folk-say, Philip had a hunting lodge on Fowling Pond, near the Leonards, and had enjoyed friendship and the exchange of courtesies with the family. When he struck his blows, in 1675, he is supposed to have instructed the Indians not to molest the Leonards.

There was a saying, "Where you can find iron works, there you will find a Leonard." The brothers, James and Henry, who planted their clan in this country, were among the assets left from the Saugus iron works venture. They came over at the same time as Joseph Jenks. Less inventive than the Jenks family, they were none the less enterprising and probably no less valuable in their contributions, founding a kind of iron-working dynasty unto at least five or six generations.

In 1801 a Leonard was rolling iron at Canton, Massachusetts, adjacent to the mill Paul Revere set up there to roll copper. They spread out, too, for though the two first brothers were among the earliest settlers in Raynham, in 1652, Henry later removed to New Jersey and founded iron works there. The Leonard forge has sometimes been called the first in America, but Jenks seems to have a clearer title to that. It hardly matters—what counts is that Jenks, the Leonards, and more and more others, were building an industry. One of the several other Massachusetts sites where the Leonards set up furnaces was Rowley. The venture did not work out well, there. That town's destiny lay in weaving.

We might as well have a look at what an iron furnace, or foundry, was like in the 17th-century colonies. The hearth was of sandstone and the furnace was brick lined, with a height of perhaps ten to twenty feet (the latter height is found in late 18th-century American furnaces, whether so a century before I am not sure). The furnace was loaded with charcoal and ore, the fire blasted from time to time by bellows which might be worked by water power. Iron was run perhaps as much as eight tons every six days (which period was called a "founday," as we call two weeks a "fortnight"). It was as much as ten weeks before a fire was at its height. A furnace was good for about forty weeks (or "foundays"), which would produce roughly 320 tons of iron, after which it was no good and a new one had to be built.

The next two stages involved hammering in the "finery" and the "chafery." A mass from the furnace of roughly 75 lbs. was beaten into a "bloom" (whence forges that did wrought-iron work derived the name "bloomery") which was a square lump. It would then be beaten into a bar with knobby ends, known as an "ancony." Then in the "chafery" the process of beating out the uniform bar of desired size was finished. It was largely manual work but water-driven hammers were used. The use of these names varied, and so did the processes, too, but this is a general sketch of 17th-century procedure.

In remarkably short time mills for rolling and slitting (literally slicing up) bar iron were established in the Colonies and became a continuing field of improvement for inventors, not spectacularly but by the slow, often anonymous process of developing techniques and tools. The best measure of progress is in the fact that England was first amazed, then admiring, then worried at the strides made. By the early years of the 18th century she was beginning to prepare restraints for colonial iron industries. Works were founded at Abington and Hanover, in Massachusetts, and at the latter the anchors for the U.S.S. *Constitution* were forged, a long time later.

Also, after the turn of the century, two Massachusetts men practiced and at least partly invented the cheaper and more expedient process of casting iron in molds of sand, instead of clay, for hollow ware. These were Jeremy Florio and Joseph Mallinson, acting independently of each other.

While these Tubal-cains were advancing their crafts, a strange creative work was going forward outside the realm of mechanics and industry. It was the achievement of John Eliot, the Apostle to the Indians, in the creation of his Indian Bible. A cynical ditty says of the Pilgrim Fathers that

> First they fell upon their knees,
> And then upon the aborigines.

In the Pequot and King Philip's wars we see the tragic aspect of this encounter between a primitive and an advanced culture. Yet running along with the violence that occasionally flared was a strain of concern for the red brothers who sometimes were regarded as a lost tribe of Israel and sometimes as the sons of Belial.

When Eleazer Wheelock founded Dartmouth it was first conceived as a school for Indians. And though Harvard certainly was not so planned, all the same, and much earlier, Harvard graduated with a bachelor's degree Caleb Cheeshahteaumuck, in 1665. The expectation that others would attend was disappointed. Roger Williams showed a talent for good relations with the Indians, but was unable to forestall the clashes between red and white.

It was before either of the outright wars occurred that the talented linguist and minister, John Eliot, began his ambitious work of capturing the Massachusetts dialect of the spoken language of the Algonquins in the English alphabet, so that he might, as he did, create not only an Indian Bible, but a Psalter, Catechism, evangelical writings, and brief primers in logic and branches of the liberal arts. Such ventures took a long time and tremendous work, all of which was continued to completion during the very years when white man and red were trying to exterminate each other. When the work was done, the Indians for love of whom it had been done had ceased to exist as a force and the spirit to work with them as Eliot had envisioned, at least on any large scale, had vanished. Thus what was actually an astonishing intellectual and linguistic *tour de force* and a labor of formidable proportions, fell very nearly into a vacuum, so far as its original vision was concerned, ultimately to become a collector's item and curiosity. Its language is long extinct.

From it we got our political word "mugwump," which current slang would call a "big wheel." This expression was in use in New England from Eliot's time and became popularized in a special meaning in the Cleveland-Blaine election. The title of this Holy Bible, Old and New Testament, edition of 1685, in Algonquin, was "Wunneetupawatamwe UP-BIBLUM GOD Naneeswe NUKKONE TESTAMENT Kah Wonk WUSKU TESTAMENT."

One of the longest words occurred in Mark i, 40: "Wutteppesittukqussunnoowehtunkquoh," meaning "kneeling down to him."

This was one of the earliest Bibles in other than standard tongues. Obviously Eliot strove for phonetic notation, though we no longer know his system of values. Equally clearly the book had first to be read to Indians until some could be taught its alphabet in the schools Eliot founded. He did better than simply teach them this basic requirement. Some in his schools learned English, Greek, and Latin and he developed Indian teachers and preachers.

He had to consult his Indian friends for equivalents of words outside their experience. His English Bible, in the Song of Deborah, said that the mother of Sisera, looking out the window, "cried through the lattice." He tried to convey the idea of lattice to the Indians and find a word to convey the sense. Only after his book was finished did he discover that Sisera's anxious mother now cried through an eel-pot.

It is hard to measure the effect of Eliot's "praying Indians," who were settled in a number of towns in Massa-

chusetts. Most of them remained loyal during the Indian
wars. I'm sure Eliot would have been the first to insist that
"effect" was to be measured only in the salvation of each
individual Indian soul involved. Here we must agree with
him, that his conversions cannot be measure as means to
some other end. It may well be, however, that his dedicated
work, which had recovered from its setbacks by the time of
his death in 1690, helped to pick up the shattered fragments of Indian-white relationships, for although local Indian power may have been broken thoroughly, the red man
was to be around for quite some time to come.

About a half century after Eliot, a drastically different
personality put in a brief and not very happy stint as a
missionary to the Indians of the Housatonic Valley. This
was damnation's mighty thunderer, Jonathan Edwards,
who in spite of his considerable impact upon his times, had
recently thundered himself out of the Northampton pulpit
he had dominated for eighteen years.

One of Edwards' famous evocations of God's wrath por-
trayed a revolted Deity holding sinners over the pit of hell
"much as anyone holds a spider, or some loathsome insect,
over the fire . . ." At the age of twelve he had written a
treatise on "The Habits of Spiders." I hate to speculate
how he may have dealt with them. He had written on "The
Nature of the Soul" at ten, and was graduated from Yale
at seventeen.

For all the undenied force of his personality and eloquence he went up an intellectual blind alley in American
history, sowing theological confusion by denying free will,
yet insisting that men use it, and adding to misconceptions
of the Puritan. He does not represent that tradition in the
sense that Cotton Mather and Ezra Stiles may be said to do,
bracketing him in time.

A grandson of Edwards leads us back into the subject of
industry and invention. Once domestic cattle had been
brought into the colonies, in 1624, it was not long before
tanyards sprang up and that ancient trade, of whose

corpses the first gravedigger in *Hamlet* had not so very long before assured us, "a tanner will last you nine year," was extensively practised here. It was one of the earliest needed arts in every village.

The tanner's techniques remained those of tradition. A tannery was always by a stream (and was never a popular location for its stench was mighty). There was a mill for crushing tanbark (sumac was used some, but hemlock and oak were preferred and were plentiful for a long time). There were vats above ground for liming and sunken vats for leaching. The liming destroyed the hair roots and a tedious scraping in the beam house was required to get rid of the hair after the several days of soaking. (Some two centuries later a Connecticut tanner of horse hides, Benjamin Gilbert, invented a machine to make fabric out of horsehair and ushered in an era of slippery upholstery.)

Then a long immersion in the sunken vats, with the crushed bark which yielded tannic acid, preserved the leather. Various finishing processes were required according to the hides and the use intended.

Colonel William Edwards, who was Jonathan's grandson, learned the tanner's trade in New Jersey, where he had been born, but it was at Northampton, Massachusetts, his grandfather's old stamping ground, sometime around 1794, that he ran the first bark mill by water (which seems late for such application) and made other more basic improvements in method.

He first introduced drains for his vats, and raised the previously sunken tanning vats above ground, in tiers, pumping the fluids into them. Presumably the tiers represented stages of progress. Over a long career, he opened numerous tanyards, extending his activities as far as to the Catskills, where there were vast hemlock forests, destined to be chewed up to meet the needs of tanneries. He continually improved the tanning procedures, developing new types of bark mills (also being the first to remove these to some distance from the rest of the operation when

the availability of bark and water power made it desirable
to do so). He took out patents on many details of the operations.

There sprang up a large shoe industry in the colonies
and Lynn was a center of that manufacture from early
days. The shoeless condition of Continental soldiers at
Valley Forge, and other crucial times in the Revolution,
was not due to limitations of manufacture or raw materials, but to tangles in the commissariat division which
may have involved combinations of inexperience, incom-
petence, and corruption, all made worse by the inflation-
ary monetary situation. The leather and the shops and the
shoes were there.

An important and surprising invention early in the 19th
century was the humble shoe peg, which is attributed to
Joseph Walker, of Hopkinton, Massachusetts. It lowered
the price of shoes, which could be made more rapidly with
the pegs than by hand sewing. The peg was the staple of the
expanding shoe industry until the modern power sewing
machines revolutionized the manufacture. The shoe peg
also attached its name to that delicious and now too-little-
seen white corn with long, tapering kernels that will not be
regimented in rows.

Since the drift of story has carried us up to the edge of
the 19th century, we might as well find brief room here for
Paul Revere and one of his good friends. The Revocation
of the Edict of Nantes caused a great emigration from
France of the Huguenots, French Calvinists. Among the
places to which many went were the New England colonies.
Several of their names remain great on our land: Vassar,
Bowdoin, Faneuil—and Rivoire, which became Revere.

Youthful Apollos Rivoire debarked on Boston's famous
Long Wharf sometime around 1716. The town which
thrust this great finger almost a half mile out into its island-
dotted harbor, beside which any ship might be brought to
rest, was rather small, all but surrounded by mud flats,
although hills rose up in its background. A causeway helped

to impound the tide to run the town's mills. All the same, this huddled town at the water's edge long ago had become "the very mart of the land." Its great wharf and another of only somewhat lesser splendor (near the base of which Apollos' family would have its home for years) were evidence of an amazing traffic in far-plying traders and fleets of small fishing craft which pursued the cod which helped to build Boston town.

Apollos was apprenticed to the prominent silversmith, John Coney, and so learned and afterward practiced the craft which he passed on to his son, that Paul Revere who outstripped his worthy but undistinguished father in all things. Huguenot blood was blended with Yankee stock through Apollos' marriage to Deborah Hitchbourne.

For the purposes of this book, it is not "Bold Revere," as he was called, who claims our attention. The young Paul became the greatest of all the colonial silversmiths (goldsmiths, they all traditionally styled themselves, notwithstanding silver was the metal of their great works). Well over five hundred known pieces by Paul Revere are in public or private collections today.

He saw short duty in the French war but had little taste for it. The turbulent politics of pre-Revolutionary Boston town held zest for him and he flung himself into them as one of the Sons of Liberty, conspirator and propagandist, making crude and sometimes frankly plagiarized (in a free custom of the time) copperplate cartoons to whip up public feeling. His most famous was the print of the so-called Boston massacre.

He was one of the spurious Indians of the Boston Tea Party. The ride which has enshrined him in mythology was an actual one (and not his only one) though the circumstances do not quite fit the Longfellow version.

When all the shooting was over, "Bold Revere" was no longer a young man and surely there must have been a sense of letdown following years of sustained pitch. It was then, after a long career in one of the most delicate and precise of crafts, that he turned to a trade that brings him within the scope of this book, though not as a primary inventor.

In 1788 he opened an iron foundry, right among the shipyards of North Boston, and set about the manufacture of miscellaneous hardware, everything from household items to tools for smiths and shipwrights. But more emotionally fulfilling things waited. The Old North Church's bell had cracked and had to be recast. No bell had ever been cast in Boston, but Paul Revere determined to cast this one—a singularly heavy and yet at the same time delicate piece of metallurgy of which he had no experience.

He got help and advice from the Hobarts, of the iron foundry in Abington, who had cast most of the relatively few bells made in America. Revere's new North Church bell was not a very good one, but it *was* a bell and it was made in Boston. More important, it had launched an enterprise which obviously became a labor of love. Paul, and his son Joseph Warren, who soon came of an age to join his father in the business, probably cast in all some four hundred bells and shipped them to many parts of the country. Their masterpiece, best in tone and heaviest, still is heard from the tower of King's Chapel, in Boston.

Once more it turns out that this is not the end. Between the casting of bells and the manufacture of ship's hardware, Revere had found himself working with various amalgams of copper and with brass. He developed by experiment incomparably the best amalgams of copper of any founder in the country and became filled with ambition to supply one of the urgent needs of American shipping, both merchant and naval, rolled copper sheathing for hulls. The young nation which was destined to fight another war with England before so very long was wholly dependent upon that country for such sheathing.

Revere was thoroughly aware of this need and personally responsive to the challenge. The *Constitution* had been built at the wharf beside his own shop. Her bolts, blocks, sheaves, virtually all her miscellaneous hardware needs, and even her bell, had come from him and he must have

chafed that he could not handle the sheet work for her hull.
It was a satisfaction that he would yet fulfill.

Risking his long-built-up fortune and credit to the limit,
aided in cash and copper by the United States Government
(but not nearly to the match of his own commitments), he
purchased a site with water power at Canton, acquired
rollers from England, and by 1801 was producing cold
rolled copper of the best quality—the first in America. In
1803, the *Constitution,* which was occupied in the effort
to break the tyranny exercised over American shipping in
the Mediterranean by the Dey of Algiers, returned home to
Boston to have her hull sheathing renewed. This time the
still young ship that would become "Old Ironsides" got a
hull of Revere copper.

Paul Revere had done a work of industrial pioneering
that might be held to overshadow the fact that he was the
greatest silversmith of his day, were it not for the fact that
the fields are so separate as not to stand in rivalry to each
other in the one man. To cap things off, the last great interest of Paul Revere was in working with Robert Fulton to
solve the problems of copper boilers to power the steamboats with which Fulton opened the first successful commercial runs.

Joseph Warren Revere was a worthy co-worker and successor. He had been named by his father for his intimate
friend and co-patriot. Joseph Warren had fallen as a hero
in the Bunker Hill battle and it was Paul Revere who established the identity of the face-mangled body by the false
teeth he had wired in for him. The copper foundry which the
Reveres, father and son, launched and developed, grew in
an unbroken continuity into the great Revere Copper establishment of today.

Paul belonged to an early association of Massachusetts
"mechanicks" as did one of his best friends, Jacob Perkins. This man, too, had begun as a silversmith, and had
a distinguished inventive and scientific career regrettable
only in that we lost him to England while still in the vigor
of it.

Perkins was born in Newburyport, in 1766, being a little better than thirty years younger than Revere. He won respect for his abilities early, devising in his youth a new way of plating gold shoe-buckles. His first formal patent was at the age of twenty-four, for the almost inevitable nail machine upon which so many inventors cut their teeth. Early work as a die-maker for the Massachusetts mint led him into engraving for the printing of currency. He developed steel-engraving techniques and methods of protection against counterfeiting, which were valuable both to this country and England, where he was much consulted on such problems. He contrived a steam cannon, pumps and ventilators for ships, cannon-boring processes, improvements in water wheels and a variety of engines. Closer to the realms of pure science, he experimented with the laws governing steam, demonstrated the compressibility of water, and invented a bathometer for testing its depth.

Paul Revere and Jacob Perkins, as we've seen, both were silversmiths. We are going to find numerous other inventors who were trained in and practiced that craft. Like the work of the clockmaker (which, also, we will find overlaps that of the silversmith), it seemed to be an inspirer and developer of precise mechanical skills. In the 19th century, especially in Providence, Rhode Island, and Meriden, Connecticut, the silverplating industry developed. Although its basic processes were brought from England, Yankee skills contributed. It is too large and too specialized a subject to fall further within the scope of this book, but fine silver wares, sterling and plated, still remain important products of New England.

Linked threads have drawn this chapter quite some distance from the 17th-century colonial times where it began. We must find our way back at least long enough to observe that far more enterprises of manufacture and processing were going on than are indicated by the few which are touched upon here as notable instances of invention or initiative.

Potash, for example, made by the leaching of wood ashes, was greatly needed by the industries of England. That country's woods already were so depleted as to make her lean heavily upon Russia as a source of potash. To the colonists, trees were a weed. The very necessity to burn them in clearing the land yielded immense by-products of ash, to which some devoted the tedious labor of turning it into potash. It remained a constant staple of shipments to England right up to the Revolution, and afterwards.

By the late 18th century, its production had dropped off in the coastal areas. The great region of land-clearing now was inland, especially Vermont, and Boston did a large business inspecting and shipping potash from the Green Mountains. The first official patent issued by the United States Government was to Samuel Hopkins, of Burlington, Vermont, in 1791, for a new process in the leaching of ashes. In that year Vermont produced about 1,000 tons of pot- and pearl ashes (a staggering amount, since it is a light substance).

Shipbuilding began at Plymouth within four years of the founding of the plantation. The first ship's carpenter arrived at the same time as the incompetent salt maker, and was ill-starred in a different way. Bradford reported: "He quickly built them two very good and strong shallops (which after did them great service), and a great and strong lighter, and had hewn timber for two ketches; but that was lost, for he fell into a fever in the hot season of the year, and though he had the best means the place could afford, yet he died; of whom they had a very great loss, and were very sorry for his death."

Between fisheries and trade, the life of the colonies was so dependent upon the sea that shipbuilding on an ever greater scale spread swiftly up and down the entire coast. Not a field noted especially for invention, in this country, before the evolution of the steamboat and the clipper ship, it was nevertheless a blend of complex crafts and a constant area for applying and developing mechanical ingenuity. The colonies were well supplied with oak for hulls and with towering pine for masts; it became a source of friction that the king's arrow was placed on many of the finest pines to reserve them for the royal navy.

It should be said, though, that Benjamin Franklin is credited with improving ship design and being the first in the country to recommend compartmented hulls with watertight bulkheads—an idea which he borrowed, in his reading, from the Chinese.

Brewing and wine making, brick making, potteries, glass furnaces, paper making, powder making—a laborious catalogue would be required to itemize all the branches and divisions of industry and manufacture, on a scale larger than the household, which were vigorously flourishing in America before the 17th century ended.

All these enterprises were being prosecuted busily on a normal day-to-day basis when the strange witchcraft hysteria raged through Salem. Yet it is those dramatic events that are most vivid in the minds of many of us when we think of the period.

The horrors of the witchcraft prosecutions—terrible as they were in themselves—have been blown up out of all proportion and relation to context as a New England—or even a Puritan—phenomenon. Those four dark months of a localized frenzy which produced an aftermath of repentance and did not recur, do not count for much against the vast measure of the colonial record. This is not because I minimize what happened, but because what did happen was part of a pattern common to Western civilization at that stage. Such forms of demonology, happily, were in their dying flurries. Both before and after Salem the same things were done, sometimes more sweepingly and cruelly, in England and all over Europe by Roman Catholics and many shades of Protestants alike. The Salem events have to be seen in this framework.

As the chronicles of invention and industry show, the Puritan colonies had a great many better things to do—and did them—besides the burning of witches.

CHAPTER 4

PURITAN HATCHES INTO YANKEE

Your factories down east beat all
natur . . . there's one manufacture that might stump all Europe
to produce the like . . . the facture of wooden nutmegs; that's a
cap sheef that bangs the bush—it's
a real Yankee patent invention.

—T. C. HALIBURTON

FROM PURITAN into Yankee seems in some ways a more
unlikely metamorphosis on nature's part than even caterpillar into butterfly. For more than a 'hundred years of
New England life, the type that became immortal as the
Yankee, and his name, were unrecognized and unheard of.
Suddenly the creature was everywhere and the name came
on all tongues.

Josh Billings said a lot about him. I've modified his
comic spelling because it's more work than it's worth to
read it straight:

The live Yankee has no home; his love of invention
breeds a love of change, and wherever a human
trail shows itself we find him pantin' on the track.

He never gits sick at the stummuk in a furrin'
land, or grows sentermental; the beauty of a river
tew him is its capacity for a steamboat; its sloping

57

banks checker into buildin' lots, and its poetry
waters might do the drudgery of a cotton mill.

This is the Yankee who traded around the globe, who
built up into a thriving industrial region the settlements of
his Puritan predecessor, and then set out to save, improve,
or exploit, according to his taste, the rest of the American
continent. The print of his foot and the work of his hand
are everywhere in our nation.

Folklore was quick to identify this character with two
qualities: Inventiveness—"They are natural mechanicks;
the history of man's necessities is the history of their in-
venshuns," and supersalesmanship—"The oil of their
langwidge is their desire tew please, and their greasy words
foreshadder a profit."

But where on earth did this Yankee come from, who in
Artemus Ward's words could "invent, chop, swap, work,
and (if necessary) fight"? He didn't, of course, spring
full panoplied from the brow of Cotton Mather. He
emerged gradually, and remained always something of a
walking exaggeration. His very name remains a mystery.

Mencken dismisses various theories deriving the word
"Yankee" from either Indian words or Indian mispro-
nunciations. He says it belonged first to the Dutch, that as
early as 1638 pirates of the Spanish Main called single
Dutchmen *Janke,* a diminutive of *Jan,* or called them col-
lectively and contemptuously *Jankees,* meaning "John
Cheese." All this would have applied to Dutchmen of the
New Netherlands, and it is the most convincing theory
about the origin of Yankee. But when it comes to the question of how the term got itself detached from Dutchmen
and fastened onto New Englanders universally, Mencken
throws up his hands and admits that no one knows or stands
any bright prospect of finding out. He acknowledges Yankee as in use by 1765 as a derisive word and says that by
1775, as indeed every schoolboy singer of *Yankee Doodle*
knows, the Yankees had taken the name to themselves with
pride and pleasure.

Since Yankee inventiveness had built up New England it was bound to rank high in the lore about him. New England's farms are apt to be a hardscrabble proposition. There are scads of "poor land" jokes, from the warning that in Essex County, Vermont, if you aren't careful when you buy land they'll slip over more than you paid for, to the yarn about the weeping rabbit that had been left a whole township to get its living from, and couldn't.

On the other hand, there *are* some prosperous New England farms and some less well known claims about good land. Along the Housatonic where I live there are old yarns about sod so rich that if hung in the sun it dripped grease, and pigs so fat and lusty that they ran around squealing "Kill me! Kill me!" And for that matter, in 1630, Massachusetts Puritans vied with the spies of Israel by speaking of grapes four inches in circumference. I've tested that measure—perhaps it isn't too fantastic for the rich virgin soil, but it's good going.

Good soil or bad, many a New England farmer had a small workshop, mill, or even factory on his place, worked both, employing all the members of his family, and felt that he needed both, to make do. Turn it around and look at it the other way, almost every miller, gunsmith, or button maker was a farmer too. You can hardly find an eminent Yankee inventor or machinist who didn't spring from what has been called "that best school of mechanics, the New England hill farm."

Enormous amounts of yarns and finished goods were carded, spun, and woven by farm women of all ages and also young boys. As for nails—they were a well-nigh universal home industry on every farm. The earliest nails, tacks, or brads were cut from wire, or cut hot or cold from thin strips or sheets of iron, and headed by pounding in a vise. It was natural for the farmer-mechanics who had been doing that for a couple of generations to turn some of their ingenuity upon this process. Nail, tack, and brad making machines of one sort or another were among the most numerous of patents for years and years in young

America. Even so, farmers and their sons went on hammering out their heavier spikes on the anvil.

New England winters were long, and in some of their aspects, bleak. Jingle bells and the merry scene at Grandma's, frolics on the ice and sleigh rides were only so much of it. Between the time that winter closed down and the time when sap began to run and sugaring was to be done the farm shop was busy. There was harness to be mended, tools needed sharpening and repair; if there was another home product, whether nails or buttons or wool cards, now was the time to turn to it. Even the apprentice to a clockmaker might find that this was the one lucky season when he had a chance to learn the trade he had bound himself over for, since like as not his craftsman master had kept him at farm chores in the summer time.

The inventive mind is not bound by seasons, but all the same, New England winter was its time for thinking, pondering, tinkering—for patient hours needed to bring to reality the model of the notion, grand or small, that may possibly have been born in the farmer's mind while his hand was at the plow. And that notion, for all its enormous range of possible varieties, was quite likely to be a better, faster, easier way to do a necessary, familiar thing. If he could make a machine to do one job for him, he was that much more free to do some other job—or to make yet another gadget to do that one, and on and on *ad infinitum*. And there was always the dream of sudden prosperity, some golden touch, for which there was little other prospect than invention on an average Yankee's farm. Then there is plain curiosity, too, which kills cats and makes wheels go round.

There were times in the early years when it seemed that every shed in New England harbored an inventor. Along with the immediately practical touches of a better plow, a better scythe, a better shovel, a better pump, something more exotic, the old dream of the perpetual motion machine haunted hosts of Yankee tinkerers as the dream of making gold from base metals had obsessed the Middle Ages.

Even the young and sober Eli Whitney, in his youth, tried patiently the prospects of perpetual motion. Claims to have solved the mystery were common and mountebanks capitalized on demonstrations of their triumphs. An enterprising Pennsylvania Dutchman named Redheffer, who obviously missed his destiny as a Yankee, toured the country exhibiting a Rube Goldberg masterpiece of wheels within wheels, weights, counterweights, flyers, balances, pulleys and gears which ran on and on, apparently world-without-end, with no visible means of propulsion and seemingly not to be stopped short of breaking it up with a stick. He collected a dollar a head from the gapers who were willing to be taken in by a real expert.

The analytical eye of Jacob Perkins, one of the most gifted of New England's authentic inventors, spotted a part of the humming contraption which he was convinced concealed a driving cord. He challenged Redheffer to allow this ostensibly solid beam to be sawed through. The "inventor" refused. Finally at another demonstration, after a prosperous career, the analytical ear of Robert Fulton caught the subtle rhythms peculiar to hand-crank motion. Denouncing the fraud to the assembled spectators, he broke through the adjoining wall and disclosed a weary old embodiment of perpetual motion patiently turning the crank. What Perkins' eye had suspected, Fulton's ear had confirmed.

The poem about Darius Green and his flying machine, and Holmes' masterpiece about the deacon's wonderful one-hoss shay, built so well that it lasted in perfect condition until the day when every part disintegrated into dust simultaneously, both bear on the Yankee tinkerer's more grandiose visions. The "cap sheef" of all the traditions of perpetual motion (which after all had intrigued the great Leonardo) is "Shepherd Tom" Hazard's story of old Ephraim Hazard, who had built a perpetual motion ma-

chine in his attic. It was "an old woolen yarn spinning-
wheel, some four feet in diameter. To one of the spokes of
this there was tied a pair of kitchen tongs, whilst from the
opposite there dangled a flat-iron."

Proudly giving a demonstration, old Eph gave the wheel
a brisk turn. It clattered wildly around until one of the
strings broke and the iron dropped off. The inventor explained: "There, cousin Tom, if that flat-iron had been a
little weightier than them kitchen tongs, and them kitchen
tongs had been a little weightier than that flat-iron, and
that old tow string hadn't broke, that wheel would have
gone round and round, just like the world, for ever and
ever."

From some Abbott and Costello of the mid-nineteenth
century there is a hoary routine that begins:

"Well, Mr. Blitz, do you know there's a place
called Nantucket where they make machines to
manufacture nutmegs?"

"What kind of machines?"

"Why, you put a tree into the machine, then turn
a crank, and the trunk comes out bacon, hams, and
tongues; the large branches, wooden clocks and nutmegs; the balance is worked into cowcumber seeds,
Brandreth's pills, ladies bustles, and so forth."

"That's a great machine."

"It's not half as great as the shad machine."

"What's that?"

"Why, they put the machine in the mouth, and
the shad in the hopper, turn the crank, the meat
goes down and the bones fly out. . . ."

But if the hokum machines and the will-o'-the-wisp of perpetual motion did nothing but nurture a crop of ingenious
frauds and vaudeville acts to enthall gaping gullibility at
side-shows or penny museums, nevertheless, the Yankee
tinker-whittler was constructively busy. He was finding his
better way to do the job at hand: to make nails, pins, wool

cards, clock movements, or rifle barrels. "A better way" might mean a lot of things: a superior product, quicker production, meaning more of it in less time, or (where the authentic key to the future lay) a *uniform* product.

When the Preacher observed that God hath made man upright, "but they have sought out many inventions," he was not talking about the main subject of this book, even though its subject cannot be separated entirely from what he *was* talking about.

The tradition of the Yankee inventor has become entangled with the Yankee's general reputation for shrewdness, which in turn overlaps with the lore of the Yankee peddler, who was the distributor of some of the inventor's products, and in his peculiar ways a thoroughly inventive cuss himself. The peddler and the mechanical inventor were not often the same except as their activities overlapped in the careers of some of the clockmakers.

The peddler was said to live by the belief that the world would not go 'round except to the tick of a New England clock. These indomitable salesmen, afoot with pack on back or with horse and wagon as the case might be, ranged widely across the young country, from Canada to Louisiana, up and down the Mississippi and sometimes across it. Their penetration of the South was so near the point of saturation, and so disconcerting to local merchants, that the canard sprang up that a plague of Yankees was the final scourge which induced Pharaoh to release the Children of Israel. And when Rip Van Winkle awoke from his twenty-year sleep to learn that his wife was dead, it was because that choleric woman "broke a blood-vessel in a fit of passion at a New England peddler."

The peddler's wide range was attained by the shipment of large stores to strategic points, whence the retail distribution fanned out. Sometimes clocks were assembled, or tinware (another of the basic staples of the peddler) was fashioned at a temporary Southern headquarters while the selling season was on. Even the horse and wagon would be acquired locally and sold before the peddler made his final way north.

The Yankee peddler preceded in type the modern "pitchman," who still works at carnivals, on city sidewalks, and now on television. He was the spiritual father of Barnum, never a regular peddler himself, but yet the apotheosis of the tradition. He was also the forerunner of what Victorians called the "drummer" and this century, the travelling salesman. With the peddler's reputation for glibness and supersalesmanship there came also a name for outright swindling and fraud which would be less than pleasant if divorced from the laughter with which it is treated commonly. To see the world and tradition of the peddler wonderfully recreated in their finest flower, in the person of an itinerant limner, read *Rainbow on the Road*, by Esther Forbes.

It was in the nature of this crittur to capitalize on the worst aspect of his reputation. It is uncertain who launched the "wooden nutmeg" legend. T. C. Haliburton immortalized it through Sam Slick in *The Clockmaker* and its tenacity has fastened a permanent nickname on the State of Connecticut. Very likely it developed from the sale of wormy nutmegs, as worthless as if they had been made of wood.

I thought the Yankee peddler was on the scene again some years ago when I bought from a counter, in New York, a half-pound bar of milk chocolate of a standard brand manufactured in Connecticut, and opened it at home to find a slab of wood. It turned out to be a device for counter display, conveniently immune to hot weather and staleness, rather than the launching of a new Yankee tradition of wooden chocolate bars.

Yet many a Yankee peddler turned his reputed sharpness into a disarming joke. As Richardson Wright portrays him, his approach might be: "Madam, are you in need of any pocket sawmills? Horn gun-flints? Basswood hams? Wooden nutmegs? White oak cheeses? Tin bungholes? Or calico hog troughs?" Whether or not this produced a smile, he would trot out his actual merchandise: "tinware, mats, glassware, brooms, washboards, clothespins, rolling pins, matches, paddy irons, kettles, and pots."

Clocks are a grievous omission from that catalogue. Their manufacture, improvement and sale were among the Yankee's most famous and characteristic activities. The figure of the Yankee clockmaker and peddler is the link between inventors and the folklore about Yankee notions, sharp traders, wooden nutmegs, and all the other elements, realistic or fantastic, that went into the image of Sam Slick, as T. C. Haliburton embodied him in *The Yankee Clockmaker*.

Although T. C. Haliburton was a Nova Scotia man removed to New England, his Sam Slick became the image of the clockmaker, peddler, hawker-of-notions, and master salesman. There is a tradition, which I wouldn't advise anyone to take too seriously, that Sam was closely based upon the characteristics and personality of Eli Terry, famous early Connecticut clockmaker, of whom we shall see much more in a later chapter, even though James Russell Lowell indignantly repudiated Sam Slick as the authentic Yankee type. (All folk figures are hyperbolic projections. Calculate the curve and you know the reality.)

Haliburton introduces us to this itinerant on horseback invading Nova Scotia with his wares, and in recounting the exploits of the Yankee trader laments that "an American can sell his wares, at whatever price he pleases, where a blue-nose [Nova Scotian] would fail to make a sale at all.

"I had heard of Yankee clock pedlars, tin pedlars, and bible pedlars, especially of him who sold Polyglot Bibles (all in English) to the amount of £16,000. The house of every substantial farmer had three substantial ornaments, a wooden clock, a tin reflector, and a Polyglot Bible."

Sam Slick does a good deal more than sell clocks and other Yankee notions among the quiet farms of Nova Scotia. He expounds the Yankee philosophy, the gospel of industry and commercial enterprise. He is made downright restive by the sight of a tempting piece of green "interval" on the farm of Deacon Flint, and exhorts him: "I wonder, Deacon, you don't put up a carding mill on it: the same works would carry a turning lathe, a shingle machine, a circular saw, grind bark, and—" "Too old," the Deacon answers, "too old for all those speculations."

Such a failure of energies, such a lack of response to opportunity, is heresy to the Yankee itinerant salesman. He expounds his doctrine further on the subject of a railroad: "This here railroad will not perhaps beget other railroads, but it will beget a spirit of enterprise, that will beget other useful improvements. It will enlarge the sphere and the means of trade, open new sources of traffic and supply— develop resources—and what is of more value perhaps than all—beget motion. It will teach the folks that go astern and stand stock still, like the statehouse in Boston (though they do say the foundation of that has moved a little this summer) not only to go *'ahead' but to nullify time and space.*"

Yet, with the contradictions that mix, even in creativity, Sam Slick, insofar as he is a valid type, also represents a narrow utilitarianism that negates other values. His materialist-pragmatism is seen in his contemptuous comment: "As for Latin and Greek, we don't valy it a cent; we teach it, and so we do painting and music, because the English do, and we like to go ahead on 'em, even in them thar things. As for reading, it's well enough for them that has nothing to do, and writing is plaguy apt to bring a man to States-prison. . . ."

He has short shrift for shiftlessness. "An idle fellow who runs away to us, is clapped into harness afore he knows where he is, and is made to work; like a horse that refuses to draw, he is put into the Team-boat; he finds some before him, and others behind him, *he must either draw* or be *dragged to death.*"

His inventiveness, as Haliburton demonstrates, extends to creative selling approaches, also. Sam explains: "It is done by a knowledge of *soft sawder* and *human natur*. We trust to *soft sawder* to get them into the house and to *hu-*

man natur that they never come out of it." Thus Sam leaves a clock at Deacon Flint's house ostensibly to disencumber himself of it while on another errand. He explains it is *not* for sale, in fact is spoken for, but when it has run there for several weeks and been admired, he allows himself to be high-pressured into selling it, over protests that he doesn't know what he will say to the fictitious promised customer.

Richardson Wright's list of wares carried by the Yankee peddlers is capable of a great deal more extension, for the field of what were universally called "Yankee notions" was vast. The term still survives in the catch-all "notion" counter of many stores. The peddler offered jack-knives, "hankychers," pins, needles, caps for men and women, miscellaneous clothing, yard goods, sewing thread, scissors, thimbles, knitting yarns, shoes, combs, razor strops, axe handles and heads, suspenders, lace, patent medicines, smelling salts, bowls and baskets, candle molds, seasonings and essences (peppermint, vanilla, cocoa, wintergreen), herbs (Shaker yarbs), seeds, pictures, portraits to order (from ready-painted backgrounds and figures, male and female, clothed appropriately for a variety of ages and professions or stations in life—the features blank, to be painted in), tea and pots for it, crockery, puzzles, books, tracts, sheets of ballads and songbooks, Bibles, and on and on into catalogues that hardly any one peddler could have stocked but which, among them, they disseminated to fabulous distances.

Amazing loads were carried on their backs by the peddlers, packed with a wonderful space-saving ingenuity. The long-shanked hawker was a familiar sight on the roads, a little stooped when on the earlier part of his route, by the great pack strapped to his back, odd-shaped items such as pans dangling from his belt, knives and whistles and buttons and buckles in his pockets and side pouches.

When this figure was spotted trudging into village or up to farmhouse, there were whoops and shouts from children, old folk got out of rockers, wives came from kitchens, loafers from taverns, and the workingman might sometimes emerge from shop or field or barn. For his arrival was not only the coming of goods, needed or merely tempting, it was also the coming of news and entertainment, a word from the world behind the hills. This was especially the reward of the family that might give the peddler a night's lodging.

For his part, this vendor was a practicing psychologist, depending in Sam Slick's words on "soft sawder and human natur' " to unload his wares. He knew that the news, yarns, gossip and gags that he brought, and the ready wit of his patter, were the softeners of thrift-dedicated hearts, the untiers of purse strings. A slick line of chatter was the one commodity he could carry in infinite supply without adding to the weight that he must tote or his horse must pull. So the customer could and did count on an artful earful, but if experienced had his salt to swallow it with, even though there were times (and these the wise man could probably discern) when an authentic piece of big news, from the sudden death of a great man to an event in politics, might first reach the hinterlands by peddler.

The more ambitious peddlers, those who worked with horse and wagon, could take in a larger area and carry a more extensive stock. All peddlers, but especially those on wheels, did a fair amount of their trading on swap, in which case sharp practice could cut both ways and devil take the hindmost. In this *caveat emptor* tradition, where most everyone clothed and in his right mind knew the score, the swap and even the cash sale was an acknowledged contest. If you were roundly bested, either through misappraisal of the man or the merchandise, you were fair game and the subject more of laughter than of indignation and redress. The peddler sometimes had the experience of accepting from a housewife a large bundle of sifted hearth ashes (for the potash trade) to later find that the center core of it was refuse.

The wagon peddler was a regular side show and among his professional skills was the rapier thrust for the local wits and hecklers. Someone would interrupt in the midst of his spiel: "Any goose-yokes?" "No, but I'll take your measure and bring 'em next time"—and the selling pitch was resumed.

The wagon might simply be the standard flat-bed, with an arched canvas cover. More elaborate ones were regular vans, with sloping sides constituting shelves of merchandise, the hinged covers of which were folded back like opening up the kitchen cupboard, to display the offerings. The inside was for larger items and the replacement stock. Sometimes these vehicles were likened to hearses, but were apt to be brightly painted, and one such had a bower of woven branches arching from the sides over the driver's seat to shelter the peddler from sun and rain.

Patent medicine is a basic Yankee tradition from Kickapoo Indian Sagwa to Peruna to the career and products of the remarkable Lydia E. Pinkham, the latter enshrined in a lugubrious ballad as "friend of the human race."

Most any peddler was apt to carry a line of cures and nostrums and some specialized in such. There was a story about a peddler who overtook the wagon of a competitor on the road and started to pass him. "What do you carry?" the first one called out. "Drugs and medicines." "Go on ahead then; I carry grave stones."

Connecticut men were quite diligent in making remedies. Samuel Lee patented and sold Lee's Windham pills, and Lee's New London pills, to aid biliousness—supposedly the first product of their kind. Elisha Perkins created a fad, around 1796, that took the nation by storm briefly, and even spread to England. He used a contraption of what he called "metallic tractors," with points of steel and brass. As they were sometimes called galvanic there is a suggestion that electric shock may have been used, too, all for the purpose of curing aches and pains. A New Hampshire man named Thomas Fessenden ridiculed the device, at the height of its publicity, with a long comic poem called "The Terrible Tractoration."

"Crazy" Lorenzo Dow, the Massachusetts-born evangelist, brewed patent medicines and combined the peddling of them, sometimes, with his amazingly far-flung preaching journeys.

That rare creature from Massachusetts, John Chapman, known to us as Johnny Appleseed, was a Yankee peddler— a "give-away" peddler at times and a dedicated Swedenborgian missionary. He carried some superstitious freight such as a belief in the anti-malarial virtues of dog-fennel, which he distributed widely enough for it to become a scourge. Still he was a peddler, pictured sometimes with horse and wagon, but more commonly afoot with seed-stuffed pack on his back, striving to make orchards in the wilderness. The whole frontier knew and loved him. But he dealt in cash, too, as a merchant. He sold trees or seeds to many who could pay and gave to those who could not. He carried ribbons and calico, at least in small quantities, chiefly to give away to girl children.

Another peddler, familiar to Virginia roads, was the New England farmer's son, Bronson Alcott, father of Louisa May. This dreamer spent many of his youthful years roaming with his wagonload of Yankee notions until he gave it up to come to Boston and "invent" the "progressive school" long before John Dewey and the Lincoln School were heard of.

In the south, one folk figure described another. Davy Crockett, backwoodsman, politician, humorist, and hero of the Alamo, sketched a lasting picture of the Yankee peddler he called Job Snelling, "a gander-shanked Yankee, who had been caught somewhere about Plymouth Bay, and been shipped to the West with a cargo of codfish and rum." Observe the sardonic tribute to Yankee invention.

> The whole family were geniuses. His father was the inventor of wooden nutmegs, by which Job said he might have made a fortune, if he had taken out a patent and kept the business in his own hand; his mother Patience manufactured the first white oak pumpkin seeds of the mammoth kind, and turned a pretty penny the first season; and his aunt Prudence was the first to discover that corn husks steeped in

tobacco water would make as handsome Spanish wrappers as ever came from Havana, and that oak leaves would answer all the purposes of filling, for no one could discover the difference except the man who smoked them, and then it would be too late to make a stir about it. Job himself bragged of having made some useful discoveries, the most profitable of which was the art of converting mahogany sawdust into cayenne pepper, which he said was a profitable and safe business; for the people have been so long accustomed to having dust thrown in their eyes, that there wasn't much danger of being found out.

So much for the peddler in his various aspects.

The outburst of mechanical invention which gave rise to all this Yankee lore—and also gave rise to American industry—was not unique to our shores. It was something happening in Western civilization, when seen in full scale, with shifting centers of especially furious activity over hundreds of years. One such center is all that can be claimed for America, but there it showed particular characteristics, related to circumstance and need, but not wholly explained by them. England pioneered the steam engine, but saw and used it chiefly as a fixed source of power. America had abundant fixed sources of power in its wealth of rushing streams. It seized upon the steam engine as a mobile power, a means to get somewhere, so that though England worked early with steamboats and locomotives it was the American who wrought the greatest advancements with these things the better to master the challenging distances of his sprawling continent.

England pioneered the fabulous textile machinery. America hastened to pirate it, to create something new of the factory system, and to make the cotton gin that would make cotton an explosive economic force.

Inventive genius, and lesser cleverness, were not limited to New England, and the story could not be told without

involving men from other sections of the new nation; but
the Yankees of Connecticut and the neighbor states form
a rare and special group, and New England a specific
locus, to capture the essence of one of the phenomena that
made the United States. And although ingenuity arrived
with the first settlers and still flourishes today, the story
which this book seeks to tell is the special one, chiefly
within a span of some fifty years, in which hand crafts
became mechanical crafts and these in turn became modern
industry.

That Connecticut was peculiarly a center of this awakening of America's mechanical genius was recognized by
Mark Twain when he sent his imperishable Connecticut
Yankee back to the sixth century to industrialize the realm
of Arthur and to confound Merlin's magic with Yankee
wizardry.

Twain's hero came from East Hartford. His explanation
of himself is practically a manifesto:

> So I am a Yankee of the Yankees—and practical;
> yes, and nearly barren of sentiment, I suppose—or
> poetry, in other words. My father was a blacksmith,
> my uncle was a horse-doctor, and I was both, along
> at first. Then I went over to the great arms factory
> and learned my real trade; learned all there was to
> it; learned to make everything: guns, revolvers, can-
> non, boilers, engines, all sorts of labor-saving ma-
> chinery. Why, I could make anything a body wanted
> —anything in the world, it didn't make any differ-
> ence what; and if there wasn't any quick new-fangled
> way to make a thing, I could invent one—and do it
> as easy as rolling off a log.

It didn't take such a fellow long to adjust to the problem
of finding himself transported through time and space
some thirteen centuries. His Yankee philosophy equipped
him for all contingencies.

I made up my mind to two things: if it was still the
nineteenth century and I was among lunatics and
couldn't get away, I would presently boss that asy-
lum or know the reason why; and if, on the other
hand, it was really the sixth century, all right, I
didn't want any softer thing: I would boss the whole
country inside of three months.

He wasted no time on nostalgia (which in his case was
the remembrance of things future) beyond an occasional
waking o' mornings and listening for the sound of Colt's
factory whistle. Instead, he founded his Man Factory, to
remodel the creature of the Dark Ages.

About half of the Yankee vision is here, the so-called
"practical" half, for Sir Boss confessed his own obtuseness
to the world of sentiment and poetry, qualities which
throve well in Yankee air in their own contexts, in New
England's celebrated flowering. Twain's particular breed
of Yankee believed in education—but as an arch utilitarian
and sometime debunker. Anything that could not be
shaped, carpentered, cast, molded, hammered, tinkered,
and combined into parts of an engine that could be made
to run lacked reality for him. To this Yankee, his transcendentalist neighbors seemed almost another race. There
were plenty of both and they had much in common, in
spite of apparent differences. One of the ironies of culture
is that the descendant of the transcendental Yankee (and
sometimes that transcendentalist himself) tends to roman-
ticize the materialist Yankee. But these basic types coexisted and frequently overlapped, for men never fit quite
perfectly into the categories we invent for them.

James Russell Lowell, agreeing with the estimate
Twain's Yankee made of himself, said of the New England nature, "If there be any poetry, it is something that
cannot be helped—the waste of the water over the dam."
Yet that mystical nature lover, Thoreau, was a maker and
improver of lead pencils, as well as a meditator on the
shores of Walden Pond.

The dean of the transcendentalists, Emerson himself,

denied the Yankee salesman but confirmed the inventor
when he declared that though a man be living in the
remotest woods, if he made a better mousetrap the world
would beat a path to his door. In fact, Emerson had turned
his long thoughts upon the inventiveness around him. He
knew what history proves about inventions, great and small,
that they are not dependent upon one man or group of
men—that they were waiting their time—bound to be invented—not to be denied. " 'Tis frivolous to fix pedantically
the date of particular inventions. They have all been invented over and over fifty times. Man is the arch machine,
of which all these shifts drawn from himself are toy
models." He knew that "invention breeds invention," and
he felt, in terms that would have been richly congenial
to Franklin, that it was not to be avoided but sought that
men should seed one another's minds with their ideas.
"Only an inventor knows how to borrow, and every man is
or should be an inventor." And he expressed the concept
of putting "creed into deed" which is certainly what the
materialist Yankee did.

There were dissenting voices, all the same, about the
Yankee faith in *things,* in work, and in salvation by invention. Moody Nathaniel Hawthorne, in his story "The
Hall of Fantasy," sharply derided the inventive spirit in a
passage almost certainly influenced by Swift's famous satirical academy of sciences visited by Gulliver on his third
voyage. In Hawthorne's great exhibition hall

> . . . were the inventors of fantastic machines . . .
> here was a machine . . . for the distillation of heat
> from moonshine, and another for the condensation
> of morning mist into square blocks of granite . . .
> One man exhibited a sort of lens whereby he had
> succeeded in making sunshine out of a lady's smile
> . . . Prof. Espy was here with a tremendous storm
> in a gum-elastic bag. I could enumerate many more
> of these Utopian inventions, but, after all, a more
> imaginative collection is to be found in the Patent
> Office at Washington.

The pessimistic Hawthorne would have been content to relegate most of the mechanical works of his fellow New Englanders to the giant bonfire, set by his Titan of Innovation, to consume all the world's vast rubble of *things,* expecting to find whatever was of lasting merit among the ashes.

A temperament almost a world apart from Hawthorne was Dr. Oliver Wendell Holmes. He practised medicine with distinction, lived the life of intellect and the arts, and tinkered in true Yankee style. In medicine he earned distinction by writing a famous paper on "The Contagiousness of Puerperal Fever," and he invented an improved stethoscope. The invention of that basic Victorian home entertainer, the stereoscope, for seeing pictures in what our age has dubbed "3-D," is attributed to him, and he might have made a fortune by it had he been fortune minded —which he was not. His poem about the "Wonderful One-Hoss Shay," so perfectly built that it lasted without a flaw until it dissolved totally in an instant, expressed on one level his sly opinion about the collapse of Calvinism, but on the face of it was a simple josh at meticulous Yankee craftsmanship.

Twain took up his Yankee at what is really the end of the focal story of invention in New England, the fulfilment of the drastic and remarkably quick change from hand craft to industry. At Colt's factory he stood in the midst of an accomplished fact, although his spirit was the spirit of those who had brought it all to pass. So the story does not begin, it ends, with Twain's Connecticut Yankee. The beginning is earlier in Connecticut days—and for all its concentration there, it does not and cannot exclude the threads of sub-plot which lead off to all the rest of New England, and to New York, Pennsylvania, Delaware, New Jersey, Maryland, Virginia, and Georgia.

The people who established Connecticut as a colony were emigrants from an emigration, coming, around 1635, under the leadership of Thomas Hooker and Roger Ludlow, from Massachusetts because of certain displeasures with the system of government as established there. The rule they set up for themselves did not differ startlingly, but it was their own. It was sufficient as they expressed at the end of their formal petition for the right to go, that they felt a "strong bent of their spirits to remove thither." The Saybrook settlement on the Connecticut River was almost simultaneous with the Hooker and Ludlow groups. The centers of the Hooker migration were Wethersfield, Windsor, and Hartford. They were a church-state, and had a £30 property qualification for voting.

Very little afterwards (1638), Puritans under John Davenport and Theophilus Eaton established an independent Plantation at New Haven. It was theocratic, ruled by Mosaic Law. This completed what could be called the seeding of Connecticut.

New Haven is of particular interest. It had about as narrowly restrictive a government as any settlement in the new world, and long was known for its blue laws. When, in 1662, by royal charter, it was incorporated with the rest of Connecticut, the people of New Haven protested and resisted clamorously, though fruitlessly. The city shared with Hartford the dignity of state capital, on an alternating basis, for some 175 years. As an aside to New Haven's political-religious rigidity, it is a curiosity that the State of Connecticut never has ratified the Bill of Rights. This technicality is likely to remain as a treasured oddity, just as Massachusetts in recent years would not revoke the banishment of Anne Hutchinson. (Likewise, the people of Vermont never ratified their emergency-born state Constitution.)

By all pat formulae we might look for a story of throttled creativity in the State of Connecticut and the city of New Haven, or almost anywhere in Puritan New England. Happily, history doesn't work with such simplicity. We've already met the humane, inventive, scientific John Winthrop, Jr., who was one of Connecticut's molders.

For all the admitted rigors and bigotry, modern liberal

horror at Puritan attitudes often has been overdone. The *New England Primer* would appall today's child psychologist. Its alphabetical preparation for life (and death) from

> In Adam's fall
> We sinned all

to

> Xerxes did die,
> And so must I

and

> While Youth do cheer
> Death may be near

may be laughed at for its lugubriousness. Yet in our age, in which people "pass on"; in which "Mr. Joyboys" preside over "Mortuary Parlors," and honest graveyards have become "Memorial Parks," the blunt factuality of the Puritan primer looks pretty good, even for the young.

Puritan life and thought were not perfect, but they had backbone, a sense of reality, a conviction of God's purpose, and will. These are the stuffs that breed accomplishment, in spite of excessive narrowness and over-zeal. No such good fruits can proceed from greater liberty and tolerance if slack, sloth, aimlessness and indifference are in place of the Puritan gifts.

Puritan theocracy and blue laws notwithstanding, Connecticut had its full share in the cultural-intellectual-educational output of New England, and in mechanical invention, something of a lion's share. New Haven, in particular, accumulated an astonishing record.

David Bushnell conceived and designed his submarine there, while an undergraduate at Yale. Eli Whitney studied at Yale, returned to New Haven to manufacture his cotton gin and to establish there his musket manufactory. Samuel Colt made his first revolvers in the Whitney plant, before setting up permanently at Hartford. Eli Whitney Blake,

nephew of the great man and one of the inheritors of
his industrial responsibilities, invented the stone-crusher
which remains basic in the production of materials for our
modern highways. Chauncey Jerome established the
Jerome Manufacturing Company with his revolutionary
methods in the clock industry. John Marlin made guns
there. Charles Goodyear did much of his obsessive, dedicated labor there, haunting its streets at times clad all in
rubber, as the man in the nursery rhyme was clad all in
leather. Ithiel Town, architect, who built both Center
Church and Trinity Church on the New Haven Green,
also was one of the pioneer inventors of archless truss
bridges. Yet all this does not exhaust the possible catalogue
of New Haven's inventive history which includes the inevitable host of patents whose claimants are forgotten, the
products of anonymous ingenuity, the still-born inventions.

Work always was honorable in the colonies. The new
country never saw a significant class to which work was a
mean thing. The greater number of our early statesmen,
philosophers, scientists, and artists were men whose hand
knew the plow, the hammer, the forge, the axe, the saw,
and the surveyor's transit. Many of them, like Washington
the aristocrat, knew the wilderness intimately as surveyors
and soldiers. The new nation to them was not an abstract
political concept, an ideological proposition. They knew its
soil, its rivers and forests, its mineral resources, its vast
potential under the application of ingenuity and labor. They
knew, too, the infinite diversity of the men it harbored,
knew them realistically, unromantically for the blend from
worth to worthlessness represented in them. The demands
of farm, frontier, workshop, college, and congress on their
several or overlapping levels, were the sifters of men. A
man was known by his works, without preconception, about
as thoroughly as possible considering the creature of prej-
udice and rooted habit that man is.

No arbitrary cleavage between men who work with their
minds and those who work with their hands had arisen. It

was not only Washingtons, Jeffersons, Franklins, Whitneys who ·counted—men who learned and worked. There were the men who worked and learned, one of the most famous being "the learned Blacksmith," Elihu Burritt, of New Britain, Connecticut, who made himself a master linguist, scholar, and pacifist organizer and tract writer. This "Apostle of Universal Brotherhood" learned Greek and Hebrew at the anvil, and is said to have acquired forty to fifty languages. The very pride of craft that impelled Pat Lyon, blacksmith of Boston, to commission the now famous portrait of himself at the anvil, by John Neagle, is part of this spirit.

This was a time when the dignity of the hand was ending the domination of the hand. With their hands, the mechanic geniuses constructed the machines that replaced the hand. The spirit of the age was a sense in many inquiring minds that discoveries were about to be made and achievements done that would change everything. They were right (as is almost every distinguished era in its similar conviction) though the fruits were not to be millennial and Utopian as the philosophic *zeitgeist* encouraged men to hope.

An immense and naive optimism as to what Man was about to make of himself coexisted on the philosophical level with the hardheaded appraisal of the value of specific men. Following the theocratic Puritanism of the first settlements, the humanistic Deism of Washington, Jefferson, Paine, Franklin, and most of the leading men of the age, filtered down the unlearned ranks of such ragged souls as "poor John Fitch," the steamboat man, giving rise to weird movements and strange quasi-messianic hopes, while at the same time the cool and unromantic mind of Hamilton, aristocrat of bastardy, saw the people as "a great beast." The age of transcendentalism would soon follow in New England, blending with politics and economics at Brook Farm, and Melville would rumble his dark and superb rhetoric, setting Ahab and his white whale upon one another, in anguish over the chaos in both man and nature that transcendentalism failed to encompass or resolve

At Waltham, and then at Lowell, the Americans would establish something new—an idealized factory system—a spinning mill that was half female seminary, to the amazement and admiration even of those travellers who viewed most of the rest of America with a jaundiced eye. Yet this, a kind of transcendentalism in industry, would pass into limbo when manufacturers need no longer staff their plants with New England's girls of respectable and gentle nurture but could draw on the vast, impersonal, unguarded resource of mass immigration.

All this was the breeding and nurturing of the Yankee, as Billings said, "Chock full of character and sissing hot with enterprise and curiosity."

CHAPTER 5

THE SWIMMER

One would not, therefore, of all
faculties or qualities of the mind,
wish for a friend or a child that he
should have that of invention.
—BENJAMIN FRANKLIN

ON A certain day in the early years of the 18th century, a
boy was seen swimming in a large New England pond. Being a lad who could carry more than one interest at a time,
he had been flying a kite on what must have been a fine
day with a stiff and steady wind. He had tied the long leash
of his kite to a stake, leaving the airfoil to fly itself at its
windy height.

If multiple interests were characteristic of this boy, so too
was the related gift of the association of ideas. The swimmer rolled in the water and watched the tugging kite and an
idea was born. He emerged naked from the pond and un-
tied the cord. The pull of the kite was strong and steady.
The boy entered the water once more, no doubt taking several turns of the cord around his wrist to prevent escape.
Then floating easily on his back, he found with delight that
he was towed strongly through the water.

Having tried the strength of this strange water wing, it
was again the lad's nature to discipline it to some specific
task. There was at least one witness to the venture, another
boy. The nautical kite flyer, having appraised the course of

the wind, bargained with the spectator to carry his clothe:
around to the far side of the pond, the better part of a mile
away. Then like Odysseus with Aeolus' gift of a guiding
wind, the swimmer "began to cross the pond with my kite
which carried me quite over without the least fatigue, and
with the greatest pleasure imaginable. I was only obliged
occasionally to halt a little in my course, and resist its progress, when it appeared that, by following too quick, I lowered the kite too much. . . ."

There are two clues to the identity of this inventive boy,
though many a Yankee might conceivably have had such a
notion. It is not too remotely unlike sail-skating. Yet in
spite of the utterly different purpose for which it was employed, the kite has so great an identification in our folklore
with Benjamin Franklin that it might lead us to guess at
him—and indeed, it was he. The other clue is the swimming. Though it is less well known, Franklin had great
skill in this sport. In later years as a young man in England, he found much opportunity for employment as a
swimming teacher to the sons of gentlemen.

The kite venture actually was the lesser of his creative
ideas applied to swimming. He devised an anticipation of
the frogman equipment. "I made two oval palettes, each
about ten inches long and six broad, with a hole for the
thumb, in order to retain it fast in the palm of my hand.
They much resembled a painter's palettes. In swimming I
pushed the edges of these forward, and I struck the water
with their flat surfaces as I drew them back. I remember I
swam faster by means of these palettes, but they fatigued
my wrists. I also fitted to the soles of my feet a kind of
sandals; but I was not satisfied with them, because I observed that the stroke is partly given by the inside of the
feet and the ankles, and not entirely with the soles of the
feet."

Franklin is at once one of the supreme inventive minds
and one of the least typical inventors. His whole philosophy
of invention was individual and almost calculated to em-
barrass those whose careers involved arduous struggles over

their patent rights. Of all his inventions, only two in any direct way gave immediate rise to businesses—the Franklin stove and the lightning rod—and in neither case did the inventor take any active interest or part in their exploitation.

Many inventors failed through inability to carry to fulfilment some idea or principle of which they had grasped the rudiments. Franklin in his constant but casual curiosity turned up the beginnings of many inventions which he could have developed but for which he simply lacked the interest in his busy career. He strewed such ideas about freely. In many cases he made one single ingenious contrivance of the sort which a modern businessman would exploit, but made it solely for his personal convenience. The fabulous library and study of his Philadelphia home was full of such gadgets: a little press for duplicating letters in anticipation of the mimeograph; an artificial arm and hand for handling books on high shelves, analogous to the claw every grocery store uses to get the puffed wheat from the top shelf; a rocking chair with a built-in fan, worked together by a pedal. To Franklin these were merely what used to be called "conceits."

His bi-focal glasses were another such casual creation. They did not arise from optical experiments or from the wish to make a marketable product. In his old age, while Ambassador to France, he found his two pairs of spectacles for close and distant seeing to be a nuisance and had the simple (for him) idea of having "the glasses cut and half of each kind associated in the same circle." The exploitation of this idea beyond his personal need, interested him not at all. He merely remarked that they were particularly handy to him, being in France: ". . . the glasses that serve me best at table to see what I eat not being the best to see the faces of those on the other side of the table who speak to me; and when one's ears are not well accustomed to the sounds of a language, a sight of the movements in the features of him that speaks helps to explain; so that I understand French better by the help of my spectacles."

Though as a printer and publisher he understood and
practiced the arts of business, and though as a statesman
he understood and practiced the arts of negotiation between
powers, there was little of the competitive spirit, as such, in
him and absolutely nothing of the monopolist. He wanted
what was his due and his need. Beyond this he was willing
that every man might seek his own profit, whether from
Benjamin Franklin's ideas or another's.

Often his ingenuity was applied for the public welfare.
It was he, in Philadelphia, who conceived the conveniences
of paved walks and the simple expedient of employing
someone at small public expense to keep them clean. He
was one of those who encouraged improvement in street
lamps which grew out of his observation of how, in London, globe lamps without proper ventilation top and bottom, became dim with soot a few hours after being lit. In
Philadelphia he introduced the street lamp of square shape
with separate panes of glass. One of these being broken
could be replaced without discarding the whole. He provided vents at the bottom and a chimney at the top, resulting in a cheaper, more convenient lamp which burnt all
night without blackening.

Franklin understood well the mishaps inevitable to inventors in the order of human nature. He knew that prophets are not without honor save in their own country and
that many men are slow to credit the achievements of others. "There are everywhere a number of people who, being
totally destitute of any inventive faculty themselves do not
readily conceive that others may possess it . . . With
these, everyone who offers a new invention is deemed a
pretender: he had it from some other country or from
some book. A man of their own acquaintance, one who
had no more sense than themselves, could not possibly, in
their opinion, have been the inventor of anything."

These are of the sort who protested: "Can any good
thing come out of Nazareth?" and: "Is not this the carpenter, the son of Mary, the brother of James . . . and
are not his sisters here with us?"

Franklin knew, too, the opposite side of the same problem in psychology. He had observed the "pretensions to invention which vanity is daily producing . . . Jealousy and envy deny the merit or the novelty of your invention; but vanity, when the novelty and merit are established, claims it for its own." This is why, he argued, the origin of so many great inventions of early times is either unknown or disputed. With a surprising pessimism he concluded: "One would not, therefore, of all faculties or qualities of the mind, wish for a friend or a child that he should have that of invention. For his attempts to benefit mankind in that way, however well imagined, if they do not succeed, expose him, though very unjustly, to general ridicule and contempt; and if they do succeed, to envy, robbery, and abuse." One can imagine the voices of John Fitch and many another chiming in with an "Amen!"

We can see in this face of the matter, the wistfulness which must have impelled George White, the early biographer of Samuel Slater, to throw in a footnote: "At Grand Cairo in Egypt, they have such a profound respect to new inventions, that whoever is the discoverer of any new art or invention is immediately clad in cloth of gold, and carried in triumph throughout the whole city, with trumpets and other musical instruments playing before him and presented to every shop to receive the joyful acclamation and general presents of his fellow citizens." An unlikely tale.

The sum of Franklin's extraordinarily disinterested attitude toward the inventor's claims is best seen in his own words about his famous stove, from the *Autobiography:*

. . . Having, in 1742, invented an open stove for the better warming of rooms, and at the same time saving fuel, as the fresh air admitted was warmed in entering, I made a present of the model to Mr Robert Grace, one of my early friends, who, having an iron-furnace, found the casting of the plates for these stoves a profitable thing, as they were growing in demand. To promote that demand, I wrote and published a pamphlet, entitled: *An Account of the*

New-Invented Pennsylvania Fireplaces; wherein their Construction and Manner of Operation is particularly explained; their Advantages above every other Method of warming Rooms demonstrated; and all Objections that have been raised against the Use of them answered and obviated, etc. This pamphlet had a good effect. Gov'r. Thomas was so pleas'd with the construction of this stove, as described in it, that he offered to give me a patent for the sole vending of them for a term of years; but I declin'd it from a principle which has ever weighed with me on such occasions, viz., *That, as we enjoy great advantages from the inventions of others, we should be glad of an opportunity to serve others by any inventions of ours; and this we should do freely and generously.*

He cites instances in which a London ironmonger, and others, at different times and with different devices, attempted to patent ideas of his. All such moves "I never contested, as having no desire of profiting by patents myself, and hating disputes."

Here is a desperate radical, indeed, rejecting the time-hallowed concept of the profit motive as the incentive to creativity. Such men are dangerous.

Before leaving this stove of Franklin's by the way, it is worth noting the strong resemblance, in principle, to the modern Heatilator-type fireplace. It is a kind of built-in Franklin stove, using his idea of a double-walled air chamber of metal to draw in, heat, and lead out, air apart from the natural radiation of the open fire.

To seek an understanding of Franklin through his origins is not greatly illuminating. His people, in England, had been franklins for a long time before that designation of status—meaning a free, landholding farmer below the level of the gentry—became a surname. His immediate ancestors numbered smiths, dyers, scriveners, and the like. They were Protestant and in Queen Mary's reign, when there were dangers for their persuasion, one of Benjamin's forebears showed a Franklinesque ingenuity:

> They had got an English Bible, and to conceal and secure it, it was fastened open with tapes under and within the cover of a joint-stool. When my great-great-grandfather read it to his family, he turned up the joint-stool upon his knees, turning over the leaves then under the tapes. One of the children stood at the door to give notice if he saw the apparitor coming, who was an officer of the spiritual court. In that case the stool was turned down again upon its feet, when the Bible remained concealed under it as before.

Franklin's father, Josiah, had come to New England in 1682, with his first wife and three children. Franklin was born of a second wife, Abiah Folger, and was the youngest but two of a grand total of seventeen children Josiah had by the two marriages. Benjamin remembered as many as thirteen at table at one time, all of whom survived to maturity.

Josiah was a man of splendid character and his son left a touching account of him, reporting incidentally that, "He had a mechanical genius too, and, on occasion, was very handy in the use of other tradesmen's tools" (he was himself a candle maker). But at the crowded family table the boy was submitted to influences the effects of which are visible in the Franklin who founded first the Junto and then the Philosophical Society.

> At his table he liked to have, as often as he could, some sensible friend or neighbor to converse with, and always took care to start some ingenious or useful topic for discourse, which might tend to improve the minds of his children. By this means he turned our attention to what was good, just, and prudent in the conduct of life; and little or no notice was ever taken of what related to the victuals on the table, whether it was well or ill dressed, in or out of season, of good or bad flavor, preferable or inferior to this

or that other thing of the kind, so that I was bro't up
in such a perfect inattention to those matters as to be
quite indifferent what kind of food was set before
me, and so unobservant of it, that to this day if I am
asked I can scarce tell a few hours after dinner what
I dined upon.

In the Boston in which Benjamin grew up, his father's
shop was near the Mill Cove, which could possibly have
been the pond of his kite-swimming notion. During Benjamin's early youth and his rather unhappy apprenticeship
to his brother as a printer, there were many other appren-
tices in the town (enough sometimes to kick up a riot). A
lad named Thomas Hancock was destined to do well for
himself and bring up, as if it were his own son, a nephew
named John. Franklin would know him. The young French
Calvinist, Apollos Rivoire, was soon to metamorphose into
Paul Revere and raise a like-named son. But Benjamin was
not to stay in Boston—he moved in larger orbits.

Hoping to discourage Benjamin from a strong inclination
to run off to sea, as one brother had done, Josiah exposed
him to the work of many trades, that he might find a congenial one. This, too, bore fruit. "It has ever since been a
pleasure to me to see good workmen handle their tools;
and it has been useful to me, having learnt so much by it
as to be able to do little jobs myself in my house when a
workman could not readily be got, and to construct little
machines for my experiments, while the intention of making the experiment was fresh and warm in my mind."

His mention of experiments reminds us that Franklin
was not just a contriver of useful, convenient, or amusing
gadgets, but was of major stature as what we would call a
scientist but his world generally called a philosopher.

In the colonial mind, or more inclusively, in the 18th-
century mind, "philosophy" was a term much involved with
mechanics, scientific experiments of all sorts, and general
speculation on the nature and behavior of physical phenomena. Every college and academy boasted of its "new and

respectable philosophical apparatus," by which was meant a limited supply of vessels and retorts, Leyden jars, mineral specimens and archaeological and paleontological curios, globes and astrolabes, orreries, and whatever else could be had by way of laboratory equipment for the study of science.

When Franklin, that most protean of all early America's diverse geniuses, in 1743 founded the American Philosophical Society (an enlarged conception of his local, intimate Junto) his printed "proposal" sent to prospective members throughout the colonies gave a glimpse of all that the word "philosophical" connoted to his era.

He saw the time as opportune in terms that cast light upon the old saw about necessity and invention. "The first drudgery of settling new colonies, which confines the attention of people to mere necessaries, is now pretty well over; and there are many in every province in circumstances that set them at ease and afford leisure to cultivate the finer arts and improve the common stock of knowledge."

To further this, he proposed meetings and correspondence to inquire into:

> . . . all new-discovered plants, herbs, trees, roots, their virtues, uses, etc.; methods of propagating them, and making such as are useful, but particular to some plantations, more general; improvements of vegetable juices, as ciders, wines, etc.; new methods of curing or preventing diseases; all new-discovered fossils in different countries, as mines, minerals, and quarries; new and useful improvements in distillation, brewing, and assaying of ores; new mechanical inventions for saving labour, as mills and carriages, and for raising and conveying of water, draining of meadows, etc.; all new arts, trades, and manufactures that may be proposed or thought of; surveys, maps, and charts of particular parts of the sea coasts or inland countries; lakes and mountains, nature of the soil and productions; new methods of improving the breed of useful animals; introducing other sorts

from foreign countries; new improvements in plant-
ing, gardening, and clearing land; and all philosophical experiments that let light into the nature of
things, tend to increase the power of man over matter, and multiply the conveniences or pleasures of
life. . . .

Through the Philosophical Society, and also the private
correspondence of many men of restless intellectual curiosity, a constant exchange of ideas and information and
passing along of puzzling questions took place. By such
means, in spite of the colonial isolation and the general
slowness of communications, the interested men were all
remarkably aware of what was afoot in one place or another, and what manner of project such and such a man
might be employed upon. John Fitch was to discover this
when he ventured out, in fresh naïveté, with the idea of a
steamboat, to find a network of men who had either attempted, or knew about attempts, at such a goal, all of
which was undreamt of by Fitch.

Yet Fitch was typical of another side of the picture. There
were many ingenious tinkerers, in out-of-the-way hamlets
and farms, who were not learned men, who had no correspondence and who read no books on the latest "philosophical" curiosities and discoveries. And these men too were
making their new-fangled wool cards, nail and pin machines, leaching processes, mill improvements, and the like.
In short, it is impossible to isolate any single pattern, or
context, in which inventors and their works are to be explained or located.

But it is worth taking time, about here, to see what
Franklin, his friends, and other contemporaries in America,
were exploring in their "philosophical" activities. We had a
glimpse of 17th-century scientific interests in John Winthrop, Jr. With Franklin we join the 18th-century scientists.
The scientific and the mechanical genius are distinct,
though we find them overlapping often. Blended or separate, both are modes of invention.

CHAPTER 6

THE NEW PROMETHEUS AND HIS FRIENDS

I am often ask'd by those to whom
I propose subscribing, Have you
consulted Franklin upon this business? And what does he think of it?
And when I tell them that I have
not (supposing it rather out of your
line), they do not subscribe, but
say they will consider of it.

—LETTER OF DR. THOMAS BOND
TO BENJAMIN FRANKLIN CON-
CERNING ESTABLISHMENT OF
THE PHILADELPHIA HOSPITAL.

WE MET the boy Franklin being towed by a kite across a
New England pond like a species of sailfish. Mythology has
absorbed (in that nearest medium of permanence that human record knows) the image of the somewhat stout man,
forty-six years old, on a hillside in Philadelphia, flying another kite in the windy gusts from lowering clouds, letting
the mysterious force from the skies flow into his knuckles
in crackling sparks from a housekey tied to the tugging
cord. The God who is said to protect drunkards and fools
sometimes even protects wise men when they try that inspired form of foolishness, "a new thing." And so some
have gone unscathed in balloons to the stratosphere and to

the sea-depths in bathyspheres, and have stood unblasted
on hilltops with a string in the lightning.

He might have been struck dead (and rightly, too, some
of the pious would have said, heads nodding). In 1753, a
year after the kite venture, a Swedish scientist experimenting in Franklin's footsteps with a lightning rod, received a
fatal bolt. The Philadelphia printer's famous indoor rod,
descending by his stairway with two bells, rung by static
charges across a gap, might well have been the death of
him, had his angel been distracted for a moment.

These charged and crackling experiments with rods and
cords had caught the fancy of the western world and were
taken up all over the colonies, England, and Europe. The
myth became almost instantaneous with the historic event.
(I interpret "myth" to mean a story embodying so much
that is universal and profound in its various implications
that it ceases to be involved with circumstantial considerations of fact. Thus there are levels in history when things
that incidentally happen to be fact also pass over into myth
in appropriate aspects. In this way Lincoln became a myth
before he was cold.) Immanuel Kant called Franklin a new
Prometheus. Another potent fire was stolen. Our age has
stolen yet another.

But there were among the Puritans those to say such
doings were impious. That Puritan-Newtonian, Cotton
Mather, would not have said so. Ezra Stiles, pious to the
teeth, would not have said so. Men in Harvard College and
Yale College, Christian centers both, defended Franklin's
experiments from religious attack, as did ministers in many
pulpits.

Yet in 1755, the year when the great earthquake in
Lisbon inspired that marvelous intellectual gallimaufry,
Candide, there was also an earthquake in New England. A
Boston divine, Thomas Prince, said portentously: "In Bos-
ton there are more iron points invented by the sagacious
Mr. Franklin than anywhere else in New England, and Bos-
ton seems to be more dreadfully shaken. Oh! there is no
getting out of the mighty hand of God!"

Franklin had been very much in that mighty hand on his kite-flying day. Indeed, I think he would have disagreed with the Prometheus "theft from the gods" concept of man's mastery of the resources of nature, for his religious view ("I never was without some religious principles . . .") rather saw the treasures and secrets of nature as bountiful gifts to be taken and used by the application of industry and God-given wit.

Only in extremists, as everywhere at every time, did that age postulate a conflict between the demands of religion and those of natural science. Lorenz Oken, priestly precursor of Darwin, summed it up nicely in defining natural science as the study of the everlasting transmutations of the Holy Ghost in the world. It was in the rising atheistic materialism, quite arbitrarily associated with science, breeding an ensuing "scientism," that theology found a basic antagonism. France was a late 18th-century focal point of this brand of materialism—bringing French science into religious controversy—but though Franklin stimulated French science and was stimulated by it, living in France for long times and being honored there, this materialism was wholly alien to his spirit as evinced in his writings throughout his life but especially, in old age, in his personal credo sent to Ezra Stiles in answer to the latter's query about his religious beliefs.

> I believe in one God, Creator of the universe. That He governs it by His providence. That He ought to be worshipped. That the most acceptable service we render Him is doing good to His other children. That the soul of man is immortal, and will be treated with justice in another life respecting its conduct in this. . . .

He calls "the system of morals" of Jesus "the best the world ever saw or is likely to see" but acknowledges that he shares current doubts as to His divinity—"though it is a question I do not dogmatize upon. . . ."

Though this personal statement of his old friend Frank-

lin did not accord with the Trinitarian orthodoxy of the
President of Yale, it is notable that he made no adverse
comment upon it in his diary, which is where the statement
was recorded for us. He respected his man. The case had
been somewhat different with Vermont's wildboy-warrior-
statesman-philosopher Ethan Allen, a bush-league Paine
in his Deistical writings. When he died of a cerebral hemorrhage, crossing the ice of Lake Champlain after a strenuous party one winter's night in 1789, very close to the
time of the Franklin statement, Stiles noted: "Died in Vermont the profane and impious Deist, Gen. Ethan Allen,
Author of The Oracles of Reason, a Book replete with
scurrilous Reflexions on Revelation. 'And in Hell he lift
up his Eyes being in Torment.' "

Stiles and the college he headed were among the staunch
encouragers of scientific inquiry and invention. His diary
is a running record of correspondences and conversations
on scientific and mechanical topics, of experiments witnessed, and workshops inspected. He was as proud of the
Bushnells and Whitneys hatched out of Yale as of the bud-
ding theologians. He himself participated in the silkworm
enthusiasm (wearing an academic robe of Connecticut silk
at one of the Commencements) and corresponded with
Franklin about the electrical experiments, some of which
he was trying out in the laboratories at the college. Linguis-
tics was probably his major scholarly field, outside of theology.

Astronomy also absorbed Stiles and other of the early
New England scholarly divines, including Cotton Mather,
again showing that Puritanism was not the intellectually
benighted thing that modern liberalism has sometimes been
inclined to make of it. The star of Newton had risen in
England. Alexander Pope cried out in poetic admiration:

> Nature and Nature's laws lay hid in night:
> God said, Let Newton be! and all was light.

That light made itself felt strongly in the colonies and all
the men we have been discussing fell under its influence.

Cotton Mather proclaimed that "Newton is the perpetual dictator of the learned world."

The absorption in Newtonian astronomy created an amazing observational activity in the colonies when the transit of Venus across the face of the sun (the importance of such events increasingly was becoming understood even to amateurs) happened to be ideally observable on the eastern seaboard. The great event occurred June 3, 1769, and elaborate preparations had been made for it long in advance at sixteen places in the American colonies, six of them in New England.

Among its observers: in Massachusetts, John Winthrop (not, of course, our old friend of early Connecticut, but a professor of science at Harvard); in Connecticut, Ezra Stiles; in Providence, Benjamin West (not the painter but a Rhode Island scientist) and also a certain Moses Brown whose story belongs to another part of this book; in Philadelphia, David Rittenhouse, and at Cape Henlopen, Lewestown, Delaware, which already had a lighthouse, Owen Biddle had set up his telescope.

These and other colonial amateur astronomers did a remarkable job for the time and with the equipment available, correlating their findings through the facilities of Franklin's Philosophical Society, which published the data and the accounts of the adventures the year following. The parallax of Venus was established to a degree of accuracy virtually consonant with our own times. General popular interest had become so aroused that the city of Providence bestowed the name of Transit Street upon the place where West's stout-timbered observation platform had been built.

This display of detached scientific concern, moreover, collaborating with the astronomers of England, was several years after the Stamp Act and at a time when the political-economic tensions with the mother country were coming rapidly to crisis.

I am not attempting to give a comprehensive picture of colonial science, which would be a large canvas, but simply to establish the tone of inquiry and intellectual curiosity, to

sketch a suggestion of the resources of knowledge, lest the
mechanical inventors be seen as in a dark vacuum. So in the
main, I shall continue to filter this picture through Franklin,
who stands astride of all that was going on.

It was to him that the Swedish naturalist, Count Peter
Kalm, came with letters of recommendation to begin his
travels and studies in the new world. Franklin opened up
paths for him, including bringing him in touch with John
Bartram, at whose farm lying just outside Philadelphia the
printer-philosopher-scientist was a frequent visitor. It was
a member of Franklin's Junto, Joseph Breitnall, who delivered Bartram up to Peter Collinson, London Quaker, merchant, and amateur of the sciences. Collinson procured the
British financial support and lent the encouragement that
made possible the career of Bartram as the greatest of
America's early naturalists. (Cotton Mather had been a
diligent amateur of flora and fauna and corn hybridiza-
tion.) Franklin later sent plants to Bartram from England,
including the Chinese rhubarb and the Kohlrabi, and while
in France, during Bartram's last years, urged the naturalist
to send American plants and seeds there. He was also one
of those active in encouraging the publication of Bartram's
important botanical journals.

Peter Collinson, through whom there flowed into England for years innumerable specimens and larger shipments
of American plants, seeds, frogs, turtles and the like from
the travelling Bartram, had sent a glass tube to Franklin, in
1746, for use in making experiments with static electricity.
This was the tangible object that set the American scientist
off upon his electrical studies. Just prior to the happy arrival
of the tube, when Franklin had been back at his place of
birth, Boston, he had seen demonstrations of electrical curiosities by a Dr. Spence (or Spencer) from Scotland. Franklin considered that "he was not very expert" but his own interest had been aroused and he would have pursued the
subject even if Collinson had not added impetus by the
present of the glass tube. Characteristically, Franklin at
once had others blown for the use of his friends, but he

called it "dividing the incumbrance" because of the rush of the curious to see the marvelous powers of the tube when rubbed with a silk cloth.

The papers which Franklin soon began to publish on electricity aroused interest and controversy in both England and France. He had occasion before long to formulate his personal views about the worth of scientific disputes just as he had done about proprietary and monopolistic rights in invention. Long drawn epistolary or pamphlet wrangles were quite common among the men of science. A Frenchman whose own theories had been brought into unfavorable light by Franklin's publications, tried to draw him into such a controversy. Franklin had come to the point of preparing an answer when the essential waste of the undertaking struck him. After all, his views had sprung from experiments "which any one might repeat and verify, and if not to be verifi'd, could not be defended." So, he concluded, "it was better to spend what time I could spare from public business in making new experiments, than in disputing about those already made." It was an attitude which might have conserved the pure creative energies of many other men—even Galileo.

Franklin's career as a printer and newspaper publisher alone could have earned him a place in history (he constructed the first copperplate press in America, by the way, for the printing of paper money for the colony of New Jersey). This profession which he practiced with great skill and diligence for business also earned him the means which made it possible, from his middle life onward, for him to divide most of his remarkable energies between scientific pursuit and service to the state.

We've seen his prospectus for the Philosophical Society. Far earlier than that, while still the hard working printer, he had organized his Junto (for the idea of which he was at least partly indebted to Cotton Mather, who had organized groups for improving intellectual discussion within the churches). The Philadelphia club, while just an intimate group of friends, he felt to be "the best school of philosophy,

morality, and politics that then existed in the province,"
everything being provided in its rules to "prevent our dis-
gusting each other."

The Junto had a set of twenty-four questions, prepared
by Franklin, which were read over at each meeting to draw
forth discussion that might be occasioned by any one of
them. They ranged from matters of morality and reputation to the welfare of strangers, the encouragement of learning and enterprise, to politics and economics. They included a query as to what had lately been read by any of
them bearing upon "history, morality, poetry, physic, travels, mechanic arts, or other parts of knowledge" and such a
practical, related query as: "Have you or any of your acquaintance been lately sick or wounded? If so, what remedies were used, and what were their effects?"

Curiosities of all sorts were collected by those of scientific
bent, I imagine not always with a sure discrimination between what was significant and what was idle. Curio col-
lecting, as it was practiced in Franklin's time, must have
stood in something of the same relationship to science that
the obsessive detail-collecting of the antiquarian bears to
history. They may often serve science or history but are
not in themselves science or history.

Franklin describes how, on his first trip to England, as a
very young man, he had with him "a purse made of the
asbestos, which purifies by fire." One of Britain's ardent
collectors of miscellania was Sir Hans Sloane, who heard of
the novel purse, invited the colonial youth to his great
house, "where he show'd me all his curiosities," and paid a
good sum for the coveted trophy of asbestos. Through one
of Collinson's letters to Bartram we learn that this same
Sir Hans had come into possession of a tame beast from
America with which he was vastly charmed, known to him
only as a "Monack." Bartram read the description and
identified it as a woodchuck.

Modern interest has been great in that "ocean river," the
Gulf Stream. While we understand the vital role it plays in

the civilizations of England and North America there remains much about it, to the oceanologist, that still is mystery. Franklin, who crossed the Atlantic many times on many errands, was possibly the first man to study the Gulf Stream speculatively (though Yankee sea captains were well acquainted with it and Franklin discussed with them their trick of cutting across it instead of bucking it as less adroit navigators did to their great loss of time). This interest lasted down to his final triumphal voyage home from France, in 1789, when Jefferson had succeeded him in Paris ("nobody can replace him," as the new Ambassador graciously said). The honored and aged man, free to come home to his "dear Philadelphia," was at the ship's rail to locate and study the Stream, dipping kegs for samples from various depths, noting the color and relative sparkle of the waters by day and night, lowering thermometers to take its temperature, and striving to tell what if any signs of differing fish inhabitation there might be between the Stream and the adjacent sea.

Quite a few years earlier he was on the waters with a different experiment. In a longboat off Portsmouth, in England, he directed a test of the quieting effects of oil poured upon sea water. That a film of oil effectively stilled the wind ripples on ponds and little streams he knew well. It was his habit to carry a bit of oil in a hollow of his bamboo walking cane in order to be able to demonstrate this phenomenon when opportunity and the fancy prompted him. In the heaving waters off Portsmouth, Franklin observed that the oil film could not influence the basic swell of the sea waves but that it did inhibit the breaking of whitecaps and smooth out the normal shimmering ripples on the swelling wave. This led him into broader generalizations on the mechanics of sea waves.

Franklin was a friend of Cadwallader Colden and encouraged the researches of this learned physician and while still actively engaged in the printing trade published at his own risk Colden's *Explication of the First Causes of Motion in Matter, and of the Cause of Gravitation*. Colden invaded Franklin's realm, inventing a stereotype printing process. The scientist-physician was also a politician, one-time Lieutenant Governor of New York. Under the Stamp Act he was serving as Acting Governor and tried to enforce that unpopular law. Angry New Yorkers burned him in effigy, adding injury to insult by doing it in his own coach. A conservative, he withdrew from public life at the outbreak of the Revolution and died before those events had time to test him further. For years he was one of Franklin's scientific friends and correspondents. His grandson, Cadwallader C. Colden, also active in New York politics with Chancellor Livingston, shared the general interest in steamboats and was a friend and the first biographer of Robert Fulton.

Medicine was always of interest to Franklin who numbered many physicians among his friends (Philadelphia's Benjamin Rush, for another example). The French honored him by appointment to a committee to study Mesmer's experiments, especially with regard to their possible harmful effects. He speculated much on the common cold and was either the first, or one of the first, to recommend white garments for tropical wear.

The progress of the techniques of inoculation, the merits of which Cotton Mather had been the first man to proclaim in America, over riotous popular opposition, was a subject particularly close to Franklin. "In 1736 I lost one of my sons, a fine boy of four years old, by the small-pox, taken in the common way. I long regretted bitterly, and still regret that I had not given it to him by inoculation." For years he was an apostle of the practice, still the subject of medical and religious controversy, but remarkably effective even though less so (and less safe) than the cow serums which the next century developed. The great Jonathan Edwards, only a short time after becoming President of Princeton (then the College of New Jersey) died of an unsuccessful inoculation in 1758. Earlier, in Boston,

Mather and his friend, the physician Boylston who did the first inoculation in the country on his own son, had been reviled and persecuted. A bomb—happily a dud—was thrown through Mather's window with a message scrawled on it (just in case), "Cotton Mather—You Dog—I'll inoculate you with this—With a pox to you."

The technique, which was called "variolus inoculation" or "variolation," used blood serum from persons having light cases through natural immunities. There sprang up veritable resorts or pleasure-palaces specializing in inoculation with the mild necessary care afterwards, sweetened by entertainments—a trade on the scale of the fashionable "water-cure" establishments that became a rage of the 19th century. Eli Whitney, just out of Yale in 1792, passing through New York on his way south to the plantation of Catherine Greene, was exposed to the pox. He could not afford a fancy inoculation place so had it done in the city and wandered around among the sights during his mild illness.

One might well ask, where did Franklin's versatility *not* lead him? He established the first public library—or strictly speaking, the library society—in Philadelphia. Music always charmed him, both as an art and a science, and he invented a complex instrument which he called the armonica (it became known as harmonica and should not be confused with the mouth-organ which now enjoys the dignity of that name) which was an elaboration of the principle of musical glasses, permanently tuned, rotating the glasses for the player's touch by a treadle.

He tried his hand at magic squares. We find him discovering by experimentation with a model why a canal boat makes less speed in low water than in high. Each time the boat moved its own length she must "move out of her way a body of water equal in bulk to the room her bottom took up in the water; . . . the water so moved must pass on each side of her and under her bottom to get behind her; . . . if the passage under her bottom was straitened by the

shallows more of the water must pass by her sides, and
with a swifter motion, which would retard her, as moving
the contrary way: or . . . the water becoming lower behind the boat than before, she was pressed back by the
weight of its difference in height, and her motion retarded
by having that weight constantly to overcome."

It was natural that the printer, so used to the composing
stick and the vagaries of our spelling, should be interested
in alphabet reforms. And apart from all his other contributions in electricity, he either coined or at least first
printed twenty or more words still basic to the vocabulary of
electricity, including "electrician," "battery," "conductor,"
"armature," "charge," and "discharge."

It is not my job to attempt evaluation of Franklin. Yet
while he engaged in all the interests and pursuits mentioned
here, America was moving painfully toward her destiny of
independence. In the French and Indian Wars he had ad-
monished the colonies with the famous picture motto of the
snake cut into thirteen parts, captioned "Join or Die." He
was not an early hothead for Revolution, for its own sake,
and labored long in England to resolve the disharmonies
between home country and colonies, but also saw with clear
eyes when the situation reached a point of no return. Then
in France he procured for us the aid in money, men, and
munitions so urgently needed with a finesse and tact that
make him one of the great diplomats of all history. At home
his counsels were mighty in the congresses of war and
peace and his weakening voice, in the shadow of death, was
heard in the Constitutional Convention, whose delegates
filed continually in and out of his home.

In the early pages of this chapter I spoke of myth in relation to Franklin. Thoreau had some interesting things to
say about myth. "So far from being false or fabulous in the
common sense, it contains only enduring and essential
truth, the I and you, the here and there, the now and then,
being omitted . . . We moderns . . . collect only the
raw materials of biography and history . . . which itself is
but materials to serve for a mythology . . . And Franklin

—there may be a line for him in the future classical dictionary, recording what that demigod did, and referring him to some new genealogy. 'Son of——and——. He aided the Americans to gain their independence, instructed mankind in economy, and drew down lightning from the clouds.' "

CHAPTER 7

OF BOATS AND STEAM

I know of nothing so perplexing
and vexatious to a man of feelings
as a turbulant Wife and Steamboat building.

—JOHN FITCH

TOWARD THE close of the 18th century it seemed as
though you couldn't throw a stone in this country without
hitting someone, whether a crank or an authentic inventor,
who was building a steamboat. Much of this activity either
was going on in New England or was the work of men who
were Yankees.

The overlapping of gifts, interests, activities, and productions among American inventors is particularly evident
among the men who built or contributed to the making of
steamboats. We find that they are also clockmakers, surveyors and mapmakers, silversmiths, painters, canal builders,
doctors, inventors of submarines, torpedoes, and locomotives, and practitioners of numerous other strange crafts.

This chapter is not at all a history of the steamboat.
Though it contains quite a bit of that history, it also omits a
great deal that would belong to such a purpose. Instead, it
is the story of the special contributions of Yankee minds to
the steamboat. The non-Yankees who play a part are there
because the story simply can't be told in their absence.

One evening in 1749, in Windsor, Connecticut, a six-year-old boy named John Fitch followed his sister as she led him with a candle to see some little treasure she had acquired that day. She let the flame touch some dressed flax in a corner. Flame flared up and Chloe Fitch fled screaming. The small boy dragged the blazing stuff from the house and battled the fire until he had put it out, getting his hair, face, and hands painfully burned in the process.

An older brother, assuming the fault to be John's, beat him for it, paying no heed to his explanations of the truth. The return of their father, a widower who had been out courting, brought no satisfaction after John's protests.

The boy brooded deeply over this incident. In later years it came to seem to him somehow symbolic of the courses of his life, so that he made a great point of it in his oddly eloquent, fantastically misspelled autobiographical writings.

Here, too, he recorded other hard aspects of his childhood. His father was a "Riged Christian . . . a bigot and one of the most Strenios of the sect of Prisberterions . . .", a factor which undoubtedly led to John's later Deistical ideas and passionate refutations of the divinity of Christ.

Fitch was born in South Windsor, on January 21, 1743. Childhood for him was a time of bitterly hard work on a meagre farm. In spite of an inward, saving ruggedness, or tenacity of life, he was thin and sickly looking. As a boy (and as a man, for that matter) he was "nearly crazey after Learning," but his school time was limited to one month in mid-winter, and even then he had to leave early for chores.

John had strong gifts for "Arithmatic." In his enthusiasm to learn, he became obsessed with a desire for a copy of Salmon's Geography, which he had seen, and he worked beyond his already heavy tasks for a year to get the money to buy one. After he acquired it, he learned it by heart. Those interests and aptitudes led him to seize an opportunity, at thirteen, to learn surveying, though he had no satisfactory or profitable occasions to practice his skill.

Only a few years earlier, in 1735, a Boston merchant, Rowland Houghton, invented his "New Theodolite" for surveyors—one of the first scientific instruments to be invented in this country. Whether Fitch ever saw or used one I do not know. About the same time that the Fitch boy was learning surveying, the young George Washington was carrying on the same work in Fairfax County and other parts of Virginia, as a public surveyor. Fitch much later was to do similar work in the employ of that same state.

At seventeen Fitch was restlessly awaiting a time to strike out for himself. This seemed to come as the result of a chance meeting with Benjamin Cheney, of East Hartford, one of the leading clockmakers of the colony. Clockmaking was a trade rich with appeal for John Fitch. It was, in a sense, mathematical in its nature, and the mysterious tools, skills, and complexities associated with clockworks lured the boy. When Cheney offered him an apprenticeship, he was eager to seize it.

Notoriously the apprentice system was brutally abused. John, in his desperate hunger for the skill, accepted hard terms, only to find himself cheated. Mrs. Cheney was a drunkard and a slovenly housekeeper who fed him scanty rations. But worse, months went by and it became clear that Cheney had no intention of teaching John the trade of clockmaking. Instead, he guarded his shop and the craft "secrets" jealously, compelling the apprentice to spend all his time at house and farm work. Under the boy's persistent protests, the clockmaker grudgingly taught him the rudiments of brass working (frequently an adjunct to the clock business) and John did learn to convert old brass kettles into buttons—but of clocks, he saw none.

In extremity, when he had worked until less than a year of his term remained to run, the boy went on strike, saying that he would work on clocks or nothing. The apprentice had no legal recourse available to him, but when Benjamin Cheney saw that nothing more would move the boy, he still would not teach him the trade, but contrived a deal to fob him off upon his brother, Timothy Cheney, of Windsor, another eminent clockmaker.

The boy was too young and eager to imagine the same

thing could happen twice. Besides, what choice had he? About as much as a baseball player who is traded to another club. An agreement was made for a year, again specifically involving instruction in the trade. Timothy at least did not have a drunken wife. Passable food was served, but precious little of it. The second Cheney was parsimonious and given to preaching against gluttony while at table. "I never got a Belly full with him at any one time," Fitch recorded.

In honoring the agreement, Timothy was as remiss as his brother had been. John spent his year doing simple brass work, utterly unrelated to the making of clocks. If he tried to watch any of his master's processes, he was rebuked. Even the clockmaking tools were kept under lock.

When the apprenticeship was ended, John "set out for home and Cryed the whole distance." He knew neither how to make clocks, nor even the names of clock parts. Yet he was supposed by all to have been trained in the trade.

He set up in Windsor to make buttons, buckles, and other small brass work. He begged the opportunity to tackle a brass clock that was out of order. By the experimental method of taking it apart and putting it together again, with his natural mechanical gifts, he learned through this and other such cleaning and repairing ventures, something of what had been denied him in his bitter four years of apprenticeship. He was afraid to confess that he had not properly learned the business, until in later years he wrote it all down for publication after his death.

The tale of Fitch's disappointments and hardships is a long one. In 1767 he married Lucy Roberts. "I cannot say that I ever was passonately fond of the Woman, but for the Sake of some Promises I determined to marry her." His attitude toward marriage and women was an odd one at best. He spoke of wedlock as "license for whoredom." Lucy proved to be a formidable shrew, but there is some question as to whether women are shrews without cause. Fitch's self-revelations, and the mere circumstances of his life, indicate that it may have been no gladsome matter to have him for husband, even though he was essentially a man of gentle and good qualities. At any rate, after about two years of marriage and much agonizing over his course, John Fitch left Lucy and the son who had been born to them and the daughter whom he did not yet know was to arrive.

In the years following, he worked first as a tinsmith, then with considerable success as a silversmith, in New Jersey. For the first time he found himself a stable and respected businessman. He played a thoroughly obscure, undistinguished part in the Revolution, largely involved in the politics of local regiments. The only tangible result of the war for him was a move to Bucks County, Pennsylvania, during British occupation of Jersey. He was practicing his crafts in Pennsylvania during the later years of the war.

Business was bad, his savings had depreciated with wartime inflation. Talk of western land speculation was in the air. Fitch decided to go to Kentucky and see what he could promote. He acquired lands there, and entered into other complicated transactions, involving both official surveying (on behalf of the State of Virginia) and private attempts at trading.

In the course of one of these ventures, he and a group of others were taken captive by Indians on the Ohio River. Fitch and his companions suffered a rigorous ordeal, including a twelve-hundred-mile march to Lake Erie and Canada, where they were given over to the British as prisoners of war near Montreal. With time on his hands while in this status, he rounded up a few tools, made many more, and managed to produce brass work, to make wooden clocks, and repaired watches, for small earnings.

When, after nine months of British internment, Fitch was shipped back to New York, he promptly headed again for the Ohio region, which was then known as the "northwest country." He believed the United States would soon open a land office there and that he would be in a position to make his fortune by filing early for valuable claims. In consequence, he did a good deal of surveying, intending, with some associates, to claim a hundred thousand acres.

With Fitch's talent for being on the wrong street corner when the parade went by, nothing direct came of all his difficult and dangerous journeys in the northwest. The United States changed the method of releasing the land so that he was unable to acquire any of it by simple claims. But home in Bucks County, discouraged and awaiting developments, he amused himself by pounding out a sheet of copper and from his hard-earned knowledge engraving a map of the northwest. Here was the spirit of the boy who had memorized Salmon's Geography.

Though he had no training in cartography and based his work partly on earlier maps, it was the most detailed and accurate one then available, including many features not represented on any prior map. Also of importance, it was the only one of a convenient size to be carried. It embraces portions of what are now Wisconsin, Illinois, Indiana, Kentucky, Ohio, West Virginia, and Michigan, and extreme western parts of Pennsylvania and New York. At the time represented, this was all virtual wilderness. The map is enhanced by numerous comments engraved upon it: "The Kentucky country is not so level as it is generally represented to be: there being a range of hilly land running thro it N.E. to S.W. also very deep valleys on the larg streams."

Fitch did all the work on his map by himself and made the first printing on a cider press. He was to print, or have it printed, many times thereafter. It was one of the few profitable productions of his life, but characteristically that small profit was to be siphoned off in the cause of the great and obsessive endeavor, upon the eve of which he now stood, all unconsciously.

By nature Fitch was a dabbler—but no more—in most of the intellectual-philosophical currents of his time: a Deist, a Mason, a liberal, a leveller. The genesis of his steamboat is odd. He writes of standing by the roadside as a large carriage went by, because he could not afford the luxury of riding his own horse to church but had to hire it out for its keep. He reflected what a wonderful thing it would be to have a carriage without a horse. It was a poor man's democratic vision, not yet taking into account that a machine might be as costly to buy and might eat as much of its own kind of fodder as the horse it was to replace.

"What cannot you do, if only you will get yourself about it." And he thought of steam, as somehow the force to drive a horseless carriage. Now the odd thing about this is that the steam engine was already an established reality, yet apparently Fitch had never heard of such a thing. The concept came to him spontaneously and he was later to be shocked when he was informed of the engine's existence. There were then three primitive engines in the United States, all English made, of the Newcomen type, and in England more progress was under way. Watt and Boulton were working on the advanced development of a double-acting engine.

This strange John Fitch started from scratch to invent a means to harness steam. It did not take him long to realize that if he contrived his horseless carriage he would have no roads of a satisfactory condition for it to run upon. (We must realize that when the internal combustion engine was perfected, it brought with it the roads that it demanded. There is no chicken-or-the-egg dilemma here. History shows that roads are developed according to the demands of the vehicles waiting to run upon them, from the Roman chariot to the Model T Ford.)

Fitch was quick to realize that water was the true medium for his vision of steam propulsion. Moreover, he was a man with a sense of geography, who had seen and mapped the great rivers of the west, where the flow of traffic was one-way, *down,* with the current.

Relying on money from the sale of his maps, Fitch went from Bucks County to Philadelphia. In this center of commerce—and more important, of science—he hoped to find some sympathetic and tangible support. He brought with him a small working model, demonstrating his propulsion mechanism (not an engine, but that which the engine was

to turn). It was something like a caterpillar tread, or a
bicycle chain with paddles on it, running along the side of
the boat.

The model and Fitch's earnest explanations won the interest of Dr. John Ewing, of the University of Pennsylvania,
who gave him a letter and passed him along to a man in
Trenton, who in turn passed him along to a man in Princeton, and so forth, until Fitch, selling maps along the way,
arrived in New York with his model and a fistful of letters
of recommendation. This city, of course, was then the seat
of Congress. Fitch petitioned that body to inspect his model,
and to give encouragement to this project, designed "to
facilitate the internal Navigation of the United States,
adapted especially to the Waters of the Mississippi."

Now whether it was because the influential men of the
coast were not anxious to nourish trade competition from
the Mississippi, or whether it was because of simple short-
sightedness, plus preoccupation with their new political
status, the men of Congress brushed off John Fitch's plea.
Not all of our early great men realized the importance of
the west, and some of those who did were jealous of it.
John Marshall was one of the Virginia group whose vision
did not go beyond the opening of the upper waters of the
Potomac. If this were achieved, he said, "we shall have but
little occasion to test the navigation of the Mississippi."

While Fitch was still hoping for Congress to act, he had a
tentative offer of backing from Spain, in return for exclusive rights to the invention. Patriotism impelled him to decline, and later, disillusioned about his own country's response, he wrote, "God forbid that I should ever be in like
error again." The "Ignorant Boys of Congress" spurned
the steamboat. Fitch went sadly back to Philadelphia.

This was the beginning of a long trail, involving knock-
ing at the doors of notable people. The first of these was
Benjamin Franklin. The aged Doctor beamed at Fitch and
listened with interest. He heard much and said little, though
Fitch considered his opinion of the project "flattering." But
for all the attention and friendliness of reception, Franklin

would say nothing about the boat in writing, and made him no promises. Fitch went away with a hopeful impression that he would hear something from the Doctor in the near future. He heard nothing. He wrote to Franklin, reviewing the advantages of the steamboat, but received no answer.

Disheartened, he headed for Kentucky again, where land matters called. In Lancaster, Pennsylvania, he made an important call, at the splendid home of William Henry, gunsmith, one of the great names associated with the American rifle. Henry had been high in the councils of the Revolution and an important supplier of arms. Thomas Paine had spent much time there, and in this house had written the fifth of his famous *Crisis* papers, in 1778.

When Fitch, with his naive eagerness, confided his steamboat ideas to Henry, he was disturbed to learn from the gunmaker that he, himself, had played with the idea as early as 1776. There were drawings, which Henry took out and showed to Fitch, to confirm it. Worse, still, at the time of Paine's visit, in 1778, the busy pamphleteer amid all his political involvements, had discussed his own independent steamboat ideas with Henry. These were so advanced as to involve the use of steam on the turbine principle, which was to be one of the latest developments in the history of steam engines.

To calm his agitated guest, Henry complimented him on his general concept, offered a few suggestions, and assured him that there would be no rivalry. The gunsmith was far too busy to work at the scheme and intended to make no issue of priority of ideas; he could not say, but felt reasonably sure that Paine would probably feel the same way.

Fresh from this encounter, which had reassuring as well as initially upsetting aspects, Fitch journeyed on to Frederick, Maryland, and walked into another worry. He visited an eminent ironmaster, proprietor of the Catoctin Ironworks, Thomas Johnson. This Johnson was a man of considerable parts. He had been a member of the Continental Congress, and the first Governor of the State of Maryland. It was he who put forward the nomination of Washington to be Chief Commander of the Continental Army, in 1775. In later years he was to be one of the strongest voices for Maryland's ratification of the Constitution, and a Justice of the Supreme Court.

From former Governor Johnson, Fitch first heard the name of James Rumsey, of Bath, Virginia—a name that was to be the bane of Fitch's life for years to come. The ironmaster told him of a strange "walking boat" which Rumsey had invented and had demonstrated, in a model, to George Washington, who had been impressed.

Was it steam propelled?

Johnson told the agitated Fitch that it was not. Its machine worked only against the current, the flow of which past the hull turned a water wheel (exactly in reverse of the paddle-wheel propulsion principle) which imparted motion to a rig which caused poles to thrust against the bottom, like men poling a flatboat upstream. The thing actually worked, at least in the model, and speeds of two to three miles an hour under favorable conditions were expected. Its awkwardness and weaknesses are self-evident, not the least of which was that it could do nothing whatever in still water, deep water, or on a muddy bottom. Yet it is a typical example of what we would hasten to call "Yankee ingenuity" but for the embarrassment of its inventor being Maryland born.

In one important respect, Johnson was not entirely candid with Fitch. He did not mention certain mysterious iron cylinders which Rumsey had asked him to make, at his Catoctin Iron Works, quite unlike any familiar iron work. They were for a steamboat, but Johnson was later to claim that Rumsey had concealed, or at least partly camouflaged, their intended use from him. The ironmaster did not feel fully free to talk. Apparently Fitch did make a good impression on Johnson and have his good will. The Governor was one of the few men who would encourage Fitch in writing, by commending him wholeheartedly to the attention of others.

His specific advice for the moment was to go down the

Potomac and call on General Washington. Perhaps the great man could set him straight about Rumsey, and if by good fortune Washington's aid could be gained by Fitch, the steamboat could have no better patron.

Fitch already was beginning to develop a complex about his dealings with the mighty. But the welfare of his dream overcame his nervousness. He ventured to Mount Vernon. Fitch was poor, untidy, unpoised, and generally uncouth. Throughout his chronicle he often speaks of "my despicable appearance." In contrast to his shabby, unprepossessing presence, his schemes were grandiose, almost always over-stated in their immediate prospects, and usually far too sweeping in their assumption of originaltity. The latter fault was not arrogance but ingenuousness. He lacked the background to know what other men had done and thought. This battler for a visionary steamboat had no money, no education, had never built a boat, and had never seen a steam engine.

That reserved spirit, Washington, nevertheless received John Fitch into his stately halls with grace. No one else was present to compete for the General's attention. Fitch began to pour out his scheme, but as he talked, the General became visibly agitated. Alarmed, Fitch stopped and asked if Rumsey's boat was anything like his own.

Washington replied somewhat stiffly that he was not free to discuss Rumsey's plan, even by negatives. Then the General excused himself, leaving Fitch alone and in anxiety for an uncomfortably long while. When his host returned, he appeared to have composed his thoughts in the face of what was clearly a surprise. The model boat which he had seen at Bath, and for which he had written a certificate of commendation, was not a steamboat. Yet he said that at a later time Rumsey had spoken of "something of the sort to him," in Richmond, but that "he had been so engaged in company that he did not attend to it."

General Washington was unwilling to put anything in writing for Fitch, or do more than express a formal good will. He softened the partial rebuff by urging the disappointed man to stay for dinner and the night. Fitch declined. He went away, his self-preserving optimism persuading him that Rumsey was not at work on a steamboat. But Rumsey *was,* and though Washington may not have known it for a surety, it is clear that he was disquieted by the whole episode and puzzled as to how to be fair to both parties. He had not shown Rumsey's hand, if indeed he had any significant knowledge, which is not likely. He would not show Fitch's hand to Rumsey, though he had heard the Fitch project explained. Yet he did feel it necessary to let Rumsey know that currents were stirring.

He wrote to him, in part, some two months later, at the end of January, 1786: "Sir; If you have no cause to change your opinion respecting your mechanical boat, and reasons unknown to me do not exist to delay the exhibition of it, I would advise you to give it to the public as soon as it can be prepared conveniently. The postponement creates distrust in the public mind; it gives time also for the imagination to work, and this is assisted by a little dropping from one, and some from another, to whom you have disclosed the secret. Should therefore a mechanical genius hit upon your plan, or something similar to it, I need not add that it would place you in an awkward situation, and perhaps disconcert all your projects concerning this useful discovery. . . ."

Thus far, in the letter, Washington had succinctly stated the dilemma that was, and always has been, the bane of the inventor, especially when working in one of the periods of proliferation. The individual inventor always felt a rival breathing down his neck. But as the General's letter continued, he further stated the unhappy but ruthless truth that has broken the heart of many an inventor, living to wonder at the heartlessness of a public that paid scanty attention to long protestations and explanations to prove (in prize-ring vernacular) that "we wuz robbed."

". . . for you are not, with your experience of life, now to learn that the shoulders of the public are too broad to feel the weight of the complaints of an individual, or to regard promises if they find it convenient, and have the shadow of possibility on their side, to retract them. I will inform you further that many people in guessing at your plan have come very near the mark; and that one, who had something of a similar nature to offer the public, wanted a certificate from me that it was different from yours. I told him that, as I was not at liberty to declare what your plan was, I did not think it proper to say what it was not."

Here it is time to pause and see just who James Rumsey was and what he had afoot. At about this point, the waters of steamboat history had become as muddy as if all the incipient paddle-wheels, poles, oars, and propellers were churning them up at once. There is no better demonstration of simultaneity and duplication in the inventive processes, and no clearer proof that there is no one of whom it could be said, even remotely, but for *him* we would not have the steamboat, or that he is *the* inventor of the steamboat. There are scads of inventors of the steamboat. In now being compelled to relinquish a single thread of pursuit, we must further remember that to a large extent the problem was one of adapting known engines to *use* on known boats, and that in France, and far more in England, steamboat plans and experiments were or had been going forward.

James Rumsey was of an age with Fitch, being born in Maryland in 1743. Their roots were similarly modest in means, and farm bound, but in Rumsey's case the setting and tone were mellower. He, too, had scanty education and was a hand-craftsman, learning the trades of milling and blacksmithing. He was a builder, and also, in the capacity in which Washington made his acquaintance at Bath, an innkeeper. Rumsey was a handsome man with valuable assets that Fitch lacked, for he had a winning presence, courtliness of manner, tact, and that shrewd complex of intangibles in human negotiations which we might call knowing how to play his cards.

He was a man of many gifts, quick to seize opportunity, ever alert to his own advantage—perhaps too much so, for there were times in his career when he out-smarted himself by making moves, apparently expedient, which resulted in defeating his purposes.

It was in the fall of 1784, in Bath (now Berkeley Springs, West Virginia), that Rumsey won Washington's approval with the working model of his pole boat and obtained from the General the later much-discussed certificate that said in part, "he has discovered the art of propelling boats by mechanism and small manual assistance against rapid currents." It was slightly later in the same year that Rumsey, in Richmond, made the casual mention to Washington of steam as a possible power agent for boats. There is some evidence that Rumsey did make steamboat plans during 1785, involving the motive power which he ultimately used, and of which we'll speak in due course. Apparently he did give orders for machinery, and for the construction of a boat which was to be fitted up to make full-size tests of *both* steam and pole propulsion, to determine which was the one to develop.

In this same year, Rumsey's sense of opportunity, plus the natural challenge of his inventive nature, and a wish to accommodate Washington, all conspired to make him undertake the post of chief engineer for an ambitious Potomac Canal project sponsored by the leading powers of Virginia. Rumsey had never built a canal—but neither had anybody else around, and the General had confidence in his candidate's native gifts. Rumsey was not to succeed in solving the problems of the canal, but at the time it appeared to offer a chance for achievement, and would it not, after all, be precisely the medium awaiting the steamboat he had in mind? So Rumsey allowed his boat plans to take second place, entrusting them largely to the hands of others.

Meanwhile, what of Fitch? From his disquieting visit to Mount Vernon, he had gone to Richmond and aroused some interest from James Madison, Henry Clay, and other legislators, but nothing tangible came of it. This was the very camp of the opposition. He gave up his intended Kentucky trip and went back to Philadelphia. There he organized a company. He sold stock to some twenty-two holders, men of various interests and moderate means. Only $300 cash was realized, with which he was to build a steamboat.

Around this time he went to Bordentown, New Jersey, to call on Thomas Paine, whose steamboat ideas William Henry had mentioned. Just now the pamphleteer was preoccupied with his designs for iron bridges. He was friendly and sympathetic to Fitch, as was his way with all men, agreeing that he would not be a rival, but could do little more for him than buy a copy of the map of the northwest which still was Fitch's economic mainstay.

A well known English mechanic, John Hall, whom we shall hear of again, was living with Paine and collaborating on the bridge. Hall was a curious personality who called inventions "saints" and inventors, "saint-makers," a usage which Paine may have picked up from him. Hall's journal, on March 10th, 1786, records the visit from Fitch, and is worth quoting in full, though it contains an allusion to what must be a garbled impression of Fitch's account of his troubles.

> March 10th. Before 7 o'c a brother saint-maker came with a model of machine to drive boats against stream. He had communicated his scheme to H. [William Henry] who had made alterations and a company had taken it and refused saint-maker partnership. [?] He would fain have given it to Mr. Paine or me, but I a stranger refused and Mr. Paine had enough hobbys of his own. Mr. Paine pointed out a mode to simplify his apparatus greatly. He gave him 5s. to send him one of his maps.

A couple of things are interesting about this. For one, it indicates, probably quite reliably, the lonely desperation with which Fitch would give himself over to almost anyone who would listen to him sympathetically. The mention of Paine's suggestion to "simplify his apparatus" (as well as prior suggestions of Henry's) is significant when we reflect that absolutely the only thing that Fitch had yet to offer, in connection with a steamboat, was a model of a chain-belt propulsion unit which subsequent testing proved to be utterly worthless. Considering the knowledgeable men with whom he was making contact, this may have much to do with the difficulties he had in getting strong support, early in the game.

The really important thing that happened to Fitch about the time he organized his company, was the meeting with Henry Voight, who was to be his partner and co-laborer in the painful struggles ahead. Voight certainly would not have built a steamboat without Fitch, but quite possibly Fitch could not have built one without Voight. Also, he, too, was in his way a sad soul, and became Fitch's closest friend, which represented another very real need of this obsessed and wandering Yankee. The German-born Voight was a watchmaker, another instance of the affinity of the men who dealt in timepieces for other mechanical enterprises.

The first move of the new partners was to make tests of Fitch's concept of chain-and-paddles as a means of propulsion. Rigged up on a skiff and operated by hand, this device proved useless. The boat spun around like a demented waterbug, to the laughter of the gallery always present to mock the enterprising. Fitch was chagrined by this, and one of Voight's first real services was to save him from a mistake, curious in its circumstances.

Shortly after Fitch's return to Philadelphia from the visit to Mount Vernon and points south, in December of 1785, an informal paper by Franklin, entitled *Maritime Observations*, was read before the American Philosophical Society. The good Doctor was not present. But in his paper he referred to a method of boat propulsion which did not originate with him.

In 1738, Daniel Bernoulli, a Swiss of a mathematical and scientific family, had published a book called *Hydrodynamica*, in which among a great many other ideas, he suggested propelling a boat by a jet of water under the stern. The idea was to employ nothing more than the force of gravity, pouring the water into the vertical member of an

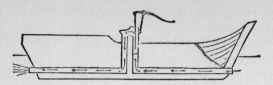

Dr. Franklin's plan of a Pumping Boat to go by ejection of water.

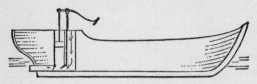

Dr. Franklin's plan of an Air Boat to go by forcing out air against water.

Franklin's conceptions of jet boats, on Bernoulli's
principle, which may have inspired Rumsey.

L-shaped tube rising in the middle of the boat, and emptying below and to the rear.

Franklin's mention of the idea was coupled with the thought of increasing its power by finding some means of pumping water into the standpipe to maintain a continuous flow and pressure. Whether or not he was stimulated by the visit from Fitch, some months earlier, the doctor included a passing mention that some form of "fire-engine" (so the earliest steam engines often were called) might be employed to pump the water.

Bernoulli's invention was a form of jet propulsion, vastly before its time. But water is not an efficient medium for the application of the principle. (Perhaps I should say, mechanically, for otherwise the squid and the octopus would not agree, having got along with it very well for a long time. Bernoulli may have borrowed the idea from them.) The energy waste involved in pumping up and forcing out the water is disproportionate to the thrust imparted. It is a good example of the pitfalls of the pre-scientific phase of invention in which often the theoretical calculation of the factors involved was far beyond the conception or ability of those who were struggling as simple mechanics with the problem of moving a vessel on water.

Now this was precisely the method of propulsion adopted by Rumsey in his steamboats. Where did Rumsey get the idea? Fitch was later to insist that Rumsey took it from Franklin's paper, using this as part of his attempt to prove that Rumsey had not conceived a steamboat before 1786. But there is good evidence that Rumsey had already ordered some of the parts for such an engine in 1785, before the reading of the paper. Had Rumsey seen or heard of Bernoulli's book, did he get the notion from Franklin, or had he thought up the idea for himself?

Soon after the paper had been read, Fitch called on Franklin to try to enlist him among the stockholders of the company. Once more, the sage of Philadelphia was polite and kind, but he bought no stock. Instead, seeing the shabbiness of his visitor, he offered him a few dollars for himself. This well-meant but possibly tactless gesture wounded the sensitive Fitch, and probably helped to give the final thrust to his latent suspicion that Franklin meant him no good and was a potential rival.

Just why Franklin acted as he did toward Fitch is a puzzle. If at these early calls he saw, correctly, that Fitch as yet had done nothing, why did he never visit, or give acknowledgement of the success of the boats Fitch later ran in and out of Philadelphia? Yet, when the Rumseian Society was founded, to finance the enterprises of Fitch's rival, Franklin did subscribe to it. Was it simply because Rumsey was following the line Franklin had endorsed, or was it because Franklin preferred the company kept by Rumsey to the random supporters of Fitch and his bibulous, watchmaking associate?

Under the spell of Franklin's name, Fitch was all set to jettison his own original ideas and adopt the Bernoulli scheme, had not the common sense of Henry Voight dissuaded him, and kept him on the right track.

Although the Boulton and Watt engine—basically what

Fitch needed—existed already, Fitch and Voight practically had to reinvent it for themselves. Much to their credit is the fact that in a few months they not only duplicated Watt's basic engine, but included in it the improvement which Watt just about then was working on himself—the double-acting feature, by which the steam operated upon not just one, but both sides of the piston in its alternate strokes. No other evidence is needed of Fitch's and Voight's authentic mechanical talents.

John Fitch's first actual steamboat ran in July of 1786, from a wharf in Philadelphia. His new method of propulsion consisted of two rows of six oars, on either side of the boat. The forward three and the rear three, on each side, entered the water alternately, so that there was a stroke, first front and then rear, of six oars at a time. The action was almost vertical, like the paddling of a canoe.

Having succeeded with this small boat, the partners, now that they had gleaned some encouragement and recognition, began construction of a considerably larger one. Still using oars, or paddles, nevertheless Fitch had made a considerable change in the method. He now used stern paddles, not of the classic stern-wheel type of later Mississippi fame. Fitch's rig dipped the paddles vertically, at the stern, then thrust them back vigorously, lifted them and brought them forward to repeat the stroke. Rembrandt Peale, the artist, watching one of the runs of the new boat, described a "coupling crank projecting over the stern to give motion to three or four paddles [there were three], resembling snow shovels, which hung into the water."

For the demonstration of this craft, in the Spring of 1787, Fitch had as spectators and sometimes passengers, some of the eminent gentlemen who had assembled there for the Constitutional Convention. During the time of the Convention, the steamboat was successfully chugging around in the Delaware and the Schuylkill on repeated runs. It was a reality, it worked; crowds saw it and many rode on it. Yet Washington never came to see it, perhaps embarrassed by his involvements with Rumsey. Franklin never came. The other gentlemen of the Philosophical Society, fond of papers on such subjects, took no official notice of the working boat, nor did they seek to honor the shabby Connecticut Yankee and the German watchmaker who had built it.

Yet it found notice in the diary of one eminent man, who was not even on the scene. At Yale, in New Haven, Ezra Stiles, in his diary entry of September 27, 1787, after noting that he had finished the first Psalm in Hebrew recitation, that day, added:

> Judge Elsworth a Member of the fœderal Convention just returned fr. Philadᵃ visited me, & tells me the Convent. will not rise under three Weeks. He there saw a steam Engine for rowing Boats against the Stream—invented by Mr. Fitch of Windsor in Connecticutt. He was on board the Boat & saw the Expᵗ succeed.

Was Rembrandt Peale, whose description of the craft was quoted a moment ago, the only painter to watch the steamboat? It hardly seems possible, for there was a youthful miniature painter living close to the river. He had come to Philadelphia from Lancaster where, as a child, he is said to have hung around the mechanics' shops, probably those of William Henry, the greatest of the gunsmiths, who as we know had thought about steamboats. The lad with the mechanical curiosity also had great aptitude with pencil and brush, and he added to this some training as a jeweler's apprentice, before coming to the city of brotherly love to earn his living as a painter. This young man cannot have failed to know about and follow the progress of the novel craft on the Delaware, anchored close by his lodgings. His name was Robert Fulton.

Meanwhile, from 1787, Fitch worked steadily at boats, producing new models and improving his engines and his paddle systems. In 1790, he achieved the best of all his boats. At its top speed it may have been capable of nearly eight miles an hour, and in the summer of that year Fitch established the world's first regular passenger steamboat run, from Philadelphia to Burlington, Bristol, Bordentown, and Trenton. He made the upriver trip one day, the return the next. On Sundays he made a southbound trip to Chester and back. Fitch's sense of success was never higher. He and Voight felt like "Lord High Admirals of the Delaware," as indeed they might, and he wrote, "Thus has been effected, by Little Johnny Fitch and Harry Voight, one of the greatest and most useful arts that has ever been introduced into the world; and although the world and my country does not thank me for it, yet it gives me heartfelt satisfaction."

Small thanks for Johnny Fitch. During all his steamboat operations there were endless harassments. His backers would gain enthusiasm with each advancing step of success, but grumble and retreat when money was needed—and it was always needed. They can't be blamed entirely, for alas, the steamboat never earned money. Only the venturesome would patronize the new contraption. Admittedly it was dirty, noisy, and liable to breakdown. Slow shallops and the stagecoaches continued to get the paying traffic. This was no fault of Fitch's. The time was not quite ripe and the location was not good. This Delaware valley experienced no pressing need for the steamboat. The Hudson valley needed it much more, and as Fitch had always insisted, so did the Mississippi—but the time was not ripe for that, either, again through no fault of his.

Meanwhile, there was Rumsey. Fitch had beaten him to the first operation of a boat, while canals had distracted him. Now he hastened to catch up. Working in Shepherdstown, Virginia, on the Potomac, he finished an engine, again basically like Watt's, but not as sound in conception as the Fitch-Voight engine. It was designed to pump water for the Bernoulli jet action. Rumsey's one true creative contribution was a pipe boiler—an important improvement over the tank type of boiler, though a somewhat premature one, for continuous pipe was not to be had and it continually sprang leaks at the joints.

In September, 1787, he tested his boat privately, but suffered the inevitable boiler troubles. Finally, on December 3rd, he gave a public demonstration, in the presence of the whole town and its leading citizen, General Horatio Gates. His boat made a short run, attaining a speed of about three miles an hour. Eight days later, Rumsey made another run, claiming four miles an hour. This boat was never run again. In fact, Rumsey never operated another steamboat, anywhere, at any time.

Without wishing to minimize Rumsey's gifts, it seems extraordinary that with the uncontested dates of actual boat operation, even if Rumsey had conceived his boat as early as he claimed, with the faulty method of propulsion he employed, and with his meagre two tests compared to Fitch's sustained commercial runs, Rumsey and his adherents should have harassed poor John Fitch for years over both honors and patent rights.

The influential friends of Rumsey, numbering Washington and Franklin among them, formed the Rumseian Society, to advance the steamboat and any or all other inventions of the Virginian. There was no Fitchian Society for the promotion of "little Johnny Fitch." Only once did the adversaries meet face to face, when Rumsey came to Philadelphia, at which time Fitch called on him and read aloud the text of a paper he had written in answer to a pamphlet of Rumsey's, laying claim to priority.

The battle of paper was just beginning. It went on for years, involving the Patent Office and several state legislatures. The later quarrels over the Fulton-Livingston monopoly revived the Fitch-Rumsey dispute, and historians and biographers have never dropped it.

Fitch applied to the Federal government for a fourteen-year exclusive patent on steamboats, in 1790. Part of his argument sums up the history of his venture: ". . . the great length of time and vast sums of money [about $8,000] expended in bringing the scheme to perfection, have been wholly occasioned by his [Fitch, speaking of himself] total ignorance of the improved state of steam engines, a perfect

knowledge of which has not been acquired without an infinite number of fruitless experiments; for not a person
could be found who was acquainted with the minutia of
Boulton & Watt's new engine; and whether your petitioner's
engine is similar or not to those in England, he is at this
moment totally ignorant; but is happy to say, that he is
now able to make a complete steam engine, which in its
effects, he believes, is equal to the best in England, the
construction of which he has never made a secret."

His case was strong enough so that in spite of the Rumsey
interests, the fourteen-year monopoly was granted, under no
less signatures than those of Washington, Thomas Jefferson, Edmund Randolph (who had been one of Fitch's
passengers in 1787), and John Quincy Adams. But by a
magnificently ironic bureaucratic fumble the specifications
described the jet-boat of Rumsey! Fitch's right later became
the precedent for the Fulton-Livingston monopoly. From
today's perspective, it could be said that both Fitch and
Rumsey, in their sweeping claims of achievement, did not
distinguish clearly between an *idea* and an *accomplishment,*
or between an experimental accomplishment and a successfully developed application.

Rumsey, in 1788, went to England, with funds from his
Society, to buy a Boulton & Watt engine, and perhaps
enter into further negotiations with those great names of
the steam-engine. He almost set up arrangements which
might have put him in the place Fulton was to fill in steamboat history, but his opportunism seems to have rebounded
against him. In reaching for too much, he affronted Boulton
and Watt, who declined to go ahead with the projected
plans.

Rumsey remained in England, with a side trip to France
to see Jefferson, who was interested in his projects, and also
Joel Barlow, of whom more presently. He became involved
in an elaborate project to build a boat on the Thames.
Financial problems drew him temporarily to Ireland, on
salary, to aid in a canal project reminiscent of the fruitless

Potomac enterprise. Finally, after almost two years of delay, in December of 1792, his British boat was nearing completion when Rumsey died of a cerebral hemorrhage which struck him in the midst of proceedings of the Society of Arts in his honor. His boat was operated experimentally, after his death, but apparently only once, and that was the last heard of it.

Fitch, for all his technical successes, had not had much better luck. Also his personal life had been involved with all sorts of complications. His Deist enthusiasms had carried him to extremes. He was almost as absorbed in a fervent, religious zeal to reject the Divinity of Christ as to build steamboats. (One Rumseian Society document calls him "the ungentlemanly, anti-Federalist, Deistic Fitch.") With a few of his friends he planned the organization of a society which was ultimately to embrace the world, to prove that "contemptible as I was and despised by all ranks of People . . . I could call in all the world into my doctrines . . . and fix a new Era that all the world would remember when the names of Jesus Christ and Washington is lost. . . . Was I a handsom man and a good riter I could now do more than ever Jesus Christ or George Fox did."

Such were the wild flights that unquestionably helped to hamstring Fitch all along the way. Even his comradeship with Voight cracked under an odd personal strain. Fitch, in his poverty, had lived for some years by the kindness of a tavern-keeping widow, Mary Kraft. Voight, the widow Kraft, and Fitch had spent many a sociable evening together, in a friendship that must have meant much to each of them, for Voight was unhappy in his marriage and in search of consolations. Fitch, as he recorded, had "kept a solemn Lent for more than seven years together." There was no tie between himself and the widow, but he was pained and astonished to discover that she and his partner, behind his back, had been disporting themselves in unseemly wise. "The productions of love appeared," in Fitch's words. Both Voight and the widow had numerous children, and Fitch, hoping to save both families, made the unusual offer to marry the widow, pledging his word of honor "never to bed with her."

This was complicated by the fact that he still had a wife in Connecticut. The widow declined the offer and went into hiding until the child was born, Fitch being on hand faithfully to aid in the arrangements. Unhappily, the lovers found themselves in the same predicament again, in spite of Fitch's exhortations. This time the widow went away, but meeting acquaintances, declared herself Fitch's wife, to save face.

Fitch was too gallant to deny the claim and found himself entangled in a web that did nothing but lose him the long friendship with Voight. The watchmaker, deprived of his "choicest pleasure," began a series of wrangles with Fitch over the credits for their achievements and over the rights involved. It was a melancholy collapse of an association that had achieved so much.

The poor steamboat man had reached almost low ebb. "All I can say of the matter is this: [so he wrote it down] I think this is a dam wicked world and when I get clear of it never wish to come back to it any more. I have frequently been apt to conclude it is a place where they transport Souls to from other Planets that is not fit to live in them, the same as Great Britain used to send Convicts to Virginia; and if I was sent here as a lunatick to Bedlam or for running into Chymereal whims, I am sure my lesson of Caution will be sufficient to make me more cautious when I get back to Jupiter again."

In all this messy shambles, his steamboat company had failed to make money, the stockholders would put up no more. Fitch was bankrupt, humiliated, wounded in heart. Then one last, possibly even cruel, hope appeared. Through the intervention of Aaron Vail, who had seen Fitch's boat run and was now a consul in France, a French patent was issued to Fitch and he was urged to come to France and build a boat there.

This was not the first French prospect. A few years before, St. Jean de Crèvecoeur, author of *Letters from an American Farmer,* had been serving the last of his time as French Consul in New York. He talked to Fitch, who aroused the Frenchman's ready enthusiams in the cause of steamboats. Franklin rather sprinkled cold water on Crèvecoeur's spirits when the Consul sought the philosopher's opinion.

Again, nothing came of all this. Fitch, who was then hopefully (but vainly) seeking land grants from Congress as a form of subsidy, was so grateful that he promised to name a town for his French friend. This would have been no novelty to Crèvecoeur, who had a knack in this line. Due to a correspondence on Deistical philosophy with Ethan Allen his name became memorialized in St. Johnsbury, Vermont, and he contributed the name of the small city of Vergennes, in the same state.

Now, in 1793, his passage across paid, Fitch sailed to France. Rumsey had been there, Fulton was there, Paine was there. He found Paine living in seclusion in Paris, his prestige waned in the treacherous shifts of the Revolution.

The political chaos of France thwarted all the great plans. Fitch went to England and in the Spring of 1794 sailed to Boston. He had to indenture himself for his passage back and worked months in Boston to bail himself out of this debt.

A bleak and fruitless time followed. 1796 found Fitch back in Kentucky, where he still owned some land. His spirit was gone. For about two years he lived in the tavern of Alexander McCowan, making over deeds to him in exchange for keeping him as long as he should live. He then set about the serious work of drinking himself to death. It took him nearly two years and some help from disease which, from the sound of it, might have been anything from cancer to cirrhosis of the liver.

He was given opium pills to ease his pain. He saved enough of these to kill himself, in July of 1798. His pathetic hope, expressed in the will in which he disposed of such meagre properties as were his, was that once a year someone might go to his grave and sing "The Song of the Brown Jug," beginning

> With my jug in one hand and my pipe in the other
> I'll drink to my neighbor and friend. . . .

and ending

> He's gone, what a True hearted fellow.

Almost automatically the label "poor John Fitch" fastened itself to this roaming Yankee. In some respects he is the classical "sad sack," the kind of person for whom everything goes wrong, consistently. Human nature, unfortunately, does not warm to this trait, and I think it can be called a trait, for there were ways in which Fitch was partly the architect of his own frustrations. He was frustration-prone as some people are accident-prone. He was a life-long prey to self pity, and was unable to keep his ideas in proportion. The astonishing thing, and in justice the tribute to him, is that he was able to do so much with so little.

Fitch was not the only Yankee in the steamboat line. The upper waters of the Connecticut River are not favorable to craft other than the flatboat, except in a few deep crossings. Nevertheless, in this relatively unlikely place, in 1790, the year of Fitch's peak success, more steamboat experiments were begun. The town of Orford, New Hampshire, a village of stately mansions some twenty miles or so north of Dartmouth College, harbored an authentic inventor in Captain Samuel Morey, dealer in lumber.

Going one better than the tea-kettle legend of James Watt, Morey's first steam experiment is said to have been the harnessing of the steam from a kettle to turn the spit in the fireplace. Apparently it was not until 1793 that Morey actually ran his boat, choosing a Sunday morning so that most of the townspeople would be in church and could not laugh at him if he failed. This boat used the first steam-powered paddle-wheel in this country (an Englishman named Symington had built a paddle-wheel boat and run it in 1789). Morey's first wheel was at the bow and pulled the boat. The craft was a tiny skiff, barely able to contain the engine, Morey, and enough slabs of wood to keep steam up. He made five miles an hour, chugging in the Connecticut between Orford and Fairlee, on the Vermont side. Then for three successive summers, Morey ran steam-boats in New York, either in the rivers or on Collect Pond, possibly both. There are persistent traditions of a steamboat on Collect Pond and this can have been none other than Morey. The story that Fitch had a boat there after his return from France has no solid foundation.

Illness in his family caused Morey to leave New York. He sailed his boat up Long Island Sound and up the Connecticut to Hartford, about 1795 or '96, the longest single voyage by steam up to that date. A year later he was back in New York again, demonstrating a boat. At some-time in these many experiments he had found it better to transfer his paddle-wheel from the bow to the stern.

According to Morey's own account, Robert Livingston, John Stevens, and others "went with me in the boat from the ferry as far as Greenwich and back, and they expressed very great satisfaction at her performance and with the engine."

He said that Livingston offered him $7,000 for the patent rights on the North River (Hudson) and to Amboy, and further held out the promise of large sums if Morey would develop a boat capable of eight miles an hour. Morey was unwilling to sell for the sum offered.

In June of 1797, Morey was in Bordentown, New Jersey. Here, on the Delaware, in Fitch's old scenes, he ran a side-wheeler with a rudimentary walking-beam. It worked well, made numerous trips, and was openly exhibited in Philadelphia. By his claim—and it is possible—only his inability to solve his financial problems kept him from beating Fulton to successful commercial operation.

Morey went back to New England. The latter years of his life were spent in Fairlee, Vermont. Near there is a small lake, now called for him, Lake Morey. Legend intrudes itself here, with the story that the Captain, defeated in the great waterways, ran his last small steamboat here, sinking her in a tragic gesture in the middle of the lake. On misty nights, she is said to rise, and be distinctly heard, chugging about in circles.

One added thing is a matter of record. Years afterward, Morey again proved his inventive capacity by making and patenting, in 1826, a liquid-fuel, internal-combustion engine, including the basic concept of the carburetor. Charles Duryea, a pioneer of the gasoline engine, paid tribute to Morey's invention as a remarkable achievement. Like the early electric motors, and Paine's vision of a steam turbine, it was premature.

Two other Yankees, one in Massachusetts and the other in Rhode Island, were tinkering with boats, at no more than the level for which the term "tinker" is apt. But there was some interest to what each one did, so that we cannot ignore them.

The more important is Nathan Read, farmer, Harvard graduate, apothecary, Hebrew student, and mechanic. We'll hear of him again in other contexts. He was more an engine man than a boatman, experimenting with both but never carrying them to fulfilment in combination.

At his home in Salem he developed a multitubular boiler, like the one independently created by John Stevens as an improvement on Rumsey's pipe boiler. He then made a double-acting engine, comparable to Watt's, which, as we have seen, Fitch did also. It has been claimed for Read that his boiler and engine contributed to the American steamboat, but it is hard to point to a significant link, other than conversations he is known to have had with Stevens. His achievements were relatively isolated, and were independently duplicated by more active men.

In 1789, he fitted out a small boat with hand-powered

paddle-wheels. This would bring him about neck-and-neck with Morey on paddle-wheels in this country except for what I consider the disqualifying fact that he never put his steam engine and his paddle-wheels together, which Morey did.

In Cranston, Rhode Island, some time after 1790, Elijah Ormsbee, carpenter, and David Wilkinson, blacksmith, tinkered up a little steamboat, more or less as a lark. They made a crude, single-acting engine, partly out of an old still, and rigged it up temporarily in a borrowed long boat.

The thing that is most interesting about this case is that Ormsbee, apparently spontaneously, duplicated more crudely the propulsion device that had been used by the Frenchman Jouffroy, in 1775, in one of the several experiments antedating all American attempts. This was another instance of the understandable but fundamentally misguided efforts to make mechanical motion conform to animal motion. Ormsbee, like his French predecessor, contrived a mechanical goose-foot, that moved back and forth in the water, opening and closing. After entertaining their neighbors with a nine-day wonder, neither Ormsbee nor Wilkinson, sheer tinkerers, made any effort to develop their ideas.

John Stevens, of Hoboken, represents yet another factor and is markedly different in nature and approach from any of our steamboaters thus far. He is the first specimen of the engineer-inventor to turn up in our story. Stevens did his work on paper, by theory. Whatever he designed he had others build for him, by specification. One of his hired mechanics was the Englishman, John Hall, who had worked for Fitch after Voight had pulled out of the partnership. Fitch had first met Hall at Thomas Paine's. Hall, the man who liked to call inventors "saint-makers," was not canonized by Stevens, who fired him on the complaint of drunkenness.

We have been dealing, generally, with men of poor and

humble origin. Stevens was a gentleman inventor. His was one of the oldest and wealthiest New Jersey families. His home, in Hoboken, had broad lawns stretching down to the waters of the Hudson, no doubt helping to make him keenly conscious of the possibilities of that avenue of shipping.

John Stevens had been an officer in the Revolution. He was thirty-eight when he began to take serious interest in scientific and mechanical matters. Transportation, in particular, attracted him, and from the time he took up the pursuit he never relinquished it.

His first act, relative to steamboats, was to correspond with Rumsey, whose pipe boiler interested him, with recommendations for its improvement. These resulted in his own, stronger, multitubular boiler. It was not long before he was applying for patents of his own, and injecting his voice into the Fitch-Rumsey controversy. Both those gentlemen wanted exclusive patents. Stevens did not want either of them to have a monopoly. He put forth arguments which were to be a consistent position with him all the way through the later battles over the Livingston-Fulton monopoly. Speaking of Fitch and Rumsey, Stevens argued: "As neither of these gentlemen, from what has yet appeared, have brought their Schemes to that degree of perfection as to answer any valuable purpose in practice, I conceive that neither of them are entitled to such an exclusive privilege as may secure to them all the benefits arising from the improvements invented by others."

In 1795, during the hard years after his return from Europe, poor Fitch called on Stevens, to try to borrow the pitiful sum of twenty dollars, offering to give him rights to a "horse boat" he had designed. This was a cumbersome treadmill device to impart motion to paddles. Stevens, who owned a ferry to New York, was interested but skeptical. Meanwhile, Voight claimed that the horse boat was his, anyhow. Fitch kept up a desperate correspondence with Stevens, in characteristic style, frantically urging that his design could not fall short of the Colonel's needs and pledging "the mechanical reputation of John Fitch," which, unfortunately deserved to be high but was not. Stevens, too much the theoretician and aristocrat, was among the many to whose discredit was a failure to give Fitch his due.

Stevens worked on rather advanced principles, so much so that they were to play second fiddle for a while to more primitive devices. In May, of 1804, while the Colonel stood on his Hoboken lawn watching, two of his sons crossed from New York in a small craft named *Little Juliana* which a spectator described as containing an engine but moving by no visible means of propulsion. In fact, it was moving by twin-screw propellers.

This was Stevens' primary contribution in the realm of the steamboat. The propeller was not new. We've mentioned before that it was a development from the screw of Archimedes; Bernoulli, the inspirer of the jet boat, had also set forth the theory of the screw; Bushnell had used it on the *Turtle,* and Fulton had used it on his submarines, which we shall speak about later. But Stevens devised the twin-screw, as a factor in steering and stability as well as thrust, and also designed the first steam-engine power transmission to operate such screws. Both Bushnell and Fulton had turned theirs by manual power.

Now we must give some attention to Mr. Robert Fulton. We know already something of his origins and of his beginnings as a painter at the time and place of Fitch's earliest steamboat trials in Philadelphia. Franklin, who had cold-shouldered Fitch in practical effect though not in personal demeanor, was helpful to young Fulton, presumably without any knowledge of him in a capacity other than that of artist. When Fulton went to England, in 1786, he bore from the sage of Philadelphia a letter of commendation to the American expatriate painter, Benjamin West, then artistic arbiter of London, with whom the young man studied.

Fulton's first years in England were rugged. He wrote of them, in 1792, to his mother:

> . . . Many Many a Silant solitary hour have I spent
> in the most unnerved Studdy Anxiously pondering
> how to make funds to support me till the fruits of my
> labours should sifficant to repay them. Thus I went
> on for near four years—happily beloved by all who
> knew me or I had long ear now been Crushed by
> Poverties Cold wind—and Freezing Rain. . . .

Just as he was emerging from this Slough of Despond,
he switched his talents abruptly to another field. Brush and
pencil became dedicated, henceforth, chiefly to technical
drawings. In England, and later in France, he devoted himself to the study of engineering.

Canals had diverted James Rumsey from his steamboats.
For Fulton, canals were the first step of his new career. He
published at least two pamphlets connected with problems
and principles of canal construction, in 1796. One of these
was in connection with a project of the Earl of Stanhope,
who was also one of England's most active (and eccentric)
experimenters with steamboats. Rumsey had had negotiations with him during his English sojourn.

We find that the switch of interests and the publishing
of canal treatises had not yet made any significant change
in Fulton's practical affairs, for in a circumlocutory note
to Lord Stanhope he confesses "That I am now Sitting
Reduced to half a Crown, Without Knowing Where to obtain a shilling for some months . . . Thus Circumstanced
My Lord, would it be an Intrusion on your goodness and
Philanthropy to Request the Loan of 20 guineas Which
I will Return as Soon as possible."

In addition to his canal studies, he patented in England
an improved marble saw, a ditch-digger, and flax-spinning
and rope-making machines. These didn't yield much
money, either.

In 1797, he went across to France. Here he met the man
who was to be his greatest friend—Joel Barlow. He was
eleven years older than Fulton, a man who had practiced
in the realms of diplomacy and literature. He had been

one of the handful of American idealists who had dabbled in the French Revolution, emerging from it more successfully than Paine, who by the way was a friend of both Barlow and Fulton and must have talked steamboats with the latter many times.

Every schoolboy learns that Barlow was the author of a pseudo-epic, *The Columbiad,* published in 1807 and dedicated to Fulton, who illustrated it. More pertinent to us is the fact that he had been at Yale with David Bushnell and quite probably knew a good deal about the *American Turtle,* whether or not Bushnell ever met Fulton in France, as some have alleged.

The thirty-two-year old Fulton had charm and good looks. One of his own submarine sketches, only a little later, contains a self-portrait in profile showing him peering through the peep-hole in the conning tower, looking extraordinarily like the late William Gillette in his prime as Sherlock Holmes. The Barlows, husband and wife, were quite taken with him. He lived in their home in Paris for seven years. They called him "Toot." Combining his painting and his inventiveness, he created a successful fad in Paris with a big diorama. For once he made quite a bit of money, all of which he dedicated to his submarine, as he did everything he could get from his friends.

Now he began what may have been his most truly inventive accomplishments, notwithstanding his considerable debt to Bushnell. He conceived, sketched, and actually carried out a series of experiments in submarine navigation and warfare. These had the encouragement of officials in the French government, of which Napoleon then was First Consul. The jargon of the Revolution was still current and annoys us now, since the accounts of the experiments and negotiations all are dated according to the Revolutionary calendar. Thus we will find *27 Vendemiaire an VI* for October 17, 1798. In spite of official interest and cooperation, Fulton financed most of the work by the proceeds from his immensely popular cyclorama and by drawing on his friends.

His motives were odd. He was infected with the most advanced Utopian thinking of his day. A pacifist, he decided that war would soonest be ended by making it too terrible to contemplate, a concept to which history has not been kind. The fearsome submarine would wipe out the navies of the world and peace would ensue. Why his vision precluded the continuation of war with the added impetus of one more weapon, who can say? Dreamers often dream with blinders.

Fulton's thoughts were quite as subversive as they were submersible. While in France, he felt that England was the oppressive villain of Europe. During Napoleon's tenure as First Consul, Fulton said in one of his long memorials to the Minister of Marine concerning his boat, the *Nautilus:*

> If by means of the Nautilus one could succeed in destroying the English navy, it would be possible with a fleet of Nautilus to blockade the Thames to the end that England would become a republic. Soon Ireland would throw off the yoke and the English monarchy would be wiped out. A rich and industrious nation would then increase the number of republics in Europe and this would be a long step toward liberty and universal peace.

If you were to block out everything but the conning tower and controls of Fulton's *Nautilus* you would have left something which was fundamentally Bushnell's *American Turtle*. Fulton elongated it, to twenty-one feet (about three times the length of the *Turtle*) and its profile was a little like that of a modern artillery shell. It had a manually operated propeller, and a rudder, at the stern. A collapsible sail was folded along the top, to be lofted for surface navigation. The use of water ballast for submerging, and the basic method of attaching a torpedo to a ship's hull were those of Bushnell. The boat was to accommodate a captain and a crew of three men. The *Nautilus* may quite possibly have been the inspiration to Verne, years later, for the name of Captain Nemo's mighty craft.

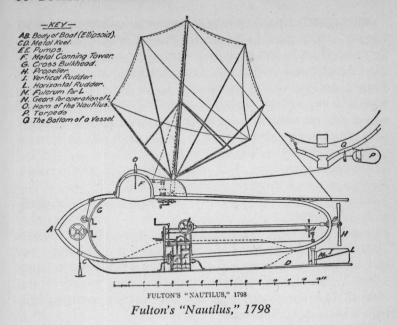

—KEY—
AB. Body of Boat (Ellipsoid).
C.D. Metal Keel.
E.E. Pumps.
F. Metal Conning Tower.
G. Cross Bulkhead.
H. Propeller.
J. Vertical Rudder.
L. Horizontal Rudder.
M. Fulcrum for L.
N. Gears for operation of L.
O. Horn of the Nautilus.
P. Torpedo.
Q The Bottom of a Vessel.

FULTON'S "NAUTILUS," 1798

Fulton's "Nautilus," 1798

Fulton built the *Nautilus* at Rouen, and tested her in the Seine and later in the harbor at Le Havre, in the summer of 1800. His greatest feat, as he reported it to his French supporters, one of whom was the scientist Pierre Laplace, was a submersion with three other men, for four hours and twenty minutes. This was achieved by carrying an auxiliary copper globe of compressed air which Fulton used to replenish the "Oxszine."

He claimed to have maneuvered with facility, both above and below the water. Also, by means of his torpedo, he blew up a sloop, provided for experiment by the French navy. These were bold and remarkable accomplishments. In spite of the debt to Bushnell, he had so developed and carried forward the conception of the submarine, in practice, as to have earned great credit in his own right. The one faintly dubious circumstance is that he dismantled the *Nautilus* with startling celerity after these tests and pled the rest of his case on paper.

He devised, also, a system of anchored submarine mines (again with a debt to Bushnell's New London and Philadelphia efforts), and proposed the laying of minefields in the Channel and in harbors, along distinctly modern lines. France decided not to use any of these devices. Napoleon now had grasped the state firmly and his swelling sense of power felt no need of help from American gadgetry. England was already strong enough at sea and was interested merely in getting Fulton out of France, which she did by adroit seductions when Fulton had persuaded himself that Napoleon was betraying the Republicanism to which the inventor had lent his sympathy. America was preoccupied with other matters than engines of war. So all across the board, Fulton was frustrated with his bombs and submarine vessels which he had seen as foreshadowing the end of war. War, it appeared, must go on for yet a little while. Fulton returned home, in 1806, after twenty years abroad, forty-two years old, not yet very prosperous, but with a destiny before him.

The turning of the tide for Fulton was a matter of contacts. The alliance that was to make his fortune had been established in France, even while so many of his submarine schemes were being frustrated. A curious figure in the annals of steamboating had come to France as Jefferson's minister. This was Chancellor Robert R. Livingston, so known from the New York State office he had held. Livingston was one of the English-stock aristocrats of the Hudson valley who had been the inheritors of the patroons. He had a great estate, Clermont, on the river some forty miles below Albany. His career has many facets. He administered the oath of office at Washington's first inauguration. On the French mission which brought him into contact with Fulton he was one of the prime movers in negotiating that epic of real estate deals, the Louisiana Purchase, which, incidentally, would make it possible for American steamboats to ply the Mississippi.

Livingston was a dabbler in many ventures, including gypsum fertilizers and sheep raising. But his pet interest was steamboats and he had the money to indulge it. Also he had advantageous connections. His brother-in-law was Colonel John Stevens, one of whose sons was named in honor of the Chancellor.

Livingston had more or less peered over the shoulder of Stevens during the latter's earliest interest in steam, and we have Morey's testimony that the Chancellor and his brother-in-law were witnesses to, and passengers on, some of his New York steam cruises. We must remember, too, that Livingston had offered to purchase at least a part of Morey's rights but that a price could not be agreed upon. The last ventures of the Chancellor, before his mission to France, involved unsuccessful attempts to build a boat with the mechanical aid of the machinist, Nicholas Roosevelt, whom he engaged for the purpose.

In France, Fulton and Livingston made some steam experiments on the Seine, even while the submarine deals were afoot. Napoleon, who had spurned the submarine and called Fulton a swindler, later was vexed that the steamboat had slipped out of his grasp. He thought it might have held the key to his cherished enterprise of invading England.

Livingston had decided to waste no more time or money on engine experiments. The Chancellor put up the cash and the one tangible fruit of all Fulton's dickerings with England that followed his rejection in France was the permission for him to bring a Boulton & Watt engine to the United States. This was a major concession for the British were chary of shipping machinery of any sort to rival countries—an economic precursor of the modern military security consciousness.

The mechanical prize package that Fulton brought home in 1806 was the engine which on the celebrated day of August 17, 1807, supplied the power for the first cruise from New York to Albany of the craft which was not then called the *Clermont,* as tradition had insisted, but was known variously as *The Steamboat, The North River Steamboat,* or simply *The North River.*

Livingston's political power was important to this history. When Fitch's exclusive patent of fourteen years, from which he was to reap nothing but disappointment, had expired, Fitch being dead, Livingston maneuvered for himself a monopolistic grant to steamboat traffic on the Hudson and adjoining waters, without even having a boat to run or one in sight. The building of Fulton's *North River* was crowding the date of expiration of this monopoly and Livingston succeeded in getting it renewed.

The monopoly caused a tremendous furor for years. It was not broken, legally, before it expired; but neither could it be enforced, effectively. Unauthorized rivals entered the field in competition. The earliest of these was brother-in-law Stevens, himself, who had first refused to join the Livingston-Fulton combine, then tried to buck it, and later came to terms with it. Not long after the Fulton boat began running, Stevens put aside his advanced but unripened ideas of screw-propulsion and high-pressure engines and built the paddle-wheel *Phoenix*. After running for a time in the waters around Amboy, in defiance of the monopoly, the *Phoenix* earned the honor of making the first ocean cruise by steam, in a rough, battering journey of several days and nights down coast to the waters of the Delaware, where it plied successfully, in the wake now of both Fitch and Morey.

Meanwhile, in 1808, only a year after the first cruise of the *North River*, John and James Winans launched the side-wheeler *Vermont* on Lake Champlain. Steamboats were burgeoning. No limitations could hold them back. By 1811, Nicholas Roosevelt, in association with Fulton, built the *New Orleans*, in Pittsburgh, and sailed her down to the city of her name. The Mississippi, focus of "little Johnny Fitch's" original steamboat vision, had met her historic destiny with the paddle-wheel which was to be celebrated at its climax in Twain's *Life on the Mississippi*.

Stevens opposed the monopoly on the generally consistent and sound view that no one should be allowed to throttle completely the natural rewards and channels of invention and enterprise. Nevertheless, he finally adhered to the old saw, "If you can't lick 'em, jine 'em." The Superintendent of the Patent Office, Dr. William Thornton, who had been an associate of Fitch in the later stages of his company, opposed the monopoly on the grounds that everything Fulton had built was a copy from somebody else. Fulton tried, rather unwisely, to defend the originality of various features. He could hardly avoid the fact that he had used a purchased Boulton & Watt engine. Later he worked at length with Paul Revere, designing copper boilers for his own engines. He made a feeble attempt to claim the paddle-wheels for his own, but leaving Symington's English experiments aside, there was the undoubted circumstance that Morey had used paddle-wheels front, rear, and sides, on his various boats, and that Livingston and Fulton were well acquainted with the fact. Morey made his voice heard in a full statement of what he had done. These legal battles drew Fulton into contact with Connecticut's greatest inventor, Eli Whitney, a veteran battler over patent rights and priorities. The circumstances, however, were markedly different.

The most curious testimony to be entered in the dispute came from a remarkable man, Oliver Evans, of Delaware, an inventor of such outstanding gifts that we shall hear more of him in due course. On December 16, 1814, Evans filed a certificate affirming "that when John Fitch and his company were engaged in constructing their steamboat in Philadelphia, he, the said Oliver, suggested to the said John Fitch, the plan of driving and propelling the said boat by paddle or flutter wheels at the sides of the boat; when the said Fitch or some other person, but he thought it was Fitch, informed him, that one of the company had already proposed and urged the use of wheels at the sides, but that he had objected to them."

He further alleged that in 1777 or '78 Fitch had spoken to him of steamboat plans for the Great Lakes, including a fantastic concept apparently not recorded anywhere else, in which he "meant to construct them with two keels, to answer as runners, and when the lakes should freeze over, he would raise his boat on the ice and by a wheel on each side, with spikes in the rims to take hold of the ice, he calculated it would be possible to run thirty miles per hour." Unconfirmed by other report as this is, it has the ring of Fitch's occasional hyperbole.

How are we to appraise Fulton? I think it is fair to say that he did nothing so breathlessly original as Bushnell, and nothing so doggedly and almost sacrificially creative as Fitch. He had a persistence of purpose which Bushnell obviously lacked, and the diplomatic adroitness (a few blunders excepted) of which Rumsey had some but Fitch none. He was an opportunist, but often we use that word in derogation, disregarding the fact that every successful man is, to some extent, a grasper and cultivator of the opportunities which knock many more times at our doors than the proverb says. The worst that can be said of Fulton is that as a man who was given to sounding off on a level of elevated idealism, these ideals miraculously never ever stood in the way of the main chance. When the main chance seemed to shift, as from France to England, Fulton found easy rationalizations as to why the channel of his idealism must make the same shift, too. He was also either self-hynotized or somewhat consciously dishonest (the former being more likely) in his willingness to claim as his own numerous inventions that were by no manner of means his own, retreating only when confronted by incontrovertible evidence.

Still, Fulton was a man of gifts, determination, and the happy destiny to be on hand at the time, and place, and with the men, under which combination the steamboat was finally ripe to be a commercial success. Fulton compiled rather than invented a steamboat. He was an anthologist of steam. But this was an intelligent operation. He had digested all the sources upon which he drew. He knew what he was doing, and as hitches arose, he knew rightly how to meet them. Even when other steamboats arose round about him, he remained the greatest builder of them all, constructing twenty-two, dedicated to them with a concentration that shortened his life, even though he had attained fame, comfort, and also wealth and social status through marriage to Livingston's niece. His last creation was the cumbersomely impressive steam warship—the first —called the *Demologos* (the word, or spirit, of the people —showing that his flair for idealizing had not diminished).

He resumed experiments with torpedoes and mines after coming back from Europe. Knowledge of these made the British captains so nervous in the War of 1812, that their ships in Long Island Sound daily dragged ropes under the length of their hulls lest infernal machines be fastened there.

So, steamboats got themselves invented, ruthlessly chewing up a number of lives and crushing some hopes and spirits in the process, as do all the great movements in which man is swept along, often deluded that he is the pilot and prime mover. There would have been steamboats even if there had been no United States, but it happened that the United States was the natural, even urgent, theatre for them. There would have been steamboats even if there had been no John Fitch, James Rumsey, Nathan Read, Elijah Ormsbee, Samuel Morey, John Stevens, or Robert Fulton. Yet the historic fact is that the stream of Yankee inventiveness and the blind power of steam met to make the specific thing that *was to be* out of the infinity of what otherwise *might have been*.

CHAPTER 8

SPINNERS

It is not probable, Samuel, that it
will always be as good as it is now,
but I have no doubt it will always
be a *fair* business, if it be well
managed.

—JEDEDIAH STRUTT TO SAMUEL
SLATER, ON THE TEXTILE
INDUSTRY.

AMONG THE *Mayflower* settlers of Plymouth skills in textile manufacture were well represented. William Bradford was a fustian maker. Samuel Fuller (later the colony's physician) and Stephen Tracey were silk makers. William White, Robert Cushman, and Richard Masterson were wool-carders, and Isaac Allerton was a tailor. Quite a few others of the company were weavers, some of whom brought their looms with them.

In spite of this collection of skills, colonial cloth making did not have its true beginnings among them. The men of Plymouth turned to other pursuits of necessity, especially farming and fishing, but more to the point than anything, they had not the raw materials for their trades. There were no sheep in the new world, as yet, nor was there time for the cultivation of yarn plants. When the irregular arrival of supply ships drove the Plymouth Plantation to the sheer edge of survival, the lack of the needed clothing and cloth supplies was one of the keenest hardships. It was a ragged crew that met the next arrivals, and from this privation arose the old, traditional "Forefathers' Song," one stanza of which bore on the matter of raiment:

And now, too, our garments begin to grow thin,
And wool is much wanted to card and to spin;
If we can get garments to cover without,
Our other in-garments are clout upon clout. [Patch.]
Our clothes we brought with us are apt to be torn—
They need to be clouted soon after they are worn—
But clouting our garments they hinder us nothing;
Clouts double are warmer than single whole clothing.

Once the flow of supplies from home became stabilized, as the whole process of colonization was spreading, most cloth stuffs were imported.

Around 1640, as we have seen, the New England colonies experienced their first depression, in our modern economic sense of the word. The convening of the Long Parliament, and the waning of the power of Charles I, ended the oppression which had been the cause of continuous emigration. Abruptly the influx of settlers in the colonies fell off. In fact, considerable numbers returned to England to take up their prior lives and for a good many years to come the Atlantic saw a two-way traffic between England and the colonies, little more than holding a balance at the best.

This sudden check in population knocked the props from under a highly profitable colonial cattle market. Within less than a year the price of cattle dropped from as high as £28 sterling per head to as low as £5, with no takers at that. "Thus the flood which brought in much wealth to many persons, the contrary ebb carried all away out of their reach." So it was put by historian William Hubbard, who was graduated in the first class from Harvard, in the midst of that depression, in 1642.

The trade in cloth from England was throttled. An urgent need for yarn and cloth of all sorts arose. It was under this pressure that the long-surviving tradition of household manufacture of yarn and cloth began on a large scale.

The Massachusetts Assembly, in 1640, issued an emergency General Court order:

> The Court, taking into serious consideration the absolute necessity for the raising of the manufacture of linen cloth, doth declare that it is the intent of this Court that there shall be an order settled about it, and therefore doth require the magistrates and deputies of the several towns to acquaint the townsmen therewith, and to make enquiry what seed is in every town, what men and women are skilful in the braking, spinning, weaving, what means for the providing of wheels; and to consider with those skilful in that manufacture, and what course may be taken for teaching the boys and girls in all towns the spinning of the yarn, and to return to the next Court their several and joint advice about this thing.—The like consideration would be had for the spinning and weaving of *cotton wool*.

Connecticut did much the same, penalizing the waste of cattle skins, and requiring all families to sow hemp and flax and to harvest the seed, so that they might "have supply of Lynen Cloath amongst ourselves."

Earnest attention was turned to sheep breeding. The first flock in New England had been brought in 1633. Wolves and Indians were so great a predatory menace that for a long time the sheep were kept on an island in Boston harbor. As others were brought, towns began to maintain small flocks under the care of common shepherds.

Flax and hemp raising were extended. This earliest hemp was a coarse native plant (*Apocynum Cannabinum*), quite unlike and much inferior to the true Asiatic hemp (*Cannabis sativa*), the source of *hashish* and *marijuana*.

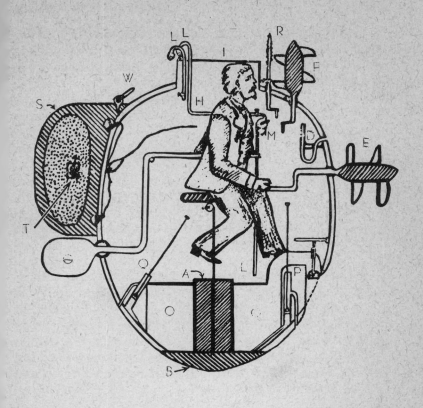

David Bushnell's fabulous American Turtle, *as Sergeant Lee operated it. Text description in Chapter I. will help to understand it.
Compare with Fulton's Nautilus in text.*

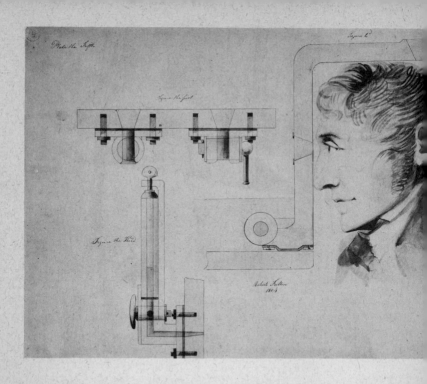

Number five of an extraordinary series of plates which Fulton prepared in 1806 for the British government. This is a detail of the conical glass peephole in the conning tower of a more advanced submarine than his Nautilus (but this one never was built). The sketch includes a self-portrait, resembling the late William Gillette as Sherlock Holmes. This vessel was proposed to the British after Fulton's disillusionment with Napoleon as a democratic savior. The original drawings — large in size — are at the New York Public Library.

NEW YORK PUBLIC LIBRARY, MSS COLL.

Jackson's Mill: watercolor by Archibald Robertson. A beautiful example of a tide mill. La Guardia air field is built approximately on this site.

COLLECTION OF CHARLES K. DAVIS

PHOTO: HARRY SHAW NEWMAN OLD PRINT SHOP, N.Y.C.

Paul Revere's engraving of British war ships landing troops in Boston, 1768. Long Wharf is in the foreground. The next largest wharf, to the right, is Clark's Wharf, at the foot of which stood Revere's shop.

NEW YORK PUBLIC LIBRARY, STOKES COLLECTION

Poor Johnny Fitch. An anonymous, posthumous engraving.

Plan of Mr. Fitch's Steam Boat.

Fitch's side-paddle boat, of about 1786. His best boat was the later stern-paddle model.

Old Slater Mill at Pawtucket, Rhode Island.

One American inventor paints another. The young Samuel Finley Breese Morse's portrait of the aging and unwell Eli Whitney, about 1822.

Lithograph of Lowell, Mass., by William S. Pendleton. This is in 1833, nine years before Charles Dickens' visit. See his description.

Chauncey Jerome, builder and chronicler of the Connecticut clock industry. This is the frontispiece of his autobiography.

Eli Whitney's gun factory. The idyllic age of industrial paintings. Note the rows of workmen's houses. "The best place God ever made about here," a contemporary called it.

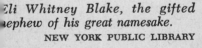

Eli Whitney Blake, the gifted nephew of his great namesake.

As the family clusters round, a walking Yankee peddler opens his pack of wares.

ASHER .B. DURAND
COURTESY OF THE NEW YORK HISTORICAL SOCIETY

A Yankee peddler with wagon of canvas-covered type. Observe the clock among his wares.

JOHN WHETTON EHNINGER
COURTESY OF THE NEWARK MUSEUM, NEWARK N. J.

There was also a boom in the importing of so-called "vegetable wool," or cotton, the American cultivation of which is a later story. At this stage, the colonies depended upon Barbadoes for their supply. In Connecticut, the chief commodity for trade for cotton was "pipe-staves" (barrel-staves), no doubt destined for rum and molasses. They were of such importance that official pipe-stave inspectors kept guard over the quality, "in regard especially of worm holes, whereby the commodity is like to be prohibited . . . to the great damage of the Countrie."

Now the spinning wheel, the flax-brake and "hetchel," the wool-card, and the loom took their place as household implements as tradition, song, picture, and story in America have recorded them. These old tools are still to be found in the remote New England barns and attics where the diligence of the antique dealer has not entirely garnered them. Ponds around New England are still, in some places, remembered as the flax ponds, where the outer stems of the flax and hemp were water-rotted (or "retted") in the preparation for heckling out the long fibers. From these necessary labors came the gatherings called "bees" (from being busily engaged in a common enterprise), half work and half game, for braking, or carding, or spinning.

In the first urgent spurt of these activities, the colonial Assemblies in some places offered bounties, up to as much as three pence per shilling's worth, on linen, woolen, and cotton cloth and yarns. Advancements in production were so swift that they forced the abandoning of bounties within three years or so, as too burdensome. The fabrics made were chiefly linen and cotton mixtures, called fustians and dimities. (The names of cloths, in this period, often are confusing for the same name may be applied by different persons, or in various places, to quite different fabrics.)

Wool was considered the most desirable fabric of all. The General Court of Massachusetts, in an order in 1645, showed the relative esteem in which wool and other fabrics were held, and afforded us, from our long perspective, a realistic glimpse of contemporary living problems.

Forasmuch as woolen cloth is so useful a commodity, &c., by reason of the cold winters, and being at present scarce and deare, and likely soon to be so in parts whence we can expect to get it, by reason of the wars in Europe destroying the flocks of sheepe, and killing and hindering the trade of those whose skill and labor tend to that end, and as for want of woolen cloth many poor people have suffered cold and hardship and impaired their health, and some hazarded their lives, and those who had provided their families with cotton cloth, (not being able to get the other) have by that means had some of their children much scorched by fire, yea, divers burnt to death; this Court, therefore, (taking into consideration our present condition in that particular, as also having an eye to the good of posterity, knowing how useful and necessary woolen cloths and stuffs would be for our more comfortable cloathing and how profitable a merchandize it is like to be to transport to other parts;) doth hereby desire all towns in general, and every one in particular within the jurisdiction, seriously to weigh the premises, and accordingly, that you will endeavor the preservation and increase of such sheepe as they have already, as also to procure more with all convenient speed into the several towns by all such lawful ways and means as God shall put into their hands . . . which being carefully endeavoured, we leave the success to God.

Every measure was taken for the protection of sheep. Liberal bounties were paid for wolf's heads. Some "fished" for wolves, as Bishop describes the grim process.

A mode of capture early practiced in Massachusetts was by binding the shanks of four fish hooks together with the barbs outward, then wrapping them in raw cotton, and dipping in melted tallow until a ball was formed the size of an egg, which was greedily swallowed by the hungry vermin.

In addition to defense against these natural foes, there were sharp restrictions on the killing of sheep for food, complete prohibition of their export, and at some times, prohibitions of the export of wool.

But the woolen industry has great need of one specialized function—fulling—the cleansing of the natural animal grease in the fibres, the lanolin so widely used in modern cosmetics. Good fuller's earth, a friable, detergent clay, which had been thought by many in that day to be almost a unique treasure of England, proved to abound in the colonies. With the growth of the household woolen manufacture, some towns acquired a fulling mill to perform this special service for the whole community. Where such facilities did not exist, the woolens were used in their dirty and malodorous unfulled state.

The first such fulling mill in the colonies was built by John Pearson, in 1643, at Rowley, in Massachusetts, which town was the earliest center of woolen making. (This was the same year in which Joseph Jenks came over and the Saugus ironworks were commenced.) It was in operation for more than fifty years. Other fulling mills followed in widely scattered areas. Towns would set aside lands, on the "eminent domain" principle, for such a purpose, and many a town record contains the equivalent of this item from Waterbury, Connecticut: ". . . there was sequesterd the great brook from edman scots lot down to samuell hickox, Jr. lot for to build a fulling mill."

In the same way, one weaver in some cases might work for all the town's yarn spinners. Chelmsford, Massachusetts, offered twelve acres of meadow and eighteen of pasture to William How, "provided he set up his trade of weaving, and perform the town's work."

Any notion of absolute freedom of the individual in colonial life would be an error (as always and anywhere). The town-meeting system of local self government throughout New England never hesitated in the early days to prescribe what nature of work, and how much of it, must be done by its able-bodied citizens for the communal good.

And it never occurred to the villager to question the propriety of this. The colonial Assemblies exercised the same type of jurisdiction with a high and firm hand. In 1656 this extremely diligent Massachusetts Assembly whose utterances we have been following, went all out in a primary example of its kind:

> For the improving as many hands as may be in spinninge woole, cotton, flaxe, &c. . . . all hands not necessarily employed on other occasions, as women, girls and boys, shall and hereby are enjoined to spin according to their skill and ability, and that the selectmen in every town do consider the condition and capacity of every family, and accordingly to assess them as one or more spinners. And because several families are necessarily employed the greater part of their time in other business, yet, if opportunities were attended, some time might be spared, at least by some of them, for this work; the said selectmen shall therefore assess such families at half or a quarter of a spinner, according to their capacities. Secondly: and that every one thus assessed for a whole spinner, do after the present year, 1656, spin for 30 weeks every yeare 3 pound per week of linen, cotton, or woolen, and so proportionally for half or quarter spinners, under the penalty of 12*d*. for every pound short . . . And it is further ordered that the selectmen in all towns within this jurisdiction shall have power to make such orders in their respective towns for the clearing of commons, for keeping of sheep, as also for the time of putting rams to their flocks, as they shall judge meet; and it is hereby ordered that the deputies in the several towns impart the mind of this Court to their inhabitants concerning the sowing of seeds both of hemp and flaxe.

Such was the sum of conditions and needs, and measures to meet them, that enabled the anonymous author of *New*

England's First Fruits to remark "that God is leading us by the hand into a way of clothing."

"I have seen his cotton factories . . . with machinery that a greedy dog could have invented. . . ." So says the Devil, about man, in Shaw's *Man and Superman*. But he was wrong. For in sheer mechanical ingenuity, manipulative complexity, very little can match the automatic, high-speed machines of the textile industry. You must turn to the realms of the electronic, the chemical, or the nuclear, to overreach them in technical achievement.

The textile industry did not just bring about, it *was* the industrial revolution. The English inventor of water-frame spinning, Arkwright, also was the inventor of the factory system and its disciplines, and was said to be the father of some of its evils. These machines took the immemorial spindles out of the hands of women, and out of the home. They herded women and children into vast barracks and slums, just to do work, and moreover, work that required little brains, for the brains had been built into the machines.

Most of the pioneer inventiveness in this revolution of textiles was British. The United States needed this industry. In a manner of speaking, the Yankees kidnapped it, and then made their own contributions. Before this story can be understood, it is necessary to know about four basic inventions that ended the countless centuries of spinning as a handcraft.

The art of spinning is the taking of short, combed fibres of wool, or cotton, or flax, rolling them so that they form a loose, soft rope (roving) and then by an intermittent stretching and twisting (spinning), lengthening, tightening, and refining the yarn. From ancient days this had been done by hand alone, twirling up the thread on the spindle, held in the hand. The only mechanical factor introduced had been the spinning wheel, to hold and turn the spindle while the fingers stretched and manipulated the fibres. This machine is of such dim antiquity, in Europe and still earlier in India, that it knows no inventor. Leonardo made some of the earliest identifiable improvements in it.

In 1738, an Englishman named Lewis Paul patented a device which spun thread by leading the roving through a series of rollers, each successive pair moving a little faster than the pair before it. This drew out, or in the proper word "attenuated," the yarn.

Around 1764, a spinner named James Hargreaves, poor and destined to die poor, invented the "jenny," which folklore says was named for his wife or daughter. It spun sixteen strands at once and by extension of the principle, an indefinite number. It remained at first partly a hand operation, as if simply multiplying the functions of a spinning wheel by mounting vertically a series of spindles and rovings turned by a single wheel.

Around 1767, Richard Arkwright, who was destined for knighthood and wealth, followed Paul with an invention that used rollers to attentuate the thread, adding a bobbin and flyer to twist it and wind it on the spindle. Because of the birdlike noise of the flyer it was called a "throstle," but became best known as the "water frame" after the application of water power to drive it. It did the first truly continuous mechanical spinning and made strong warp threads, whereas the jenny made only softer, weft threads. Arkwright originally had been a barber. Tradition says he was a coarse and ruthless man, responsible for many of the abuses which Dickens and other "reform" novelists were to agitate about. Carlyle called him a "bag-cheeked, pot-bellied barber" with "fat, vulgar face" and "goggling, heavy-lidded eyes."

Then, between 1774 and '79, Samuel Crompton invented the "mule," said to be so-called because it was a cross between the jenny and the Arkwright frame. It carried the spindles on a movable carriage which rolled outward to stretch the yarn and inward to wind it. Its special merit was it versatility in making fine yarns.

The whole machine-spinning industry has been based on improvements and developments of the machines of Paul, Hargreaves, Arkwright, and Crompton. And remember that all the developments with which this chapter is concerned are toward the spinning of threads and yarns by machinery. The subsequent process of weaving them into cloth is considered afterwards.

As we have seen, colonial America largely clothed itself by household spinning and weaving. From at least 1640, colonial legislative bodies exhorted and encouraged such industry. Connecticut had inspectors in every town, in 1644, to appraise the quality of linen and woolen yarns and set prices for them. Flax, native hemp, wool, and cotton (the latter then chiefly from the Barbadoes) were the staples of this home cloth manufacture. The late 1700's witnessed a great silk raising enthusiasm in all of New England and most of the eastern seaboard. In 1788, President Stiles wore a gown of Connecticut silk at the Yale Commencement. The silk enterprise survived into the 19th century, but died away, disappointing great hopes.

Symptoms of alarm over the possible effect of American cloth making upon the English industry were seen as early as Lord Cornbury's report on the Province of New York, in 1705.

> . . . I am well informed that upon Long Island and Connecticut they are setting up a woollen Manufacture, and I myself have seen Serge made upon Long Island that any man may wear . . . I hope I may be pardoned if I declare my opinion to be that all these Colloneys . . . ought to be kept entirely dependent upon and subservient to England . . . if once they can see they can cloathe themselves, not only comfortably, but handsomely, too, without the help of England, they, who are already not very fond of submitting to government, would soon think of putting in execution designs they had long harbourd

in their breasts. This will not seem strange, when you consider what sort of people this country is inhabited by.

The same emotions were stirring English ironmasters over the growth of that industry in America.

The economic tensions and boycotts in the years leading up to the Revolution added continual impetus to American cloth manufactures. Spinning matches became fashionable among young ladies. Spinning schools and weaving rooms, all on a hand-work basis, were established and encouraged, an unconscious step toward leading these processes out of the home.

Hamilton's Report on Manufactures proclaimed that as of 1791:

> Great quantities of coarse cloths, coatings, serges, and flannels, linsey woolseys, hose of wool, cotton, and thread, coarse fustians, jeans, and muslins, checked and striped cotton and linen goods, bed ticks, coverlets and counterpanes, tow linens, coarse shirtings, sheetings, towelling, and table linen, and various mixtures of wool and cotton, and of cotton and flax, are made in the household way.

Even so, this was not sufficient for the need. Already a new element was ready to make itself felt on the textile scene, but first we should see what native ingenuity had been doing and attempting.

Some fantastic and versatile personalities dart across the American cloth and yarn manufacturing picture, many of them in a kind of shuttle motion, weaving this particular interest into the warp of many other activities. Not all of them made successful or substantial contributions, even though they were talented.

Abel Buell, for instance, had a major gift for dissipating and misdirecting his talents. This Killingworth, Connecticut, lad served apprenticeship as a silversmith and engraver. With a fine precocity, at twenty-one, in 1762, he turned his engraver's skill to the promising business of upping Connecticut five-shilling notes to the improved value of five pounds.

This colonial crime did not pay. Within two years he had his goods confiscated, was branded as a counterfeiter, and sent to prison. While serving his time, he invented a machine for cutting and polishing gems. This won him some favorable opinion and helped give him a fresh start. He went into the businesses of map engraving (which John Fitch had practiced as an amateur) and type-founding. He is generally credited with casting the first type in this country.

The State of Connecticut showed its good will toward the reformed counterfeiter by giving him a grant of £100 to establish a large type foundry. Buell took the money, but the foundry never was created. The state's impatience wore thin, as did that of one James Rivington, to whom he owed money also, and Buell fled the state in 1775 to avoid debtor's prison.

The love of a good woman now came to his aid. Aletta Buell continued her husband's business in the silversmithing shop, "The Sign of the Coffee Pot." She paid back the delinquent £100 to the Connecticut Assembly. Rivington, a Tory, conveniently joined the British army, forfeiting his rights in civil suits. So after three years, Buell was able to come home. He had not been idle. In his "exile" and later, his fertile brain lent itself to various enterprises, from quarrying, to boat lines, a little investment in privateering, the invention of a corn-planter, and the exhibiting of freaks (he promoted a negro allegedly in the process of turning white).

In 1785, he invented a coining machine. Again the State of Connecticut reposed its trust in him, with better luck, and he coined copper for the commonwealth.

His relatively brief and unproductive relationship to the textile field, began around 1789, when as we shall see further, the feeling that America must match British accomplishments in this industry was widespread. Buell went to England to spy out their machinery. After his return, he set up a factory in New York, in 1793, to attempt spinning by British methods. Here his ingenuity failed him. The enterprise was not a success and the British "secret" had already been implanted in America through other channels.

Buell closed out his career in one of the conventional patterns of his time. He decried his occasional former rascalities, denounced Thomas Paine for the baleful influence of his deistical teachings (a much-adopted pious move for aging scoundrels just then) and died in an almshouse in New Haven.

By contrast with Buell, Jeremiah Wilkinson was a much more solid and productive citizen. A farmer's son, from Cumberland, R. I., he became a blacksmith and also, as did so many other skilful and inventive men, took up the crafts of silver- and goldsmith.

Now the first process in the spinning of any fibres, animal or vegetable, is carding, which means combing them so that they lie parallel, ready to be twisted into thread. In home manufacture, this was a hand operation, using a card, generally of stiff leather, with many rows of bent wire hooks in it, with which the tangled mass of wool or cotton was combed out.

As a smith, Wilkinson invented techniques of drawing a superior iron wire, for card teeth, much in demand among other card makers. Next he devised a complex machine, hand operated, which with one motion would cut and bend the teeth, and also punch all the required holes in the leather. Wire was an imported commodity, in his day, and sometimes hard to come by and of variable quality. Wilkinson was one of the first men to draw wire in the colonies, which he did by horsepower, having made by hand his own plates and dies. Joseph Jenks had failed to get support for a wire-drawing venture, nearly a century before, but there were tools for it in the colonies even in his time.

There is a typical story of improvisation in necessity leading to another of Wilkinson's inventions. In 1775, in his card-making shop, he ran out of the tacks that fastened the card-leather to the wooden backing. He took a thin plate of iron, lying discarded on the floor, and with shears cut it into pointed strips. He headed these in a vise by hammering the wide ends. These may have been the earliest cold-iron tacks in the colonies. He later cut small nails from old Spanish cask hoops, heading them the same way as the tacks. A considerable industry in cold-iron nails and tacks was developed by others after Wilkinson's experiment. Wilkinson, on his part, took up the manufacture of steel pins and needles. His wife once traded three steel darning needles for a spinning wheel—an interesting glimpse of values in barter. Ezekiel Reed, of Abington, in 1786 invented a machine for the cold cutting of tacks and nails, producing great quantities there for many years.

Wilkinson's ingenuity was widely applied. He built a machine for chopping cornstalks and made corn syrup in a cider press. But if Jeremiah was more stable than Buell, the Wilkinson family still was not without its streak of flamboyance. What could this solid and creative smith have thought of his fabulous sister Jemima? An off-beat inventive genius of sorts surely was in her.

In the latter phase of the 18th-century colonial evangelical revival known as "The Great Awakening," which was subsiding, later to give rise to the "New Light" revival after the turn of the century, Jemima Wilkinson, then twenty-two years old and darkly handsome beyond the common fashion of New England women, heard the celebrated evangelist George Whitefield preach. Not long afterward, she became sick and passed into a supposed trance. Upon returning to consciousness, she claimed that the person known as Jemima Wilkinson had died and gone to Heaven. That mere husk, her body, now was occupied by the "Spirit of Life" sent by a merciful God to enlighten mankind. This was around 1768, when her stable brother, Jeremiah, eleven years older, was busily manufacturing hand cards.

The erstwhile Jemima Wilkinson had begun a long,

profitable, and colorful career. She was now the "Public Universal Friend." She travelled widely, with a vast following, holding mass meetings. The "Friend," as befitted one no longer male or female after the manner of this earth, wore men's clothing except for a long, flowing robe. Tall and slender, black-eyed, dark of hair, she cut quite a figure. There were those who whispered that she was Jesus Christ. The "Friend" was not heard to deny it.

When her vogue had died out in New England, she went to western New York, one of the "burned over" areas of frenzied revival, and established her colony, "Jerusalem," on a 12,000 acre estate. Rich, tyrannical, and in the last years grotesquely dropsical, she died there in 1819. Brother Jeremiah outlived her by twelve years.

Incidentally, the great George Whitefield, who died shortly after his unbeknownst inspiring of Jemima, had had a long and interesting acquaintance with Franklin, who respected him without subscribing to his theology. A characteristic experiment of Franklin's occurred at one of Whitefield's early open-air sermons in Philadelphia. Franklin became curious as to how far the preacher's stentorian tones carried, and made a test by backing off toward the river from the point at Second and Market streets where the speaker stood.

> . . . I found his voice distinct till I came near Front Street, when some noise in that street obscured it. Imagining then a semicircle, of which my distance should be the radius, and that it were filled with auditors to each of whom I allowed two square feet, I computed that he might be heard by more than thirty thousand. This reconciled me to the newspaper accounts of his having preached to twenty-five thousand people in the fields, and to the ancient stories of generals haranguing whole armies, of which I had sometimes doubted.

Another minor figure in the textile scene is more interesting for his general diversity than for significant contributions. Nathaniel Niles, born in South Kingston, R. I., was the grandson of the Rev. Samuel Niles, in his day a celebrated and turbulent Massachusetts divine. Nathaniel began his studies at Harvard but finished at the College of New Jersey, having studied law, theology, and medicine. He never practiced the law; he preached diligently throughout his long life, yet never was ordained; and in his latter days in Vermont, he tended the sick if there were no doctors at hand, yet had never formally practiced medicine

He married Nancy, the daughter of Elijah Lathrop, a manufacturer in Norwich, Connecticut. He entered Lathrop's factory, and in what might be considered his mechanic phase, invented an improved wool card, and a new method of wire-drawing.

Politics interested him. He served in the Connecticut legislature, and later that of Vermont. Upon his removal to Vermont, he settled in West Fairlee (near the haunts of John Morey, the steamboat builder, whom he must have known). Here Niles pursued politics and preached, and wrote poetry. His ode, "The American Hero," inspired by Bunker Hill, was set to music and much sung, during the Revolution. As an old man, his versatile attainments and classical scholarship caused him to be known as "The Athenian of the East Side of the Green Mountains," probably as large a mouthful of encomium as any minor American inventor ever won.

With Hugh Orr, we begin to draw a little closer to the main stream. He was by nature the true manufacturer, rather than the tinkerer or lone hand-craftsman. Scottish born, he did not come to America until 1740, when he was twenty-five years old. He settled in East Bridgewater, Massachusetts, going to work for a scythemaker named Keith. When his employer retired, Orr took over the business.

Hugh Orr, in an almost forgotten word, was a whitesmith, a worker in hard edged tools. ("Whitesmith" is a loose term; it then meant one who was a finisher and polisher, rather than an original forger of iron; in later general usage it would apply to a worker in "white" metals, such as tin, and to a galvanizer of iron.) He is said to have made a razor from a skillet handle to show Keith his abilities.

Orr turned to the trades of gunmaker and cannon founder. He bored the first cannon in this country and the first five hundred muskets to be made here are credited to him. When the Revolution came he was one of the important arms makers. When Independence had been won, he later served in the Massachusetts State Senate, doing everything in his power to encourage industry.

As early as 1753 he had taken enough interest in textiles to invent a flax-cleaning machine. Beginning in 1786, during his tenure as State Senator, Orr became absorbed in the question of textile machinery to compete with the English. He engaged two fellow Scots, the Barr brothers, Robert and Alex, to make machines for carding, spinning, and roving. Likewise, in the next year, he hired an English midshipman named Thomas Somers to make a spinning jenny along Hargreaves' line. Various craftsmen in wood and metal, of Massachusetts and Rhode Island, bore a hand in these experiments. The machines they produced, the first major attempts at such in America, were known as the State Models. They aroused widespread interest—in fact, they did everything except work satisfactorily. They will turn up again in the story, shortly.

This not very fruitful promotion was the end of Orr's direct contribution in textiles. The credit due him for the concerted effort is considerable, even though success did not follow. Orr's career is one of the major ones in New England industry. Apart from all the things mentioned thus far, he may have built the first triphammer to be used in an American ironshop, and may have produced the first machine-made nails. He was a diligent and knowing amateur mineralogist and collector of ores. One of his ten children, Robert Orr, followed his calling, becoming the state's armorer, at Springfield, and also the earliest producer of iron shovels in Massachusetts.

The small state of Rhode Island had a particular destiny

in American textile manufacture. In Providence there was a man of shrewd mind and gentle spirit, named Moses Brown. He came from an educated family and was well versed in mathematics and surveying. His brother Joseph spent $500 on equipment for observing the 1769 transit of Venus, and Moses, with another friend, Stephen Hopkins, assisted. Their station was on what afterwards was called Transit Street. Whether this was an independent venture or was in collaboration with the Rhode Island scientist, Benjamin West, I do not know. Their friend Stephen Hopkins was a remarkable man in his own right, from a gifted family. He became Colonial Governor of Rhode Island, was a friend of Franklin and a signer of the Declaration of Independence. He served in the Assembly with Brown and was first chancellor of Rhode Island College. His brother Esek was Revolutionary Commander-in-Chief of the American Navy.

Brown lost his first wife just before the Revolution, and under this blow withdrew from his profitable business as merchant and trader, and almost all other worldly activity. He found solace in Quakerism, and under its teachings, freed the slaves he owned and became an ardent abolitionist. There is little doubt that he felt in his spiritual life some impact from the preaching of John Woolman, who had so lately performed his rambling ministry in Rhode Island.

When the war for independence was over, which had caused Brown some embarrassment because of his pacifist principles, he joined with his son-in-law, William Almy, in the enterprise of carding cotton by machine. This is a typical case of mercantile fortunes capitalizing industry. The West Indies trade was the original source of Brown's means.

Carding machines had been made to work, here, although they were far from perfect. Brown became interested in the State Models that Orr had caused to be built, and he obtained permission to have these machines duplicated for Almy and Brown, in a water mill at Pawtucket.

Up until then, their enterprises had been carried on in the "cellars of dwelling houses," with stocking frames, and hand spinning. But the State Model copies were a great disappointment. They simply did not work.

At the time of this impasse, in December of 1789—the year of Washington's inauguration as President—Moses Brown received a famous letter. It was dated December 2, from New York, and said in part:

> Sir,—A few days ago I was informed that you wanted a manager of *cotton spinning,* &c., in which business I flatter myself that I can give the greatest satisfaction, in making machinery, making good yarn, either for *stocking* or *twist,* as any that is made in England; as I have had opportunity, and an over-sight, of Sir Richard Arkwright's works, and in Mr. Strutt's mill upwards of eight years . . . *My intention* is to erect a *perpetual card and spinning.* (Meaning the Arkwright patents.). . . .

This letter was signed, "Samuel Slater," mentioning that he was lately arrived, presently employed with a firm in New York, but wished to leave as they had no satisfactory equipment (nor apparently intended to make any).

What was the history of Samuel Slater? He had been born in the village of Belper, County of Derby, in 1768, son of a respectable farmer who fell from a hayload and died when the boy was fourteen. At Belper was the mill of Jedediah Strutt, inventor of a ribbed-stocking machine and partner of the celebrated Arkwright. The Slater boy was apprenticed to Strutt, having first asked anxiously, mindful of his future, if the textile industry was apt to prove a "permanent business." The conservative Strutt assured him: "It is not probable, Samuel, that it will always be as good as it is now, but I have no doubt it will always be a *fair* business, if it be well managed."

Young Slater was an apprentice to gladden a master's heart. He absorbed every phase of the business in the eight years that he was there. He watched Strutt tinkering unsuccessfully with an effort to increase the thickness of the winding of the yarn on the middle of a bobbin, and devoted his own Sundays to the problem, coming up with what was called the "heart-motion" to impart the variable thickness in the winding of the bobbin.

Yet all along, Slater was worried about the prospects for this industry in England. It appeared "overdone" to him. A Philadelphia paper fell into his hands, and he discovered from "ads" in this, that some people in the United States were willing to offer bounties and inducements to anyone who could bring over the English textile processes.

The plan to emigrate required a well-buttoned lip. Not only could no textile machinery, or plans or drawings for such machinery, be taken abroad; no known worker in the industry would be permitted to emigrate.

In 1789, at the end of his apprenticeship, Slater, twenty-one years old, well-versed in his industry, slipped quietly away from the Arkwright-Strutt mills, and with no jot or scrap of writing or drawing concerning the machinery, and under an assumed name, took ship for the United States. As his early biographer put it, handsomely, "The whole art was treasured in his own mind; that alone, which could not be rummaged and pillaged by any custom-house regulation."

This was the Slater whose letter Moses Brown received. Promptly, on the 10th of December, Brown answered:

Friend,—I received thine of 2nd inst . . . We are destitute of a person acquainted with water-frame spinning . . . As the frame we have is the first attempt of the kind that has been made in America, it is too imperfect to afford much encouragement; we hardly know what to say to thee, but if thou thought thou couldst perfect and conduct them to profit, if thou wilt come and do it, thou shalt have all the profits made of them over and above the interest of the money they cost, and the wear and tear of them. We will find stock and be repaid in yarn as we may agree, for six months and this we do for the information thou can give, if fully acquainted with the business. . . .

Slater came to Providence, filled with hope of finding machinery that he could correct and adapt to use. The visit with the gentle Brown to Pawtucket, to look over the mill, was disillusioning. As the Quaker recalled it, later, "When Samuel saw the old machines, he felt down-hearted, with disappointment, and shook his head, and said, 'these will not do; they are good for nothing in their present condition, nor can they be made to answer.' " They were, to the Englishman, as "so much old iron."

The offer of the cleared profits in return for perfecting and operating these machines no longer made sense. Almy and Brown were not men of narrow vision. They entered into a partnership with Slater, in which he was to build a complete outfit of machinery on the Arkwright principles, and would have a half-ownership of the business.

The feat that the young Englishman, just twenty-two years old, then accomplished was extraordinary and gave a major impetus to American industrialization. Can it properly be called invention? You could argue against it. Yet who can deny that his job of recreating the complexity of a spinning mill (he who had been only an apprentice) was an immensely creative act? No one else had been able to do it.

He had the incalculable advantage of knowing such machines could be made, of having seen them and worked with them. But we can't suppose he knew, or could remember, every mechanical detail. In part, at least, he must have had to re-invent the machinery, with some inevitable trial and error.

Slater had to make everything—including some of the tools. He had a carpenter to help him with the woodwork, and he had inestimable good fortune in his lodgings. Brown had found a place for him, boarding with the family of Oziel Wilkinson, in Pawtucket.

Oziel Wilkinson (no kin to Jeremiah and Jemima) was

a blacksmith who had come to Pawtucket for its water power advantages. (Its name means "Fall of the Waters.") With the aid of these he was moving far beyond the stage of a manual shop and was, at the time of Slater's arrival, well on the way to being the major iron worker and machine manufacturer of New England—a position he held without doubt by 1800. He made farm implements, utensils, and cut nails, forged anchors, rolled and slit sheet metal. Oziel had a gifted son, David, in business with him.

This was the family with which Slater boarded. Where else should he turn for the metal work involved in his project? So the Wilkinsons, father and son, played a part in the venture. There was also a daughter, Hannah, whom in due course Slater married, over some initial objections because he was not a Quaker, and she too was to make a contribution to the family industry.

Slater labored day and night, from the time when the new agreement with his associates was worked out. He was no fly-by-night workman. He said, in late life, that he had worked sixteen hours a day for twenty years successively in building his career. In this first challenge of reconstruction, he labored manfully. Within less than a full year, between January and December, 1790, he completed the task. The twentieth of December found three carding machines, drawing and roving machines, and seventy-two spindles working successfully for Almy, Brown and Slater, powered by the water wheel of an old fulling mill. Hamilton was able to include in his Report on Manufactures, just about to be released, the fact that the British power spinning secrets had been brought to these shores.

Some folklore attached itself to Slater. At the time of his death, one of the obituaries carried the details of a current story about him.

> Of course, in the earliest infancy of the business, and before the machinery to be constructed was itself thoroughly understood, or the means for making it as ample as could have been desired, imperfections to a greater or lesser extent were to be anticipated.

At length, however, the work was completed, and high were the hopes of the artist and his employees. All was ready, but the machinery would not move, at least it would not move as intended, or to any purpose. The disappointment was great, and the now deceased machinist was in great perplexity. Day after day did he labor to discover, that he might remedy, the defect—but in vain. But what he could not discover waking was revealed to him in his sleep.

It was perfectly natural that the subject which engrossed all his thoughts by day, should be dancing through his uncurbed imagination by night, and it so happened that on one occasion, having fallen into a slumber with all the shafts and wheels of his mill whirling in his mind with the complexity of Ezekiel's vision, he dreamed of the absence of an essential band upon one of the wheels. The dream was fresh in his mind on the following morning, and repairing bright and early to his works, he in an instant detected the deficiency!

The revelation was true, and in a few hours afterward, the machinery was in full and successful operation.

This beautiful story happens to be apocryphal, though stranger things have happened in the annals of invention. The reality on which that mythical accretion was founded had to do with the working of one of the carding machines. Such a machine is a complex series of rollers, large and small, through which the cotton fibres are passed, automatically. Delicate adjustments of the wire teeth on the various rollers alternately comb the fibres and then brush them lightly off one roller to carry them on to another.

In Slater's machine, something was wrong with this process of cleaning the roller. Fibres rolled up on certain cylinders instead of being lifted and passed through. He wrestled with this frustrating maladjustment for days. It was fundamental to the operation. The partners were waiting expectantly. Slater, as each attempt failed, was fearful of being considered an impostor.

Finally he found that the teeth in the card cylinders were not firmly enough fixed in the necessary delicacy of position. As the cylinder revolved, they slipped just enough out of alignment to fail in their function. An inferior card leather was at fault. At last, by sufficient adjustment in the angle of the teeth, he managed to overcome the problem and the machine worked.

This was only one of his troubles. It was winter when the whole plant was ready to roll. The old fulling mill was a crude structure and its outdoor wheel was completely unsheltered. Every night the water in the sluice froze. For whatever reason, he could get no one to break the ice for him, so rose before dawn each morning to spend an hour or more, wet, cold, and numb, freeing the wheel of ice for the day's operation. When he built his own first mill, he made sure to have his wheel under cover.

By the time the new plant had settled down to steady operation, the firm already had accumulated several thousand pounds of yarn, far more than the labors of all their weavers could use. As often happens, the first shock of this accomplishment was economically unsettling. "Who would buy or could use up such quantities of yarn?" demanded the same type of people who later would ask of Eli Terry and Chauncey Jerome, "Who will buy so many clocks?"

England and Ireland were dumping goods on the American market at low prices and long terms, to deter competition. The next year was financially difficult, and it was here that all Moses Brown's resources and business skill came into play, to hang on until both his product and his market were properly developed.

It was clear that power weaving must be the next step, yet oddly, though this development rapidly followed as we shall see shortly, Slater's was the last of all the New England textile industries to convert from hand weaving, not giving it up until 1828.

Now, however, his enterprises boomed. With Almy and

Brown he built a larger, improved plant, in 1793. (It still stands.) By 1799, Slater opened an independent mill of his own, while still with Almy and Brown. His salary as superintendent of each of these mills was $1.50 per day, apart from his other financial participation in the profits. One of his mills was at Smithfield (where Oziel Wilkinson, his father-in-law, had been born) and the town later became known as Slatersville—as complete an Americanization for an immigrant mechanic as could be imagined.

Mills on Slater's principle, carried by his employees in spite of all pledges and deterrents to imitation, spread to Connecticut, New Hampshire, and New York. Hannah Wilkinson Slater, who was not destined to live a long life with her husband, thought up the idea of making a fine cotton sewing thread (linen then being universally used for the purpose). She experimented with Sea Island cotton, making so good a thread that the family industries took it up. In tests, the Slaters found that in a sheet made half of cotton, half of linen, threads, the linen gave way first. The new cotton thread became popular quickly in America and Europe.

Arthur Scholfield, who came here about the same time as Slater, performed a similar feat at Pittsfield, Massachusetts, though less spectacular and less far-reaching in its effects. He had to make one or more return trips to England to spy out the mills, refresh his memory, and even smuggle in small parts before he could finally complete his carding machines. Wool was his material, not cotton. Black broadcloth of yarn spun by Scholfield at Pittsfield was presented to James Madison, who wore a suit made from it at his inauguration as President. (In 1790, President Washington delivered his first annual message to Congress wearing a suit of New Haven broadcloth—but entirely a hand-spun, hand-woven product.)

The iron-working Wilkinsons followed a logical course. Oziel's sons, David and Daniel, established the firm of David Wilkinson and Co., to manufacture textile machinery, in Pawtucket. David's other enterprises are worth noting. He built a blast-furnace and cast cannon, inventing a novel method of boring by which the cannon barrel was rotated against a stationary bit.

His most notable invention was patented in 1798, after years of experiment arising out of the problems of cutting and finishing screw threads involved in the making of oil presses. His thread-cutting machine incorporated the independent invention, on his part, of one of the basic contributions to machine tools—the slide rest. This essential guiding and supporting feature of many lathe-type tools is largely credited to the Englishman, Henry Maudslay.

David Wilkinson thought little about this particular feature in his screw-threader. It was much imitated by others. The panic of 1829 ruined Wilkinson. For the rest of his life he was an itinerant workman, never succeeding in re-establishing himself as a manufacturer. But by a thoroughly surprising circumstance, unlike most of the stories of inventors, in 1848, when Wilkinson was an old man and in need, the government granted him $10,000 for his slide rest, which had been widely adopted in arms factories, including government arsenals.

That quiet merchant, Moses Brown, whose foresight and confidence were so important to our industry, died in 1836, at the age of ninety-eight. Vertigo had forced his early retirement from active business, but his interests in matters of science and medicine continued. He became something of an amateur physician through study of his own ailment. He entertained guests at his farm near Providence with ice cream and strawberries, the earliest mention I've ever found of that noble American dish. (Ice cream is said to have been made first in this country by David Robinson, in Wiscasset, Maine, in 1823, for a reception honoring Lafayette.) When Brown was ninety-five years old, President Andrew Jackson visited Providence. The old man said to him, "I am glad to see thee. I have known all thy predecessors in office and I wanted to see thee."

As Brown had been one of the early endowers of Rhode

Island University, instrumental in bringing it to the city of Providence, it was in his honor, with others of his distinguished family, that its name was changed to Brown University. The Quaker industrialist also served his State in the legislature for seven years.

The story of early American inventions, since it relates the birth and infancy of our industrial life, also is a part of our political-philosophical history. This point, midway between the power spinning and power weaving developments, is as good a place as any to pause and consider the great clash between the conceptions of Jefferson and those of Hamilton as to what was best for the future of the new nation with regard to the fruits of our mechanic genius.

First, there was a cleavage between these two men as to the meaning of "best for the future." Power and strength, conceived in economic terms, was "best" in Hamilton's eyes. His policies were so directed, and in those terms they prevailed. The good life and private welfare of the citizen as individual was Jefferson's broad concept of "best." He felt that questions of economic power and strength, as values in themselves, did not coincide with individual welfare.

Of course our history has been a blend of, or an oscillation between, these two views. America's economic-industrial might is partly a tribute to Hamilton's genius. Her idealistic concern for the state's obligation to the individual, even when this is denounced as a trend toward the "welfare state" or "creeping socialism," is the thread of Jeffersonianism.

Political and economic theories may either look back retrospectively, or anticipate prophetically, but they do not altogether *create* what is happening, even though they may influence it in some measure. The story of American invention is the record that an industrial-manufacturing era *was happening*. It would not be stopped. Hamilton did not create it but was glad it was happening and sought to encourage it. Jefferson was reluctant to have it happen and expressed his forebodings about what he could not check, and in spite of himself often enouraged.

It is astonishing for an unprepared modern American to read Hamilton's famous Report on Manufacures, of 1791, and find that there was a time, actually, when it was necessary to argue about the desirability of encouraging manufacturing in this country. But we find Hamilton saying:

> The expediency of encouraging manufactures in the United States, which was not long since deemed very questionable, appears at this time to be pretty generally admitted.

He proceeds at length, with a survey of the current state of industries in England and Europe, and of the transition from home manufacture in America. Development of native industry is "the next great work to be accomplished." That it would be accomplished he was certain, because our people possessed "a peculiar aptitude for mechanical improvements."

Jefferson dreaded the social effects of industrialization and the rootless mob, or proletariat, he saw as certain to proceed from it. In early America there was no such class.

His argument went along these lines, culled from his *Notes on Virginia:*

> The political economists of Europe have established it as a principle, that every State should endeavor to manufacture for itself; and this principle, like many others, we transfer to America. . . . But we have an immensity of land courting the industry of the husbandman. . . . Those who labor in the earth are the chosen people of God, if ever he had a chosen people, whose breasts he has made his peculiar deposit for substantial and genuine virtue. . . . Corruption of morals in the mass of cultivators is a phenomenon of which no age nor nation has furnished an example. It is the mark set on those, who not looking up to heaven, to their own soil and industry, as does the husbandman, for

their subsistence, depend for it on casualties and caprice of customers. . . . While we have land to labor then, let us never wish to see our citizens occupied at a work-bench, or twirling a distaff . . . for the general operations of manufacture, let our work-shops remain in Europe. It is better to carry provisions and materials to work-men there, than bring them to the provisions and materials, and with them their manners and principles. . . .

The ironies of history are sharply shown in Jefferson's distress of spirit. He was, himself, one of the greatest encouragers of invention, and an inventor. It may be true that he was most given to inventions that pertained to agrarian interests, as with his own mold-board plow, and his keen interest in the cotton gin. Yet the exigencies of statecraft forced him to be a patron of Whitney's development of mass-produced arms and when once the Whitney concept of manufacture was let loose, there was no stopping it. For that matter, once the ginned green-seed cotton was available, the textile industry could never be kept from home shores. Jefferson's age could no more back away from these developments than our age can back away from the nucleus of the atom.

He was overly romantic (as peasantry then and now bear witness) about the uniformly idyllic nature of the life of the soil and its moral incorruptibility. But his anxieties were well-founded, as the social frictions ultimately bred of industrialization bore out. Jefferson supposedly represented the antithesis of Hamilton's "great beast" attitude toward the people, but his "mobs of great cities," as he described the coming proletariat, was very close in meaning.

Hamilton, in turn, was not interested in denying such possibilities in social consequence. He was coldly indifferent to them, and also evinced a hard-boiled view of the work-for-idle-hands sort.

It is worthy of particular remark, that, in general, women and children are rendered more useful, and the latter more early useful, by manufacturing establishments, than they would otherwise be. Of the number of persons employed in the cotton manufactories of Great Britain, it is computed that four-sevenths, nearly, are women and children; of whom the greatest proportion are children, and many of them of a tender age.

And lest there be any mistake, this is part of Hamilton's recommendation of the advantages, in his Report on Manufactures.

While the debate over theory went on, the endless diligence of American inventors made an accomplished fact of the transition from household industry to factory.

That thoughtful and humane man, John Winthrop the Younger, on a day of depressed mood, expressed in his Journal, while still in the Massachusetts colony, a determination to give up inventing. He could not see that any gadgets, labor-saving devices, or mechanical improvements were enhancing the prospects of salvation and the soul's welfare for him or any others. Were they not, then, vanity?

This embraces the extremes of the Hamilton-Jefferson dilemma. Which is better, gaining the whole world, or saving one's own soul? The trend of Hamilton was to the former, the trend of Jefferson to the latter. The trend of history, ever since this flawed and aspiring creature called man has been recording it, is the record of the effort to do both at the same time. I think if it were possible to succeed entirely in either or both, we would not be what we understand as human.

CHAPTER 9

WEAVERS

To prepare the clothing of the world seems to have been regarded as womanly work in all ages. The spindle and the distaff, the picturesque accompaniment of many an ancient legend—of Penelope and Lucretia, of the Fatal Sisters themselves—have, to be sure, changed somewhat in their modern adaptation to the machinery which robes the human millions; but there are, in effect, the same instruments, used to supply the same need, at whatever period of the world's history.

—LUCY LARCOM

AFTER SLATER had brought power spinning there came a veritable rage for spinning mills in New England, on a scale large or small. Every stream that could turn a wheel, every brook that crossed a cow pasture was said to be put to use for spinning. The tale sprang up about a small mill in which suddenly, unaccountably, the spindles faltered and stopped, the carding rollers ceased turning. The foreman rushed out to see what the matter was and found a cow placidly drinking from the stream. When she had her

176

fill and ambled off, the waterwheel began to turn again, the spindles flew, the carders rumbled.

The linked processes of our lives are such that where power spinning had come power weaving had to follow. The power loom was pioneered in England by Edmund Cartwright and others. Cartwright, whose name is most commonly mentioned in relation to it, did not create the mechanisms which were finally to become the modern power loom. Samuel Slater, as we have seen, was a spinner, obtuse to the problems of weaving. Power weaving in America gained its impetus from the promotional, mechanical, and organizational imagination of Francis Cabot Lowell.

He was a man of means and well connected. Travelling in England and Europe, he became impressed with the possibilities in textile manufacture and sought every opportunity to inspect the mills where such work went on. Coming home, where by the eve of the War of 1812 the youthful industry of power spinning had burgeoned beyond description, he immersed himself in experiments and by the Fall of 1812 had perfected the model of a power loom, embodying many original concepts distinctly different from the English looms.

Lowell was of the newer breed of inventors who were not themselves craftsmen, beyond the model-making stage. (The celebrated Colonel John Stevens, of Hoboken, also was such a one.) He hired Paul Moody, an Amesbury, Massachusetts mechanic, and together they built the first efficient power loom in America. It was finished in 1814.

A year before this, in anticipation of it, a significant business organization took place. Lowell, his brother-in-law, Patrick Tracy Jackson, Nathan Appleton (like many contemporary businessmen he pursued intellectual studies and wrote a book on original sin), and others, formed a company and acquired a mill at Waltham. It was a combination of inventiveness, pooled financial resources, and business and merchandizing brains. In short, on the American scene, it was as close as any single enterprise could be to being the "invention" or birth of capitalism as we have come to know it. It was a joint stock operation, capitalized at $400,000 at its inception. The firm was prepared, as an impersonal institution, to develop its techniques and machinery, integrate all aspects of its production, and concern itself with every phase of its sources of raw materials and outlets for finished goods. In short, it was not a simple venture in partnership, but was that most concrete of abstractions, a corporate entity. Hence, the Waltham mills, and those at Lowell which were their outgrowth, are more than a simple development in manufacturing and machinery, they mark the rise of the historic American capitalism, and for a while they represented a unique, short-lived social philosophy.

The mill at Waltham was first opened as one more of the already numerous spinning mills. But in 1814, the power weaving machinery was ready. Lowell had leaped beyond Slater. For the first time, not only in America but anywhere, fibre was carded, spun into yarn, and then woven into finished cloth, all by automatic machinery, within the walls of one mill.

This concept of Lowell's, and his loom, were not his only contributions. He improved the flyer which filled the spools in spinning, working out "the nicest mathematical calculations" concerning its motion for the guidance of Moody, who carried out the work. Here again is an important aspect of the Waltham mills. They pioneered the idea of intramural shop invention. Lowell and his mechanics were continually at work, improving every phase of the mechanical operation. It was more than a one-man proposition; it became teamwork, the beginning of shop-developed, cooperative invention, as American industry has practiced it so constructively.

There are other aspects to this particular question, however. From Slater's first mill, as if doubly mindful of the very defection from Strutt which made the Slater mill possible, each of the textile establishments had a formidable "loyalty oath" which its employees had to sign. This pledged them not to disclose the secrets of machinery or processes which they had learned in this mill, in the event of their seeking employment in another. Even though Wilkinson and others had begun the manufacture of textile machinery, enough of such equipment was still built, or improved, within the mill's private shops, to make such a pledge important. But it did not serve as more than a deterrent, at best. Slater's men ran off with what they learned from him as he had run from Strutt.

As a corollary to the matter of secrecy, every mechanic was required to sign an agreement that any improvement or invention he might make, while working for the mill, was to be the property of the company. The merits and justice of this policy have been long argued, and the debate goes on today. From the perspective of history, the policy had at least one constructive result. It helped to stimulate the branching out of industry and the springing up of competition. If a truly gifted mechanic saw the possibilities of an improvement or invention in the machines or processes with which he worked, the only thing for him to do, if personally ambitious, was to quit his job and set up in business for himself so that he might own and develop his own new idea. This occurred over and over in the early days of industry, nowhere more conspicuously and fruitfully (and with general good will) than in the amazing proliferation of machine-tool industries and inventions around Springfield, Vermont.

It was a major loss to the growing industry when Francis Lowell died at forty-two, in 1817, only a few years after the launching of the great enterprise he had sparked. When, in 1821, the Waltham mills reorganized the firm on an even larger and more complex basis (with the capable Paul Moody now one of the numerous large stockholders, also Nathaniel Bowditch, the great master of navigation), the enterprise was moved to a new site. The place was named Lowell, in honor of that man of vision and ingenuity.

Here, at the Lowell Mills, the unique social philosophy

of this early textile industry reached its brief peak. But first, as being also a part of the sociological picture, a word about the hand-craftsman versus the machine. The social upheavals precipitated in England and Europe by the machine processes have become famous in history, fiction, and drama. The smashing of power looms and power spinners by enraged and fearful handworkers, seeing the loss of their livelihood and the change of their ways of life, made the industrial transition truly a "revolution." Some resulting technological unemployment and general congestion of population led to the rapid development of a proletariat, divorced from the tools and materials of production and largely at the mercy of its employers. It was from this reality that Marxism took its impetus.

The situation was markedly different in America. This is not to idealize matters. A change did develop, a proletariat did come into existence, with the tides of immigration, as we shall see, after a while. Even so, at no point did the industrial-social situation develop in this country to fit the neat (and logical) expectations of Marx's thesis. This is a subject for social historians and is amply discussed by them.

The young United States simply did not have large classes of people with a wage-earning livelihood threatened by textile machinery. With the exception of some small groups of hand weavers which had developed during the brief lag between power spinning and power weaving, there was no one to be hurt. To the contrary, there were many to gain.

The whole attitude toward a factory in those early days was interesting. The general tendency of our time is to regard the factory as a blight (though the increasing reforms in modern factory design and practice are slowly altering this). In general, the spirit craves to escape from the environment of factories and all associated with them (especially heavy industry) and to seek the unspoiled rural scene. The contemporary artist may paint the factory as a social study, or as a study in form, mass, and movement. It is not a sentimental subject of popular art.

But the old engravings, even the earlier Currier & Ives prints, show a pride and pleasure approaching the romantic about these first mills and factories. They were frequent subjects of pictures for hanging in the home. In this vein, Tench Coxe, one of the ardent promoters of our early industries, described "delightful villages, suddenly rising as it were by magic along the banks of some meandering rivulet, flourishing by the influence and fostered by the protecting arm of manufactures."

At the beginning of the 19th century the factory was a dream realized, a source of pride and thus a thing of beauty. It was not yet a slum-breeder, nor foreseen as one, except by a few rare birds such as Jefferson. The factory or mill was a tidy frame or brick building beside a swift stream, framed still in a setting of rural green—not soot and cinders. The railroad yard had not yet entered the picture. From within this sedate building, which by its look might have been an academy, came the clackety-clack and whirr and buzz that were sounds of work and productiveness, and as such were pleasing to the ears of Yankees who still had enough of quiet in their lives. So an engraving of the local factory might well adorn the parlor wall. And Nancy and Lucy might go happily forth from that parlor for a stint in the mill, in company with other refined and respectable girls, before settling down to matrimony.

It was in keeping with the character of Moses Brown, of son-in-law Almy, and of Samuel Slater, too, that all should be concerned with the social and moral welfare of those who would work in the mills they were creating. These were largely women and children. Slater established Sunday Schools in all his mills (he had seen this pious practice in England under Jedediah Strutt) and even day schools, at his own cost, at some of the plants. Even the practical necessities were related to this attitude. One of the

objections of those who said that manufacture need not
and should not be encouraged in America was that labor
was high, there was no waiting labor pool.

Particularly the young women were needed in the spinning and weaving mills. These would have gone, ordinarily,
from parental home to marital home with no stop-overs.
The necessity of the early textile manufacturers was to
induce a goodly number of such girls to spend at least a
year or two in the mill. The inducement of wages, alone,
was not enough. There must be guarantees of standards
of behavior and treatment to ensure that young ladies of
respectable family could be permitted and might wish to
engage in such work. At Lowell, positive cultural advantages went beyond mere safeguards to virtue and health.

The best perspective on this phenomenon is through
the eyes of some British visitors to our shores, who were
amazed at what they saw in Lowell. Anthony Trollope,
the novelist, was the son of Mrs. Frances Trollope, possibly
the most poisoned-pen visitor we have ever entertained,
not excepting Ilya Ehrenburg. The younger Trollope was
given a handbook when he arrived at Lowell, and received
it with a natural skepticism, but when he had concluded
his report, he conceded that: "Lowell is the realization of a
commercial Utopia. Of all the statements made in the
little book which I have quoted I cannot point out one
which is exaggerated, much less false."

The women at Lowell, he found, were paid at least a
third more than those of Manchester. Even so, their wages
were only around three dollars a week. But the great difference did not lie simply in the money. These New England
working girls "are not exposed to the chances of an open
labour market. They are taken in, as it were, to a phil-
anthropical manufacturing college, and then looked after
and regulated more as girls and lads at a great seminary
than as hands by whose industry profit is to be made out
of capital. This is all very nice and pretty at Lowell, but I
am afraid it could not be done at Manchester."

"The nuns of Lowell," remarked the travelling Frenchman Michel Chevalier, "instead of working *sacred hearts,* spin and weave cotton."

Charles Dickens, who liked quite a number of things in America (especially our lake and river steamboats which mostly struck him as sumptuously luxurious) was enthralled by Lowell. It was winter of 1842, and the mills had then been in operation for twenty-one years.

> Those indications of [the town's] youth which first attract the eye, give it a quaintness and oddity of character which, to a visitor from the old country, is amusing enough. It was a very dirty winter's day, and nothing in the whole town looked old to me, except the mud, which in some parts was almost knee-deep, and might have been deposited there, on the subsiding of the waters after the Deluge. In one place there was a new wooden church, which, having no steeple, and being yet unpainted, looked like an enormous packing-case without any direction upon it . . . The very river that moves the machinery in the mills (for they are all worked by water power), seems to acquire a new character from the fresh buildings of bright red brick and painted wood among which it takes its course . . . One would swear that every 'Bakery,' 'Grocery,' and 'Bookbindery,' and other kind of store, took its shutters down for the first time, and started in business yesterday.

Dickens, emphasizing that he knew the manufacturing towns of England well, and the human types to be seen in them, found the girls here, "all well dressed, but not to my thinking above their condition; for I like to see the humbler class of society careful of their dress and appearance . . . These girls . . . were all well dressed: and that phrase necessarily includes extreme cleanliness."

Compared to the "careless, moping, slatternly, degraded" types that he had seen in English factories, these "were healthy in appearance, many of them remarkably so, and had the manners and deportment of young women: not of degraded brutes of burden." He did not see one girl whom he "would have removed from those works if I had had the power."

He was impressed by the community hospital, and the ability of the girls to pay for needed medical care. ". . . in July, 1841, no fewer than nine hundred and seventy-eight of these girls were depositors in the Lowell Savings Bank: the amount of whose joint savings was estimated at one hundred thousand dollars."

> I am now going to state three facts, which will startle a large class of readers on this side of the Atlantic [England], very much.

> Firstly, there is a joint-stock piano in a great many of the boarding houses. Secondly, nearly all these young ladies subscribe to circulating libraries. Thirdly, they have got up among themselves a periodical called THE LOWELL OFFERING, 'A repository of original articles, written exclusively by females actively employed in the mills,'—which is duly printed, published, and sold; and whereof I brought away from Lowell four hundred good solid pages, which I have read from beginning to end . . . Of the merits of the Lowell Offering as a literary production, I will only observe, putting entirely out of sight the fact of the articles having been written by these girls after the arduous labours of the day, that it will compare advantageously with a great many English Annuals.

The English had a chance to verify this for themselves a few years later. Selections from the *Offering* were published there as *Mind Among the Spindles*. At home the *Offering* had a subscription list of 4,000, and some of the girls went out on rounds as agents for it.

Of the literary talents flowering at Lowell, the most famous was that of Lucy Larcom, whose poems, *An Idyl of*

Work, and personal story, *A New-England Girlhood,* and yet other writings, can still be read.

Lucy was born in 1826. At age eleven she was a bobbin girl at Lowell. This work was not considered hard. All she had to do was change a series of bobbins once every three-quarters of an hour. Between times she could stand by the windows, read, write, or chatter with the other bobbin girls. But the hours sometimes ran from five in the morning 'til seven at night—a normal stint for those days. Her favorite window nook she called the Poet's Corner and papered it with clippings of verse. She worked for five years in the spinning rooms and then asked to be transferred into book-keeping, where she remained until a few years later she left the mills to go west with the family of a married sister. Later she became a schoolteacher.

Mrs. Larcom ran one of the approved boarding houses, which gave the Larcom daughters still further intimate knowledge of the mill girls. Sister Emeline had literary enthusiasms, too, and started a series of the small papers which were issued under such moving and symbolic titles as *The Casket,* and *The Bouquet.* Another of them, *The Diving Bell,* implied profound delvings after improving thoughts.

> Our Diving Bell shall deep descend,
> And bring from the immortal mind
> Thoughts that to improve us tend,
> Of each variety and kind.

Lucy's ambitious, book-length poem about Lowell, in blank verse, *An Idyl of Work,* is quite readable. No doubt it is naive, in some respects. If it were a painting it would be classed as a "primitive" for I think it has, as writing, the same qualities Grandma Moses has as a painter. That it has an emotional integrity cannot be questioned.

Lucy creates a picture of the life of the mills through the eyes of a girl working among them. A series of lives are unfolded through incidents and conversations. It ranges from the melancholy to the joyous and the contemplative. It most certainly is an authentic voice of its time and place. More than anything else it reminds me of that fragment, *The Spooniad*, by Jonathan Swift Somers, which inspired *The Spoon River Anthology*. I wish at the least there were someone to take up the themes of Lucy Larcom with the touch of a Frost or a Robinson.

> Not always to be here among the looms,—
> Scarcely a girl she knew expected that;
> Means to one end, their labor was,—to put
> Gold nest eggs in the bank, or to redeem
> A mortgaged homestead, or to pay the way
> Through classic years at some academy;
> More commonly to lay a dowry by
> For future housekeeping.

Like most of the New Englanders concerned with finer things, Lucy was a passionate abolitionist. She extols Garrison, in one passage, and her narrator reflects the troubles of a sensitive conscience.

> When I have thought what soil the cotton plant
> We weave is rooted in, what waters it—
> The blood of souls in bondage—I have felt
> That I was sinning against light, to stay
> And turn the accursed fibre into cloth
> For human wearing.

Although we have found ourselves assured by the official literature of the mills and the reports of the admiring visitors that all lives on the premises were conducted at an elevated level, little Lucy, the laureate of the looms, gives us a glimpse of reality through the eyes and ears of "bashful Ann," the bobbin girl.

> Sometimes the spinners are such pleasant girls—
> They come and play with us. But some are cross,

And some say dreadful words; if mother knew,
She would not let us work there. But we must,
And so we do not tell her.

The person and nature of Lucy are quite visible in *An
Idyl of Work,* which she dedicated to "Working Women,
By One of Their Sisterhood." It is pious but human, sometimes sentimental but deeply perceptive, too, and in the
fundamentals—real. The poem sings with unself-conscious
simplicity of Yankee democracy, the dignity of work, and
Christianity.

In her Preface, Lucy makes a sage observation for one immersed in a milieu which tended to elevate work almost to
idolatry. "Labor, in itself, is neither elevating nor otherwise. It is the laborer's privilege to ennoble his work by
the aim with which he undertakes it, and by the enthusiasm and faithfulness he puts into it."

But encomiums upon this experiment in small-scale
Utopia would not be complete without a characteristic word from that caustic Yankee peddler-clockmaker,
Sam Slick. He rebukes his Nova Scotian customers for
their idle chatter.

> . . . it's all talk and no work; now, with *us* it's all
> work and no talk—in our shipyards, our factories,
> our mills, and even in our vessels, there's no talk—
> a man can't work and talk too. I guess if you were at
> the factories in Lowell we'd show you a wonder—
> *five hundred gals at work together and all in silence.*
> I don't think our great country has such a real
> natural curiosity as that. I expect the world don't
> contain the beat of that.

Alas, the mid-century saw the inescapable waning of this
strange institution. It had been the growth of an essentially non-industrial culture. As the entire industrial front
expanded, as great waves of working-class immigration—a
ready-made, imported proletariat—began arriving, the labor
pool was overflowing. Wages and conditions of work were

bound to slip into decline. With a large competing, strange, and impersonal labor pool, who now would be concerned for the respectability, manners, and education of the millworker?

The remarkable things that happened in the wake of Francis Lowell's enterprise have led the story off-course a bit. Close on his heels, other American power looms were invented. One of these was David Wilkinson's improvement on a Scotch loom, which he put into manufacture at a price much cheaper than the cost of Lowell's machines. Many of the earliest power looms were so delicate and temperamental—so subject to mechanical breakdown and delay in repair, that some mills could not afford to pay that relative novelty, a weekly wage, but continued payment by the piece, as customary with hand work.

Two other New England men made fundamental contributions to machine spinning. John Thorp, son of a Massachusetts coach maker, took out a power loom patent in 1816. But his major invention, unobtrusive yet in the category of basic details, was the technique of winding the spindle known as "ring spinning." It eliminated the "flyer" for that purpose, and Thorp's ring spinner is used in the industry today. One of the least commonly known, it is yet one of the most far-reaching American textile inventions. Thorp also invented a netting machine of a type still in use, and also the first power-operated "gang loom" for weaving narrow fabrics.

Charles Danforth, a Massachusetts farmer's son, entered a cotton mill at fourteen and began devising improvements at once. After a varied career as soldier (War of 1812), sailor, and school teacher, he came back to the cotton industry, in Sloatsburg, New York, as a machinist, and invented what is known as the "cap spinner" in which a type of spool revolves upon a stationary spindle. The cap spinner and the ring spinner both were important as means of stepping up the speed of yarn making. Danforth, later in his career, went into the machine-tool field and ended up as a locomotive manufacturer for a world-wide market. His Paterson, N. J., firm, Danforth, Cooke & Co., finally became absorbed in the American Locomotive Co.

Through most of this story, the emphasis has been upon water power as the prime mover in mills. But by 1812, the versatile Delaware inventor, Oliver Evans, had put on the market his high-pressure steam engine, the first of its kind. At least ten of them were in operation, by that year, in mills of various kinds, as far distributed as Florida, Louisiana, Mississippi, Kentucky, Ohio, and Middletown, Connecticut. In the latter case the steam engine was used to power a textile mill.

Evans also invented, when only twenty-three, an automatic multiple-operation machine (a considerable step in itself), which did almost all the work of card-making, cutting and bending the teeth, punching the leather, and setting the teeth in it.

Sometimes this machine, or its equivalent, has been credited to Amos Whittemore, of Massachusetts, but there is strong evidence that it was pirated from Evans—a practice quite common. Whittemore was a highly successful manufacturer of hand carding brushes, his factories, around 1795, turning out as many as 12,000 dozen a year, employing sixty men and two thousand children. He is credited further with a nail-cutting machine, a loom, and a mechanical ship's log (called the "nautical perambulator").

Whoever invented the automatic card-making machine, it was one of the devices which excited the admiration of Father Giovanni Grassi, a Jesuit, who came to America from Italy in 1810 and remained for some years as President of Georgetown College. He produced a book on his travels, reporting that, "The ingenious Americans make up for the lack of hands to do their work by the invention of mechanical tools." He was impressed by "a machine which cuts an iron wire into pieces, bends it as desired, inserts it into leather, and in a short time forms a very exact card."

As early as October, 1789, President Washington had

visited the factory of Giles Richards & Co., in Boston, which was manufacturing hand cards of Evans' invention, by agreement with him. The President entered in his diary in somewhat blurred syntax, that, "I went to the Card Manufactory, where I was informed about 900 hands of one kind and for one purpose or another—all kinds of Cards are made; and there are Machines for executing every part of the work in a new and expeditious man'r, especially in cutting and bending the teeth, wch. is done at one stroke. They have made 63,000 pr. of Cards in a year, and can undersell the Imported Cards—nay, Cards of this Manufactory have been smuggled into England."

None of these accounts exhaust the multi-faceted story of early American ingenuity in textile manufacture, and least of all do they do justice (as I fear only dry statistics and cataloguings could do) to the astonishing multiplication of independent firms in the spreading of the industry thus engendered. Yet one name has not been mentioned which, though it is not confined to the textile field alone, so drastically affected it that he must be given a chapter to himself—Eli Whitney, of New Haven.

CHAPTER 10

A YALE MAN GOES TO GEORGIA

Eli would say I can make just such
ones if I had tools and I could
make tools if I had tools to make
them with.

—ELIZABETH WHITNEY BLAKE

ONE DAY in 1784, an American ship sailed into Liverpool with a small item in its cargo that stirred up a disproportionate rumpus. The authorities impounded the suspect material on the grounds that its source was fraudulently represented; it *must* have come from some other place. It seemed certain to the customs officials that the item could not, as claimed, have come from the United States, for that country was felt to be quite incapable of producing so large an amount for export at one time. The item in question was simply eight bags of cotton.

That was nine years before Eli Whitney made his cotton gin. The year of Whitney's death, 1825, saw two hundred and fifteen million pounds of cotton produced in the United States, of which one hundred forty-two and a quarter million pounds were for export. That, too, was still only the beginning.

The immense impetus imparted to cotton raising by Whitney's machine cannot be overestimated. Even so, many other men had a foresight of the great importance of

191

this cultivation, and the industries it would feed. Substantial advancements in production over that notable shipment of eight bags were taking place during the nine years before the Whitney saw gin was introduced.

In the involved chronicle of early American manufactures, the name of Tench Coxe recurs continually in relation to a multiplicity of enterprises. His name doesn't get into the general histories and encyclopedias very much, but the United States owes him considerable remembrance for his vision and diligence. When Alexander Hamilton became the first Secretary of the Treasury, he took Tench Coxe as his Assistant, in which role he continued for a long time as one of many comparably influential posts during his career. There is no doubt that Coxe supplied much of the data and assisted in the writing of the famous Report on Manufactures. The writings issued under his own name also are of importance, especially his lengthy discussion of the economic state of the nation, published under the title *View of the United States.*

Coxe's avowed principle was "to foster and encourage but not to force manufactures." In 1786, by a dazzling feat of industrial espionage, he had procured brass models of all Arkwright's spinning machines, through an operative in England who had them packed and ready for shipment. They were discovered and seized by British customs officials at shipside. He fostered an elaborate scheme for a model manufacturing town, to feed the port of Philadelphia with export goods, and indirectly out of this conception grew the town of Paterson, New Jersey, at the falls of the Passaic. His consistent and vigorous encouragement both of textile manufacture and cotton growing caused Coxe to be known, in the first half of the 19th century, as "the father of the Cotton culture in America."

Cotton, as it came into ascendancy, forced another culture out which had been for long a major staple in the southern colonies. This was the cultivation of indigo, which ranged through Louisiana, Georgia, and the Carolinas and had even seen early (but abortive) experiments as far north as Albany, when the Dutch were there. Some early American prints show the processing of indigo by slave labor in the southern colonies. The raising of indigo and extraction of the dye are part of what could be a rather fascinating story of early American dyestuffs, of wide color range, from a host of vegetable and insect sources.

In the early 1700's the growing of cotton in the colonies was on little more than a garden basis. It was in the sea-island and coastal areas that cotton cultivation increased. Here the long-staple, black-seed cotton could be grown. Inland were vast areas where the short-staple, green-seed cotton throve but was not worth cultivating on any large scale. Such use as was made of it required the slow, patient work of slaves, young and old, at night, tediously picking out with their fingers the sticky, tenacious green seeds. The amount that could be so cleaned by one person in a day was not economically worth the man-hours it cost in a generally short-handed young nation.

The cleaning of the black-seed, "bald-headed" seed, cotton had been done by slow hand-turned roller gins for a long time in India where the machine was called a *charkha*. The word "gin" is simply an ancient abbreviation of "engine." Why the contraction identified itself so specifically with cotton-cleaning machines is anybody's guess.

A good deal of inventiveness in the American south went into the improvement of roller gins. A Frenchman, M. Debreuil, in 1742 invented an improved one, on his plantation where part of the city of New Orleans now stands. He gave considerable impetus to black-seed cotton growing in that section of the Gulf Coast. Incidentally, he later built the first sugar mill in Louisiana.

A man named Crebs, in what is now Alabama, invented a gin around 1772, and also a technique for packing cotton in bags in roughly the equivalent of the modern bale.

During the Revolution, Kinsey Borden, a noted Carolina grower of sea-island cotton, made a gin of "pieces of iron gun-barrels, burnished and fixed in wooden rollers, with wooden screws to secure them, and wooden cranks to turn in the manner of the steel corn mill." This, like many others, was turned by one person and fed by another. There were numerous one-man, foot-treadle gins contrived by inventive planters, too.

In 1788, a Georgia planter named Bissell made a gin similar to Crebs'.

Joseph Eve, a Providence, Rhode Island, man who was living in the Bahamas, invented a double gin, for horse or water power. This was in 1803, subsequent to Whitney's invention and Eve became one of the piraters of the saw gin.

The fundamental principle of all these roller gins was the use of two rollers of metal (wood, in primitive Indian ones), longitudinally fluted, set close together and rotated in opposite directions. The fibres passed between the rollers, the black seeds, easily detached, fell off on the side.

The direction of all the improvements being made was toward the capacity and speed of such machines. They were completely useless for green-seed cotton, which appeared to have a dim future.

In September of 1793, an elderly farmer mechanic named Eli Whitney, in Westboro, Massachusetts, received a long letter from New Haven, Connecticut. It was from his son, Eli, who had been away in the South, presumably to teach school, since being graduated from Yale little more than a year before. The family had heard scanty and unsatisfactory news from him up until now. At last the younger Eli was ready to pour out the story of what he had afoot.

New Haven, Sept. 11th, 1793

Dear Parent,

. . . When I wrote you last I expected to have been able to come to Westboro' sooner than I now fear will be in my power. I presume, sir, you are desirous to hear how I have spent my time since I left College. This I conceive you have a right to know and that it is my duty to inform you . . . I will give you a summary account of my southern expedition.

. . . I went from N. York with the family of the late Major General Greene to Georgia. I went immediately with the family to their Plantation about twelve miles from Savannah with an expectation of spending four or five days and then proceed into Carolina to take the school as I have mentioned in former letters. During this time I heard much said of the extreme difficulty of ginning Cotton, that is, separating it from its seeds. There were a number of very respectable Gentlemen at Mrs. Greene's who all agreed that if a machine could be invented which would clean the cotton with expedition, it would be a great thing both to the Country and to the inventor. I involuntarily happened to be thinking on the subject and struck out a plan of a Machine in my mind, which I communicated to Miller (who is agent to the Executors of Genl. Greene and resides in the family, a man of respectability and property), he was pleased with the Plan and said if I would pursue it and try an experiment to see if it would answer, he would be at the whole expense, I should loose nothing but my time, and if I succeeded we would share the profits. Previous to this I found I was like to be disappointed in my school, that is, instead of a hundred, I found I could get only fifty Guineas a year. I however held the refusal of the school untill I tried some experiments. In about ten Days I made a little model, for which I was offered, if I would give up all right and title to it, a Hundred Guineas. I concluded to relinquish my school and turn my attention to perfecting the Machine. I made one before I came away which required the labor of one man to turn it and with which one man will clean ten times as much cotton as he can in any other way before known and also cleanse it much

better than in the usual mode. This machine may
be turned by water or with a horse, with the greatest
ease, and one man and a horse will do more than
fifty men with the old machines. It makes the labor
fifty times less without throwing any class of People
out of business.

I returned to the Northward for the purpose of
having a machine made on a large scale and obtaining a Patent for the invintion. I went to Philadelphia
soon after I arrived, made myself acquainted with
the steps necessary to obtain a Patent, took several
of the steps and the Secretary of State Mr. Jefferson
agreed to send the Pattent to me as soon as it could
be made out—so that I apprehended no difficulty
in obtaining the Patent— Since I have been here
I have employed several workmen in making machines and as soon as my business is such that I
can leave it a few days, I shall come to Westboro'.
I think it is probable I shall go to Philadelphia again
before I come to Westboro', and when I do come I
shall be able to stay but a few days. I am certain
I can obtain a patent in England. As soon as I have
got a Patent in America I shall go with the machine
which I am now making, to Georgia, where I shall
stay a few weeks to see it at work. From thence I
expect to go to England, where I shall probably continue two or three years. How advantageous this
business will eventually prove to me, I cannot say.
It is generally said by those who know anything
about it, that I shall make a Fortune by it. I have
no expectation that I shall make an independent
fortune by it, but think I had better pursue it than
any other business into which I can enter. Something which cannot be foreseen may frustrate my
expectations and defeat my Plan; but I am so sure
of success that ten thousand dollars, if I saw the
money counted out to me, would not tempt me to
give up my right and relinquish the object. I wish

you, sir, not to show this letter nor communicate
anything of its contents to any body except My
Brothers and Sister, *enjoining* it on them to keep the
whole a *profound secret.*

. . . Only two or three of my friends know
what I am about tho' there are many surmises in
town. . . .

With respects to Mama I am,
kind Parent, your most obt. Son
Eli Whitney, Junr.

The letter was carried by a "Mr. Robbinson" for
12½ ¢ from New Haven to Westboro (yet it only cost 14¢
for a letter from New Haven to the Greene plantation, Mulberry Grove). The postman was curious enough to prompt
Eli to add the warning, "If Mr. R. says anything about it,
you can tell him I wished not to have it mentioned."

A great deal lay behind this concise summation of
events, a great deal both in incident and in the growth
and nature of a character. A key to Whitney's genius—
and to that of many other of the great inventors—is in the
words, "I involuntarily happened to be thinking on the
subject and struck out a plan of a Machine in my mind."
It was not exactly that *Whitney* invented—his *mind* invented. He could no more help it than he could help
breathing.

To observe this fact is not to deprecate Whitney. He and
his mind are one. But we see that invention is a *process
going on,* and that Whitney did not invent by sitting down
and saying to himself consciously, "Now I *must* contrive a
cotton gin," and squeezing his head between his hands
until he had forced out an idea.

The mind of Eli Whitney always worked involuntarily.
Eli Sr. was a farmer, but like every really good one, was
something of a mechanic too, who maintained a work shed
of his own and had a good many tools, including a lathe
for turning chair posts. Young Eli knew tools from child-

hood. His sister Elizabeth said of him, "As soon as he could handle tools he was always making some thing in the shop and seemed not to relish working on the farm . . . [he] did his days works and gained time to make tools for his own use—put in penknife blades and do many little jobs for other people."

It was not laziness, but energy, that dictated his preference for tinkering. Eli had a sharp eye, even as a boy, for needs and opportunities. During the Revolution, this teenage lad with his father's consent added a forge to the shop and set about the making of nails and the fashioning of new tools for himself. Without even informing his father, Eli went off one day and fetched back a hired man to help in the nail business. He had calculated that the venture could sustain the labor, and the trip of forty miles or more in which he found his "hand" he further turned to profit by visiting other shops and forges and picking up fresh ideas.

When the war ended and renewed trade brought cheap nails from over the sea, Eli quickly dropped this venture and turned for a while to the manufacture of steel hatpins. Even earlier than this he had shown diverse ingenuities, including a precocious aptitude for mathematics and the ability to make a violin capable of producing "tolerable good musick."

Eli's mother died when he was quite young and some years later a stepmother came into the home. Elizabeth reports that she took a dim view of Eli's abilities. But when the new mother broke one of a set of beautiful knives, of which she was greatly proud, Eli made a matching one to replace it, thereby winning her respect, if not her affection. He had made the boast, when she displayed the set, "I can make just such ones if I had tools and I could make tools if I had tools to make them with."

Eli Whitney was admitted to Yale College as a freshman on the very day that George Washington was inaugurated as President of the United States—April 30, 1789. Benjamin Franklin had died only a few days earlier. It was the

same year in which Samuel Slater came to these shores
with the secrets of the Arkwright mill. Slater was then
twenty-two, and Whitney, the college freshman, slower in
preparation for a career, was twenty-three.

Eli had made the decision to seek formal education,
and had been preparing the way for it, from about the age
of eighteen or nineteen. His stepmother was wholly un-
sympathetic, and even his somewhat remarkable father,
perceptive of Eli's gifts in many ways, was at first short-
sighted in this particular. Their thinking was not uncom-
mon. As Elizabeth records: "When Esq. Parkman was
informed of E's going to college he said a young man possessed of such extraordinary mechanical powers he
thought might be more useful and it was a pitty he should
spend four years in a colledge and the publick be deprived of his services for so long a time."

Of course there was much preparatory study to be done
and this would have to be paid for. With typical audacity
of decision, Eli sought and obtained a schoolteaching position not far from New Haven, Connecticut, applying the
classic and honorable principle of resorting to teaching as
a means of learning. He kept himself sufficiently ahead of
his pupils, and with the money earned teaching in the
wintertime he paid his tuition for more intensive study at
Leicester Academy during the summers.

His sister Elizabeth's account of his schoolteaching days
contains a remarkable notation concerning his method in
teaching penmanship and instructing his pupils in the
proper shaping of a quill pen. "He kept a large quill cane
in complete shape of a writing pen, for a pattern for his
pupils to copy and enjoin'd them to make their own pens."
Who can ignore the link between the standard model of a
quill pen for schoolboys and the musket assembled from
interchangeable parts which, more than the cotton gin, was
this remarkable man's vital contribution to American industry?

Once Eli was ensconced in Yale, his father, overcoming
his previous reluctance, helped him staunchly insofar as

his means permitted. Even so, the years of college were years of money pinch for young Eli. He availed himself of any opportunity to apply either his ingenuity or his energy to making a little spare cash. He collected a dollar apiece for coloring the maps in Guthry's Geography for fellow students too idle to do it for themselves.

The oddest thing about these years is that Eli had as yet no conscious sense about his future career. His studies were directed toward the law, simply as an expedient. When he was graduated, in 1792, he had taken steps with the help of his always valuable friend, guide, and counsellor, President Ezra Stiles, to procure a tutoring job in South Carolina, for the family of a Major Dupont.

The person responsible for hiring him for this post, on behalf of the Carolinian planter, was another Connecticut man and Yale graduate, Mr. Phineas Miller, who was manager of the Georgia estate of the late Revolutionary War general and hero, Nathanael Greene. The gratitude of the people of Georgia for the general's military services, had led them to present to him the large, confiscated estate, Mulberry Grove. (The name reflects the era of silk-worm enthusiasm—north and south.) On his way south, by sea from New York, Whitney was to travel with Miller and the widow of the general, Mrs. Catherine Greene. This now brings us up to the events concisely summarized for the elder Whitney in Eli's long letter of September 11, 1793.

Catherine Greene deserves a good deal more time than this story can afford to give her. She had been Catherine Littlefield, named for her aunt, Catherine Ray Greene (also kin to her husband) who had shared the most famous of Benjamin Franklin's tender, partly erotic, partly pater-nal correspondences and friendships between the older man and young women. Our Catherine Greene was one of the remarkable women of her age, a person of sophistica-tion and worldly wisdom, who had been married to a shrewd, wise, but plain and simple man. With him she endured the two most terrible winters of the Revolution, at Valley Forge and at Morristown, giving birth to her fourth child during the course of the latter year.

Fate did not leave Nathanael Greene much time to enjoy the estate which had been given into his hands as the fruit of his labors and battles. He died of a heart attack brought on by the vigor with which he set himself to putting his new property into shipshape order. Phineas Miller, who had been his secretary, carried on as manager to aid the bereaved woman. He, too, was a man of ability and honor, who ultimately married the widow Greene.

The folklore concerning Whitney's gin carries a tale that Catherine solved a riddle on which Whitney was hung up, by offering him her hearthbrush, saying, "This is what your gin needs,"—presumably a reference to the rotary brush which swept the cotton fibres off the wire prongs which had torn them from the sticky seeds.

According to other traditions, he had drawn Catherine's attention to his ingenuity by fashioning a new kind of tambour embroidery frame for her, inspiring her to say to the planters discussing green-seed cotton in her home, "Gentlemen, apply to my young friend, Whitney, he can make anything." Further accounts say that it was not the season for cotton in the seed and that Eli, his curiosity aroused, went into Savannah and searched the warehouses until he found enough to use for experiment. Reports that he also drew his own wire for the cylinder teeth are quite unfounded, for in later years, in his patent disputes, he said that he used some wire that had been intended for a birdcage. He is said to have got the idea of using wire teeth by happening to test the clinging power of the seed with a toothpick, while walking and pondering the problem.

Regardless of the truth of these several legends, Catherine Greene made considerable impact upon Eli and became so staunch a friend that her death, years later (once more a widow), was felt as a profound loss by him. If he had acquired learning at Yale College, from Catherine Greene he learned important lessons about a cultivated world with a different pace, and a kind of leisured grace not native to his temperament. We find her writing to him in the early days, "Come here and let me teach you by *My example,* how to enjoy the few fleeting years which any can calculate upon."

As for Whitney's machine itself, his brief description of it prepared in connection with his patent presentation broke it down into five basic parts: the frame, the cylinder, the breastwork, the clearer, and the hopper. The cylinder was of wood with many close set rows of wire teeth bristling upon it. These combed the green-seed cotton through a fine breastwork of metal, through which the teeth could pull the cotton fibres, but through which neither whole nor broken seeds could pass. The fibres were then cleared from the wire teeth by a rapidly rotating brush. The final sentence of his description remarked that: "There are several modes of making the various parts of this machine . . ." a statement which in a while will be seen as a matter of some importance.

It has frequently been said, and was often insisted upon by Whitney, that his machine was something altogether new and unrelated to any device going before it. Insofar as the attempt to clean cotton was concerned, this was unquestionably true. But apart from this context, the claim overlooks a resemblance of which Whitney was in fact conscious—the resemblance to carding machines, which as the last chapter showed were already current by the time Whitney made his first gin. It is hard to imagine that Whitney did not know about them, whether he had seen one or not, and the simple hand card is a much more likely inspiration (possibly unconscious) for the gin teeth than the toothpick anecdote. Even his clearing brush is like a simplification of the small interspersed cylinders that automatically lifted wool or cotton fibres from one carding cylinder and delivered them onto the next.

I think this is implicitly recognized in some of Whitney's correspondence with Thomas Jefferson, who was then

Secretary of State and the person through whom the application for patent had to be made. Inevitably, Jefferson was keenly interested in Whitney's device, not only because of his own mechanical interests but also because of his status as a southern planter.

In an exchange of letters while Whitney was attempting to complete the working model which was required in filing for patent, Jefferson inquired whether the gin was adaptable to "family use." To this, Whitney promptly replied: "I think the machine is well calculated for family use. It may be made on a very small scale and yet perform in proportion to its size. I believe one might be made within the compass of two cubic feet, that would cleanse all the cotton which any one family manufactures for its own use. The machine itself does considerable towards carding the cotton, and I have no doubt but by leaving out the clearer and adding three or four cylinders with card-teeth, it would deliver the cotton completely prepared for spinning."

In the long and ultimately fruitless struggle which ensued to protect patent rights, perhaps breaking the heart of Miller, his partner, and all but doing the same for Whitney, one of the most formidable challenges was in the form of infringement of the patent based on claims of originality for mere variations of the scheme. Whitney's gin has come down in history under the name of the "saw" gin. The gins now in operation use rows of circular saws with slightly blunted teeth in place of the wire teeth of Whitney's model.

This does not show the supplanting of Whitney's concepts by something else, nor does it show that Whitney was not aware of the possibility of using the disc saw for his purpose. The names of Edward Lyon ("that ignorant low fellow" the usually mild Miller called him) and Hodgen Holmes—particularly the latter—are most associated with this variation.

Remember Whitney's observation about "several modes of making the various parts of this machine." His contention, which there is no cause to disbelieve, was that he perceived in the first instance the convenience of the circular saw form, which could be made by either a series of circular saws slightly separated by dividers, or by stamping out the centers of circular saws and sliding the toothed rims over a wooden cylinder. At the time of his first model in Georgia, however, he had not at hand either the tools or the metal to use this principle. There happened to be wire in Mrs. Greene's house that had been intended for the making of a birdcage, and Whitney availed himself of this and made cylinder teeth. Subsequently he insisted that the wire teeth yielded a better result because they were springier and more sensitive and would not force between the prongs of the breastwork tangles or lumps of cotton as the rigid saw tooth would do.

In spite of many grievous disillusionments in courtrooms in the south, in this one question Whitney was sustained in a famous decision of Circuit Court Judge William Johnson in December, 1806, in Louisville, Georgia. Johnson, a South Carolinian, later was appointed by Jefferson to the Supreme Court, where he served under Marshall with such independence of judgment that he has been called the first great dissenter, in anticipation of the later Justice Holmes.

Judge Johnson affirmed the Holmes saw-tooth to be merely a variation in method on the undeniably original principle of Whitney. In the course of his opinion, the Judge summed up concisely the debt which southern society in particular but all society in general owed to Whitney's creativeness:

> With regard to the utility of this discovery, the court would deem it a waste of time to dwell long upon this topic. Is there a man who hears us, who has not experienced its utility? The whole interior of the Southern States was languishing, and its inhabitants emigrating for want of some object to gain their attention, and employ their industry, when the invention of this machine at once opened views to

them, which set the whole country in active motion. From childhood to age it has presented to us a lucrative employment. Individuals who were depressed with poverty, and sunk in idleness, have suddenly risen in wealth and respectability. Our debts have been paid off, our capitals have been increased; and our lands trebled themselves in value. We cannot express the weight of the obligation which the country owes to this invention—the extent of it cannot now be seen . . . Our sister States, also, participate in the benefits of this invention; for, besides affording the raw material for their manufactures, the bulkiness and quantity of the article afford a valuable employment for their shipping. . . .

While the Johnson decision was a vindication in principle, it is no index to the practical success that Whitney and his partner Miller were able to achieve in southern courts, in their years of protracted litigation over piracy and infringement. In later years Whitney's cooperation was sought by two of his most brilliant fellow inventors, Oliver Evans and Robert Fulton, in behalf of measures to strengthen and improve American patent law. On March 30, 1811, Whitney remarked ruefully in a letter to Fulton:

My invention was *new* & distinct—it stood alone— was not interwoven with anything before known . . . There was a time when there was but few men in Georgia dared to come into court and testify to the most simple facts in their knowledge relative to the use of the machines. In one instance I had great difficulty to prove that the machine had been used in Georgia & at the same moment there were three separate sets of this machinery in motion [within] fifty yards of the building in which the court sat & all so near that the rattling was distinctly heard on the steps of the courthouse . . .

> A man's right to property in his inventions, although
> better founded in motive than any other right of
> property, has been but recently recognized in this
> country . . . It is a species of right which but
> few can acquire & will always be liable to be tram-
> pled under foot by the many.

Although in his earliest letters to his father about the
cotton gin Whitney made what was obviously a conscious
and cautious effort to lean away from great expectations,
the thread of excitement can be traced through his words.
He is guarding his tongue, as one under the ancient super-
stition of not boasting his good fortune and prospects lest
jealous gods overhear and blight them. But the eavesdrop-
ping fates overheard and luck was to run strongly against
him. Almost the last of these expressions of cautious optimism, while things still ran smoothly, occurs in his letter
of March 30, 1794, before he left New Haven again for
Georgia and, according to his plan, thence to England. He
regrets that he cannot get up to Westboro, but hopes that
his father or his brothers might be able to pay him a quick
visit in New Haven and see the machines.

> I am extremely sorry I cannot come and see all my
> friends, but as I have a fair prospect of making a
> handsome property, and as I am so much in need
> of it, I think I ought not to neglect the opportunity.
> Though I have as yet expended much more money
> than the profits of the machine have been hereto-
> fore, and am at present a little pressed for money, I
> am by no means in the least discouraged. And I shall
> probably gain some honour as well as profit by the
> Invention. It was said by one of the most respectable
> Gentlemen in N. Haven that he would rather be the
> author of the invention than to be prime minister
> of England. But I mean not to be elated by my
> success so much as to be vain.
>   I have a fair character and am in good Credit,
> as far as I am acquainted with myself.

Slightly less than a month later, on the 22nd of February, Ezra Stiles noted in his diary, in one of many such entries revealing his alert interest in things mechanical:

> Mr. Whitney brot to my house & shewed us his Machine, by him invented for cleaning Cotton of its seed. He shewed us the model which he has finished to lodge at Philadelphia in the Secretary of States Office, when he takes out his Patent. This miniature Model is pfect, & will clean about a dozen pounds a day, or about 40^{lb} before clean^g. He has completed six large ones, Barrel phps five feet long to carry to Georgia. In one of these I saw about a *dozen pounds* of Cotton with seeds cleaned by one pson in about twenty minutes, from which was delivered above *three pounds* of Cotton purely cleansed of seed. It will clean 100^{cwt} a day. A curious & very ingenious piece of Mechanism.

In the course of the following year, Miller and Whitney's troubles began to pile up. Probably they made a fundamentally wrong decision in trying to exploit the gin on the monopolistic basis of cleaning all the cotton of the South at a fee—though it is not easy to say that any other plan would actually have been a success—and the challenge to their rights began immediately. Also, enemies of their claims began to spread rumors, especially in England, that cotton from Whitney's gin was inferior, that it was knotted by the action of the machine. Eli (who never made his projected trip to England) at once asserted that far from knotting the staple, his gin removed knots from all but the most inferior and useless material. (Samuel Slater always refused to use anything but Barbadoes cotton in his mills until the product of Whitney's process converted him to the use of American cotton.)

In 1795 a new blow fell. Whitney's best friend, Josiah Stebbins, a tutor at Yale, wrote of it to a classmate:

> Wednesday morning last the bells jingled, and the cry of fire! was heard. On turning out among the

crowd, and starting toward the smoke, which I could
see from my windows, I was after a while surprised
to see that the fire proceeded from Whitney's laboratory, which is near Captain Hunts in the New Township. It was irrecoverably on fire, and soon fell. The
fire broke out while the laborers were gone to break-
fast.

This was a severe financial blow, but incalculably
greater was the loss of his ingenious, carefully constructed
machines and tools for the production of gins. This calam-
ity dashed Whitney into black despair. Before his wres-
tlings with infringers were over a distinct note of bitterness
was coloring his utterances. He complained: "Many of the
Citizens of Georgia are amassing fortunes, living volup-
tuously and rolling in splendour by the surreptitious use of
it [the gin], while I am and for more than six years past
have been, chained down to this spot, struggling under a
heavy load of debt contracted for my very subsistence and
expenses while I was solely employed in inventing and perfecting this machine."

His worthy and loyal partner, Miller, died in 1803 and
while the struggles over the gin cannot be blamed for his
death, they certainly did nothing to prolong his life or to
bring to the latter years of it the tranquillity and pleasure
which might have been the expected lot of the fortunate
spouse of Catherine Greene Miller.

For all his harassments he had been a man of taste, culture, and wit, as his tie with Catherine would lead us to expect. His personality shows in a letter to Whitney about
one of the interminable courtroom scenes, explaining why
he had failed to press one final argument upon a tired,
hungry jury: "I recollected Goldsmith's character of Edmund Burke, 'who went on refining, and thought of convincing, while they thought of dining.' So I kept my speech to
myself."

About six months before the sharp blow of Miller's
death, Whitney already had written to his close friend,

Josiah Stebbins: "So large a proportion of Mankind are such infernal Rascals that I shall never be able to realize but a trifling proportion of [the gin's] value. You know I always believed in the *'Depravity of Human nature.'* I thought I was long ago sufficiently *'grounded & established'* in this Doctrine. But God Almighty is continually pouring down *cataracts* of testimony upon me to convince me of this fact. 'Lord I believe, help thou,' not 'mine unbelief,' but me to overcome the rascality of mankind."

What was the mistake, if it was a mistake, in Miller and Whitney's attempt to exploit their machine? Seeing little prospect of being able to manufacture enough machines within a short time to fill the potential demand, they attempted to establish a monopoly, proposing to erect their own ginneries to clean cotton delivered to them and return it to the grower, charging a substantial fee in the form of a percentage of the cotton cleaned. There were two immediate problems. In the first place, the news of the gin, and what it could do, and its simplicity of construction, had leaked out beginning with the very first demonstration of the crude model in the Greene household, in 1793. Whitney's "enjoining" of his family to keep it a "profound secret" was already much too late.

Piratical imitations were being built before Whitney had completed his patents and advanced very far with the construction of bigger and better machines. So great was the economic pressure of the latent fortune in green-seed cotton in the south that the whole region simply would not wait—indeed by hindsight could not conceivably have been expected to wait—for processes of individual claims, and the slow manufacture and supply which was the most that Whitney could produce.

Also it was inevitable that with the burgeoning cotton fields ready to yield annually bigger and bigger crops, the planters were bound to resent and resist unto bitterness on their own part the notion that this natural crop of theirs must be subjected to a virtual tax on the part of a man trying to keep within his own hands a device of such utter simplicity. What matter that he had thought of it and they had not? Now it existed. The concept of the property right in invention was a hazy one at best at that time, particularly so in the agricultural south where minds had not been running on such problems. So the claims of Whitney appeared to the impatient and eager southern planters both fantastic and unjust on what seemed to them the simple, natural morality of the situation. It was not villainy and blackness of heart or human depravity, although it was natural enough for Whitney to think it was, that resulted in sweeping infringement. This was the conflict of two diametrically opposed interests and philosophies and attitudes toward the problem.

Later, Miller and Whitney made an effort to retrieve something by selling licenses for the use of the machine to such few as could be reached and prevailed upon to accept the licensing arrangement rather than engage in court battles over the question. Probably it would have been wiser for them to have worked on the licensing basis from the very beginning. It would not have prevented all piracy, but it would have simplified matters and removed the terrible bottleneck of their attempt to produce all the gins for all the cotton of the south. They could then have manufactured as many gins as they could make, being sure of a ready market for all of them.

But before any such reappraisal of the problem was possible, the south was rattling with pirated gins and those who made and used them were defiant. Whitney and Miller made some money from sale of machines, from licensing, and from one or two southern legislatures which had the grace to make modest grants to them in recognition of the contribution of the machine. Still, the money taken in was never remotely proportionate to the profits reaped by users of the machine, or to the costs of the interminable battles which Miller and Whitney fought over it.

The fact was, Eli Whitney had done a rare thing. He had been the one (there would have been another in short order, we may be sure) to create a simple, basic invention with which, in Shaw's phrase, the age was visibly pregnant. It was charged with such explosive and expansive economic consequences that it was utterly uncontrollable. It might possibly have been uncontrollable at any age, but in the context of the general status of technology at that time and of the confusion of attitudes involving patent rights, the attempt to establish and defend individual claims to that admirable and profitable invention was hopeless before it got started.

The thing that saved Eli Whitney and preserved his unique services for his nation was a resiliency which prevented the bitterness expressed in the heat of the cotton-gin battle from poisoning the well of his creativity. He had learned a hard lesson. What application he could make of it remained to be seen. "Verily," he wrote to Stebbins, "I have had much vexation of spirit in this business. I shall spend forty thousand dollars to obtain thirty, and it will all end in vanity at last." But he was not the subjective neurotic that we saw in poor John Fitch. He must do something with his energies and resourcefulness, something to recoup his financial losses. Not only did he do so, but characteristically he had already begun, years before the cotton-gin story had run its course.

It is given to few men to make two distinct major strikes in a single career. The new enterprise that he had embarked upon, before the old one had been wrapped up, was productive of equally important economic results, though they did not make themselves visible with the same dramatic splash. This time he was to reap his legitimate rewards—which were quite modest. The story of Whitney's second and actually greatest accomplishment is a part of the history of American armaments, and in that context it must be told.

So we turn away from Eli Whitney, who let loose a vast flood of raw materials for the American cotton mills of his contemporary, Samuel Slater, and we take up the story of Eli Whitney, gunmaker.

CHAPTER 11

ARMS AND THE MEN

One of my primary objects is to
form the tools so the tools themselves shall fashion the work and
give to every part its just proportion—which when once accomplished, will give expedition,
uniformity, and exactness to the
whole . . .

—ELI WHITNEY TO
OLIVER WOLCOTT

AT THE beginning of a new year and a new century, 1801,
a famous demonstration (or quite likely a series of them)
took place in Washington. The large-framed, somewhat
tired-looking man responsible had journeyed over what he
recorded as "deep" and bad roads, slowly, tediously, in
the winter weather in cold and cumbersome coaches from
New Haven to Washington.

This was a hard trip. His previous negotiations with the
government, of which there had been many, had been in
the more convenient capital of Philadelphia. Now, after
sitting in as many as eight different sites as opportunity or
emergency had dictated, the Federal government was like a
dweller who has just moved into a brand new house. It had
occupied this capital, designed specifically to be the seat of

212

government, for less than a year. The city was still unchartered. The building of it had been under way for about ten years, under the guiding hand of the Frenchman, L'Enfant, with that architect of no mean abilities, Jefferson, who had dickered with Hamilton to establish this southern site, taking an active interest in the development. So although Washington was a muddy city, and a somewhat bare one, scaffold-new, it had at the same time an air of spacious dignity about it, and promise.

Moses-like, George Washington had died a year too soon to see the government occupy the city that honored him with its name. He, too, had guided its making, appointing Jefferson as one of its commissioners, entrusting the planning to L'Enfant, and concurring in the sentiments of Jefferson that: "The acquisition of ground is really noble . . . I think very liberal reserves should be made for the public."

Here, then, came Eli Whitney, to show something of his wares. To the President of the United States, the Honorable John Adams, to many members of the cabinet, certainly including the heads of the Treasury and War Departments, and to numerous other important persons, one of whom was the waiting President-Elect, Thomas Jefferson, Whitney made his demonstration. Also on hand was one of his staunch friends and supporters, Elizur Goodrich, Jr., a congressman from Connecticut, where the venerable Elizur Sr., one of the adornments of the early days of Yale College, had tutored Eli for admission not so very many years before.

For a matter of two years Whitney had been working toward the fulfilment of his famous contract made in 1798 for a stand of 10,000 muskets for the U. S. Government. These were late for delivery and Whitney needed some further advances on the monies agreed upon. Some officials of the Adams administration were restive over the fearfully large commitment, the considerable advances for it, and the absence of any deliveries of finished muskets.

Whitney had come to allay these fears brought to a crisis by a shake-up in the top echelons of Adams' administration. Whether all the people mentioned saw the same single demonstration, or as seems more probable, different ones saw it at different times, the astonishing thing which the Connecticut inventor had brought to them consisted of the disassembled parts of ten muskets laid out upon a table. From this array, before the eyes of his watchers, inviting different ones of them to select the next requisite part at random, Whitney assembled gun after gun.

This was an unheard of thing—or virtually so, certainly for most of them and for the world at large. These were guns with interchangeable parts. The handmade gun from the lone gunsmith, however great or rare craftsman he might be, was always a unique thing. Its parts fitted each other, but did not fit any other gun, even from the same maker, and if one part were broken, or lost, another must be specially hand made to replace it or the whole gun was a total loss. These extraordinary muskets of Whitney's lent themselves to flexible manipulation. If one were broken, any of its parts salvaged undamaged could be used as replacements in another gun.

The demonstration was worth Whitney's arduous trip. In spite of the fact that Adams' new Secretary of the Treasury, a lame duck official, was rather suspicious of Whitney and coldly hostile toward him, a few months changed this picture. The interested, alert, thoroughly perceptive Thomas Jefferson was inaugurated as the third President of the United States. He was prepared to back Whitney to the limit and was a man competent to understand both Whitney's immediate accomplishment and the merit of his product, but even more, the implications of Whitney's feat applied to the entire field of industrial production. (His fears about industry, as discussed in Chapter Eight, may not have been removed, but he was wise enough to see that industrial development, being inevitable, was therefore essential.) Now Jefferson's first move was to take the matter of the Whitney muskets out of the hands of the Treasury Department and put it in the War Department, under Secretary Henry Dearborn, of Maine.

This, then, was the man with whom Whitney must deal specifically in the immediate future. Some reflection of Whitney himself is seen in his confidential questions to a friend, also from Maine, about the new Secretary: "Perhaps you may know something about him. I know nothing of him but expect soon to have occasion to negociate some business with him & shuld like to have some Idea of the cut of his *Gib*. Is he a man of talents? Has he extensive information? Is he a man of integrity? in short has he a *soul?* Write me all you know of him without reserve . . ."

However, this is not the moment to pursue the story of Whitney's government transactions. First it needs the context of the earlier scenes in the story of American firearms.

In 1798, the year in which Whitney signed his audacious contract for 10,000 muskets, Hugh Orr, of Massachusetts, died at the age of eighty-two. He it was, as a state senator, who had taken the initiative in having the so-called State Models of power spinning machines made—those models which proved to be in themselves inadequate, and which Slater rejected, but which were one of the strongest expressions of the growing determination to match the textile accomplishments of Great Britain. Until Slater came, no one had done more than Hugh Orr in groping toward this objective.

Early in his career, Orr's skill and reputation as a worker in edge-tools was so great that customers would travel twenty miles in that day of slow movement to have him renew the temper of an axe, an adze, a scythe, or an auger. The Massachusetts Bay Province had received 500 stand of muskets from him sometime around 1748—an astonishing performance—which are considered to be the first muskets manufactured in this country. Probably it would be safer to add "on any such scale" for I would suppose individual blacksmiths to have tinkered-up guns here or there, especially in Pennsylvania which was to become famous for its rifles.

Orr also was a pioneer in new and improved methods of

boring cannon, and his son, Robert, became Master Armorer of the Springfield Arsenal.

The fabulous Jacob Perkins, whose exploits properly belong elsewhere in this story, also dabbled in armaments, chiefly cannon, in such exotic variations as steam cannon.

Various small-scale gun manufactories sprang up around the time of the revolution, widely distributed throughout the colonies, north and south. William Henry's arms shop, in Lancaster, Pennsylvania, where Thomas Paine had talked with Henry about steamboats, where John Fitch had stopped and had his illusions of uniqueness in the steamboat dream shattered, and near which shop the child Robert Fulton had grown up, was one of the important suppliers of rifles. Some of Henry's old gun works still exist, with the ancient machinery in partial preservation.

Henry was a rifle maker. The "Pennsylvania rifle" came to be the generic name of those finely-wrought, long-barrelled weapons, wherever made. Never mass-produced, they played a role of importance in American history out of all proportion to their actual numbers. (They were the famous Kentucky "long rifles.")

The art of rifling a gun barrel has been known since at least the 15th century. It grew from the discovery that spiral grooves within the barrel helped the primitive, soft bullets to conform to the shape of the barrel, improving the compression, and also imparted a spinning motion to the projectile which enhanced its accuracy and carrying power, as every pitcher knows.

The Pennsylvania Germans brought the technique of rifling to the new world, which accounts for the irony of the Quaker State being the chief source of this particularly lethal weapon. One version of the motive which impelled the British to bring Hessian mercenaries to fight on these shores says that it was because they were equipped with rifles instead of smooth-bore muskets. However, the more-or-less mass-produced Hessian rifle was not the equal of the lovingly-fashioned, greatly elongated weapons which became the partners of the Pennsylvania woodsmen and frontiersmen. It was the Pennsylvania rifle that Natty Bumppo carried through his mighty exploits. The accuracy and range of this weapon, even in the hands of a few, imparted a major advantage in the essentially guerrilla warfare which the Americans waged against the more organized British forces.

Most of the guns produced in American gunshops, and all of the early production of Whitney's plant, were smooth-bore muskets of the French Charleville type. Years later, the Whitney plant converted to the rifle, which at last completely supplanted the obsolete musket.

In 1774, Parliament passed an Act prohibiting the export of firearms, gunpowder, or other military stores to the restive colonies. A Philadelphian wrote to a member of Parliament that the action was too late. He claimed that there were enough gunmakers in Pennsylvania to make 100,000 stand of arms within a year. The figure seems most improbable, but is still some sort of testimony to the fact that Pennsylvania, alone, was well equipped to arm herself.

In Maryland, a gunsmith named Elisha Winters made 600 stand of muskets at the rate of forty per month. At the same time, in Maryland and elsewhere, there was a tendency toward division of labor in terms of complete units, such as the whole lock mechanism. True interchange of parts was not involved, but it shows a direction. In Pennsylvania, Benjamin Rittenhouse had charge of a gun-lock factory. Winters, in Maryland, took over a gun-lock factory. A Henry Hollingsworth was a maker of gun barrels. Some men specialized in bayonets, and a few pursued such fine particulars as priming wires and brushes. A man named Messersmith, again in Maryland, could make ten gun-locks per week, charging three dollars each.

In every case, though, the several parts of a lock mechanism, or of the musket if it were the entire work of a single artisan, were unique to the specific piece and did not have the absolute uniformity which was the essence of the Whitney conception.

Immediately after the Revolutionary War, Congress felt

it expedient to establish national armories. The town of
Springfield, Massachusetts had been used as a depot for military stores and a repair center for arms. Cannon had been
made there, too. In 1794, Congress established the first national armory, at Springfield, the one of which Robert Orr
was superintendent. This was "The Arsenal at Springfield,"
of Longfellow's famous poem:

> This is the Arsenal. From floor to ceiling,
>   Like a huge organ, rise the burnished arms;
> But from their silent pipes no anthem pealing
>   Startles the villages with strange alarms.
>
> Ah! what a sound will rise, how wild and dreary,
>   When the death-angel touches those swift keys! . . .

In 1798 a second Federal arsenal was established, at
Harper's Ferry, Virginia. This, of course, became immortalized as the objective of John Brown's tragic raid. For
many years the arsenals at Springfield and Harper's Ferry,
and the Whitney plant as a private enterprise, were the
three major sources of muskets and rifles for the United
States Government, with the Whitney plant producing the
decidedly superior product by the most significant methods.

Now it is a curious and meaningful circumstance that
Eli Whitney never had made a gun in his life at a time
when he boldly solicited of the U. S. government a contract
for the largest delivery of arms ever undertaken, for which
he wanted substantial cash advances. He had not invented
a gun—in fact, the one which he contracted to manufacture in such quantity deserved to be obsolete at the time.
He had invented an approach to the making of guns. As
far as he was concerned, he was signing a contract to make
objects of various shapes out of various materials, which
objects, when finished, could be assembled into guns—a
climax which was the least of Whitney's interests.

The government wanted guns, it could pay for guns, so

Whitney offered to make guns. They gave him a specimen of the gun they wanted—an indifferent matter to him. He took the Charleville musket home and began at once to analyze its components, figuring how to make this part and that part, and even how to subcontract for others if it were something he need not keep under his own supervision (thus he obtained stocks and barrels, at times, from other suppliers).

Whitney explained it to the Secretary of the Treasury, Oliver Wolcott (another Yale man):

> My general plan does not consist in one great complicated machine, wherever one small part being out of order or not answering to the purpose expected, the whole must stop & be considered useless. If the mode in which I propose to make one part of the musket should prove by experiment not to answer, it will in no way affect my mode of making any other part. One of my primary objects is to form the tools so the tools themselves shall fashion the work and give to every part its just proportion—which when once accomplished, will give expedition, uniformity, and exactness to the whole . . . In short, the tools which I contemplate are similar to an engraving on copper plate from which may be taken a great number of impressions perceptibly alike . . . Machines for forging, rolling, floating, boring, grinding, polishing, etc. may all be made use of to advantage.

Here, for this country, was the birth of the whole concept of our machine-tool and mass-production industry.

Again, it can't be claimed that but for Whitney—or but for America—this development would not have arisen, even though America gave it the impetus that history records. The great English mechanic, Henry Maudslay, built the first all-metal lathe around 1794, and invented the slide rest, which David Wilkinson later duplicated independently. Without impugning either the inventions of Maudslay or Wilkinson, it is true that Diderot's Encyclopedia, some years earlier, contained an illustration of a lathe bench with a form of slide rest. The Greeks and the ancient Hindus knew the lathe, and the potter's wheel, which of course is a type of lathe, is of so profound an antiquity as to be used as a ready symbol by the prophet Jeremiah (Jer. 18:3-6).

A lathe basically is a machine for gripping and rotating a piece of wood or metal while one or more tools for cutting or otherwise shaping it are held against the moving material. In primitive lathes, the tool is held in the free hand, just as the fingers of the potter are freely applied to the clay. Obviously this would limit the precision of work in many types of cutting and shaping—screw cutting being a good example.

The slide rest, created by Maudslay, Wilkinson, and possibly others, enormously extended the capacity and versatility of the lathe. The "rest" part of it consists of a clamp to hold any applied tool steadily fixed at any chosen angle of application. The "slide" part refers to its movable adjustment to any position on the piece being worked, or its automatic adjustment to move in a desired manner while the work is being done.

The lathe is a machine of tremendous versatility whether it be the delicate instrument used by a watchmaker or the vast lathes used in steel mills to bore cannon. The modern machine-tool industry depends extensively on the "turret" or "capstan" lathe, basically invented or developed by James Hartness, of the Jones and Lamson Company, in Springfield, Vermont. This, however, is a modern refinement, and the "turret" is an adaptation permitting the application of several types of tools at once, or in an automatic succession.

The basic principle of the lathe and screw-cutting machines was known to Leonardo, and the Frenchman Jacques Besson built remarkable lathes in the 16th century. Maudslay's making of a metal lathe introduced the age of precision. It anticipated Whitney's independent creation of the first milling machine in America. A milling machine may be a type of lathe, but in any case its purpose is to "mill," that is to cut or shape, one piece, over and over, with absolute precision. A gear-cutter is such a milling machine. Whitney devised many of these one-track-minded lathes to make the separate pieces of his gun locks.

Two other men who with Maudslay developed techniques of precision duplication in England were the naval architect, Samuel Bentham (brother of the philosopher, Jeremy), and Marc Isambard Brunel. Bentham went to Russia on behalf of the Empress Catherine's lover, Count Potemkin, and brought some order to highly disorganized Russian factories, as an "efficiency expert." Brunel, like Paine, claimed British, French, and United States citizenship. He was the inventor of the tunneling shield and the father of Isambard Kingdom Brunel, builder of the *Great Eastern*. Also John Wilkinson, an Englishman not to be confused with our American Wilkinson families in Chapter Six, developed cylinder-boring mechanisms of an accuracy to make possible Boulton & Watt's most advanced steam-engine developments.

Yet there is a still more singular anticipation of Whitney's concept and achievement in gunmaking. In 1785, Thomas Jefferson, in France, was introduced to a man named Le Blanc, a meeting which the American Minister described in a letter to John Jay, August 30, 1785:

> An improvement is made here in the construction of muskets, which it may be interesting to Congress to know, should they at any time propose to procure any. It consists in the making every part of them so exactly alike that what belongs to any one, may be used for every other musket in the magazine. The government here has examined and approved the method, and is establishing a large manufactory for the purpose of putting it into execution. As yet, the inventor has only completed the lock of the musket, on this plan. He will proceed immediately to have the barrel, stock, and other parts executed in the same way. Supposing it might be useful in the United States, I went to the workman. He pre-

sented me the parts of fifty locks taken to pieces,
and arranged in compartments. I put several together myself, taking pieces at hazard as they came
to hand, and they fitted in the most perfect manner.
The advantages of this, when arms need repair, are
evident. He effects it by tools of his own contrivance,
which, at the same time, abridge the work, so that
he thinks he shall be able to furnish the musket two
livres cheaper than the common price. But it will
be two or three years before he will be able to furnish any quantity. I mention it now, as it may have
an influence on the plan for furnishing our maga-
zines with this arm.

In a letter to James Monroe, after Whitney's demonstration of 1801, Jefferson recapitulated the story, adding, "I
endeavored to get the U. S. to bring him over, which he
was ready for on moderate terms. I failed and I do not
know what became of him."

This was substantially the sight that the then President-
Elect witnessed again when Whitney showed his wares. The
time extension for which Whitney had come to plead corre-
sponds remarkably with the two or three years Jefferson
told Jay that Le Blanc would require to complete his process. Seventeen years had elapsed from that encounter in
France. What must have been Jefferson's complex emotions
at this reenactment, in his own land by his own country-
man? The French did not go ahead with the development
of Le Blanc's principle—who can say why not? Jefferson
had not been enthused about manufactures when he was in
France, in spite of his natural mechanical interest. In 1801
he had a different perspective on needs and values. There
is no reason to believe that Whitney knew of Le Blanc until
the private conversations he had with Jefferson during that
Washington visit. Le Blanc stands in the record as one of
the many examples of a concept grasped, worked out, and
mysteriously let slip.

Samuel Bentham, in England, had anticipated the approach to manufacture as a series of separate operations. Boring, grinding, pattern-cutting and the like were fundamental operations performed by men skilled in their particular tool. What did it matter to the operator of that tool whether the shape he bored, ground, or cut to pattern was to be assembled into a gun or into an engine? That was for the planner. The workman's job was to duplicate. Bentham and Whitney alike saw how much more readily green labor could be trained to this sort of work than to complex craft operations requiring initiative and multiple skills.

Whitney built his plant at a fine fall of water near that landmark of old New Haven known as East Rock, in the section called Hamden. He wrote about it, in relatively high spirits, to his closest friend, Stebbins.

> I . . . purchased the place called Jabin's Mill and the farm adjoining belonging to Capt. Daniel Talmage . . . The old mill & Buildings were to take away—materials to collect and new buildings to erect . . . I continue to Date from N. Haven tho' in fact I live in the town of Hamden—My situation may be made a pleasant and valuable one—The New Turnpike Road from New Haven to Hartford which is laid out, granted & subscribed for, passes directly by my Door—between the house & the Mill —indeed it cuts off a part of the House and comes hard on my New building which I have erected for my waterworks . . .

He had a splendid foundation for his plant, the whole resting upon massive rock ledge formations which were a continuation of New Haven's East Rock, and known near Whitney's site as Mill Rock.

> . . . I have a very good stream of water—much superior to that on which Dixon's Cotton factory stands . . . John Miles says "it is the best place God ever made about here" . . .

The section soon became known as Whitneyville. Timothy Dwight described Whitney's Mill Rock site as both "healthy" and "romantic." A print of 1825 shows the creek, the rolling Connecticut hills, the neat row of workmen's houses and the shop buildings—the typical early industrial scene, suitable for framing. In the right foreground a hunter and his dog overlook the works from a bluff.

Robert Orr, at the Springfield Arsenal, had given the advice that dissuaded Whitney from an original thought of dividing his operation between the old gin factory and the new plant. Orr cautioned that it would cost $4,000 a year more to do the work in two places. The government required Whitney to post a bond for the advances on his contract. Ten leading New Haven men, the greater number of them Yale men, including Elizur Goodrich, went on the bond for him. Whitney's own home and the works were at mortgage to the government, as well. Eli's letters reveal that even this calm and confident man had his nightmare moments about the size of his commitment. To his friend Stebbins he admitted that the task was "I fear a greater one than is in the power of any man to perform in the given time—but it is too late to go back."

Indeed it could not be performed in the given time. It was to appease fretfulness on this account on the part of the Federalist administration that he journeyed to Washington to make the demonstration with which this chapter opened. Whitney never found consistently smooth sailing in his many ensuing years of manufacturing arms for the government. There was always some minor official to wrangle with about details. On the whole, however, his decision after the fiascos of the gin, to do business with one steady, paying customer, justified itself. In turn the government of the United States, through its more far-seeing leaders, did not fail to appreciate and support the work of this brilliant, stable man.

Whitney married only eight years before his death, in

1825. His son, Eli, Jr., was too young to succeed to the management of the family industry. Here, circumstances had been kind. One of the more appealing aspects of Whitney's personal life was the kindly, generous, brow-furrowed concern with which he, then still a bachelor, cared for his three nephews, the sons of his widowed sister Elizabeth (who has sketched for us so much of Whitney's youth). One of these, Eli Whitney Blake, was sent through Yale by his uncle.

In a remarkable instance of familial harmony, it was young Blake, trained by his uncle, who took charge of the arms business at the founder's death, and then in due course fulfilled this trusteeship by turning the reins over to Eli, Jr.

Both nephew and son were deserving of the name they bore. The son introduced steel gun barrels, improved boring techniques and was in the vanguard of percussion-cap development. Eli Whitney Blake, apart from his excellent stewardship of the plant, branched out on his own. His brother Philos shared in the work at the arms factory. As Eli, Jr. came into the business, the cousins set up as hardware merchants. E.W. Blake supplanted the old-fashioned outside box lock, for doors, by mortised locks. He was also an authority on gear teeth and the intricate mathematics of geared power transmission. Most important of all, E. W. Blake was the man who introduced the age of concrete. That ancient material, known at least since Roman days, was not available for massive work because of the time and cost involved in rock breaking. It was said, in his day, to take two days' work to produce one cubic yard of crushed rock. He was led to the invention through being made a New Haven commissioner for the paving of Whalley Avenue.

The Blake stonecrusher, two massive, upright grinding jaws, was made on the principle that is today the basis of the entire traprock and concrete industry. Little known, by name, Blake's machine, chewing up rock like grapenuts, is a major American invention of vast economic significance. Blake lived to the age of ninety-two, studying and writing papers on aerodynamics in his latter years.

Though Eli, Jr.'s name is not attached to any specific inventions of major importance, he inherited some of his father's aptitudes. His management of the arms factory was wise, until the time it was sold to the Winchester Repeating Arms Co., in 1888. The younger Whitney devised many improvements in methods and machines. It was he who manufactured the revolver for Samuel Colt until the latter was ready to open his own plant in Hartford.

Only twenty-some odd miles north of New Haven, at the time Eli Whitney was beginning his career as gunmaker, another remarkable instance of parallel achievement was under way. In the small village of Berlin, Connecticut, there was a farmer-scythemaker-gunsmith named Simeon North. He had been born in the same year as Whitney. The information about him is limited largely to what two great-grandsons exhumed from Army and Navy files and their own family tradition. Two things about him are certain— that he was the first official pistol maker to the U. S. government, and that he developed independently a system of interchangeable parts manufacture. Is he therefore a second Whitney? Somehow, not quite.

North has been called a typical "Connecticut man"— meaning that he was endowed with individuality, resourcefulness, and self-reliance. He had no college training, himself, but sent the youngest of his four sons down to Yale College. This lad, Simeon, Jr., became an educator serving from 1839 to 1857 as President of Hamilton College, and in turn, a nephew of his became the famous classics professor known to Hamilton history as "Old Greek."

The elder Simeon North began as a scythemaker. A four-foot scythe, in his time, would bring $1.50. Smaller ones could be had for 75¢—all hand work. Even his descendants are not quite sure when or why he turned to pistol making. It is supposed that he learned the trade from

Elias Beckley, a gunsmith of Berlin. However that may be, he brought to it a mind that envisioned the advantages of duplicate parts, and the inventive-mechanical skill to devise machinery and methods for making pistols this way.

His first contract with the War Department was drawn in 1799, the year following Whitney's, and was for 500 horse pistols. He seems to have made deliveries more promptly than Whitney. Many contracts followed. How rapidly his system of interchangeability was developed is uncertain, but his contract of 1813 was the first known government contract to contain the specification: "The component parts of pistols are to correspond so exactly that any limb or part of one Pistol may be fitted to any other Pistol of the 20,000."

Because of this, a family claim has been advanced for priority over Whitney in this type of manufacture. It does not hold up, and to argue it is not to the advantage of a man whose achievement is considerable in any event. Whitney's early contracts are lost—quite probably in the burning of Washington by the British—but the documentary evidence of the fact of Whitney's development of his principle by 1789 is, as we've seen, so sweeping as to be unanswerable.

After 1828, the North plant made only rifles and carbines. In 1825 it is worth noting (apropos the story of Colt and the revolver) that North made a ten-shooter repeating rifle.

This "Connecticut man" was called Colonel North, somewhat in Kentucky style, on the basis of two years in the 6th Connecticut regiment. His relationship with his workmen was highly paternal. He would go through the factory, greeting each man personally, whenever he returned from a business trip, and there was a tradition of winter evening fraternization around the fireplace in his home. Some workmen boarded with various of the North families, at $1.25 per week, missed meals deducted, and washing included.

The records of wages are interesting. One workman "agreed to blow and strike awelding pistols at $12.00 per month." Also, "Selah Goodrich came to work for three months at $6.00 per month and three months after at $8.00 per month."

North's brother-in-law, Elisha Cheney, a clockmaker (possibly kin to the other Connecticut Cheney families for which John Fitch served his unhappy apprenticeship) sometimes made screws and pins for him.

The pistol maker was a patron of Berlin Academy, which opened in 1802, and had as one of its teachers Emma Hart, later and better known as Emma Willard, pioneer in the education of women, founder of a distinguished academy for girls, still flourishing in Troy, New York. The crowning tribute to this Yankee pistol maker is the story that he rashly consented to endorse a note for a man he trusted but who proved unreliable. The circumstances had been misrepresented to North and it would have been possible for him to repudiate the note. Unwilling to do so, he is said to have siphoned off what might have been the cream of his wealth, for years, to satisfy an unjust account of over $100,000, not paid off until his 83rd year.

North was a thoroughly successful and distinguished inventor. Though the case is less well known, he stands in relation to Whitney in something of the way Gray stands to Bell in the story of the telephone: a man travelling a parallel path. North did serve as a valuable counselor in setting up operations in the Harper's Ferry Arsenal. But that his influence and creativity were the match of Whitney's is a contention that can only be found in his great-grandsons' memoir—a valued contribution to the record, but written in familial pride in the "we who have sprung from his loins" vein.

Another great inventor, not popularly famous nor ever adequately recompensed, comes into the arms picture—though his influence is far from confined to that field.

There is something Archimedean in the story of Thomas Blanchard, driving his carriage homeward through the town of Brimfield, Massachusetts, suddenly shouting to the startled streets, "I have got it! I have got it!" The object of this latter-day cry of *eureka* was the basic concept of the Blanchard lathe for turning irregular forms—in this particular case, the difficult shape of gunstocks. The inventor had created a machine which automatically turned musket barrels. At the very end of these, the cylindrical form required to have its sides flattened. Blanchard's machine cleverly changed its motion at the right time in a manner to effect this adjustment. When he installed one of these machines in the Springfield Arsenal, a watchful (and possibly worried) workman, seeing a manual job disappear from one of his fellows, said, "Well, you can never make a machine to take my job away." "What do you make?" Blanchard asked. The answer was, "Gunstocks." Blanchard allowed that he would think about it and drove away, pondering, only to have the inspiration strike as he passed through Brimfield.

Today if you watch a key blank put into a handy little machine to duplicate your house key, you are seeing in simplified miniature the general principle of Blanchard's copying lathe, whereby a replica of the object to be duplicated controls the cutting or shaping action of the machine. To do this with something as difficult as a gunstock was a great accomplishment and the machine was extremely complicated in its appearance. Blanchard went on to adapt the device to such a variety of objects as hat-blocks, wigblocks, shoe-lasts, wheel spokes, and axe handles. He could duplicate a basic shape and yet make it longer or shorter, larger or smaller. Also, as with shoe-lasts, he could make right or left forms, alternately.

Blanchard was five years in government employ, and also during the life of his patents received a royalty of 9¢ on every musket made at Springfield and Harper's Ferry because of the contributions of his machines—some thirteen different ones in all. But his inventions were widely pirated so that his earnings from them were never commensurate with their importance.

Thomas Blanchard was born in Sutton, Massachusetts,

in 1788, and was the traditional farmer's son and whittling boy. The story that he invented an apple-parer at thirteen may be apocryphal (with its hint of the lathe). But he had an older brother who was a maker of tacks, by hand—a tedious job if there ever was one. Thomas, at about eighteen, invented a tack-counter for him, and then set to work on an automatic tack-maker. In six years he produced a machine with a hopper into which the iron was placed, and which then turned out finished, headed tacks at 500 per minute. They were so light and fine that a half ounce weight would balance a thousand. Thomas sold his rights for $5,000—and so a career was launched. Almost at the same time, a tack-making machine said to be capable of producing 60,000 per day was invented, in 1807, by Jesse Reed, of Abington, whose father Ezekiel had invented machinery for cold-cut nails and tacks, and founded an industry, in 1786.

In addition to his lathe devices, Blanchard invented a machine for cutting and folding envelopes. He tried to interest Governor Clinton of New York in a steam railroad from Albany to Schenectady but the Governor felt that the Erie Canal, still new, was sufficient to the needs. But Blanchard also earns a secondary place among the steamboat builders, for he built a stern-wheeler that ran between Hartford and Springfield, and also made shallow-draft steamers for the western rivers.

Another of his most widely useful inventions was a process and device for bending ship's timbers without cracking. Blanchard's mechanical skill was so renowned in his time, and his mind possessed such precision and clarity that he was called upon frequently by the courts as a technical witness in patent suits—an irony for one who suffered from so many infringements himself.

In the years around 1831 to 1834, many audiences in Canada, in New England, or in the southern states assembled for a "scientific" lecture by a talented showman, or "pitchman." This performer billed himself as "Dr. Coult."

His chief attraction, at the center of all the pseudo-scientific, pseudo-medical doubletalk and entertainment, was a demonstration upon the persons of volunteers from the audience, of the effects of nitrous oxide gas—popularly known as "laughing gas," a discovery of the British scientist, Sir Humphrey Davy.

The motive of this journeyman was more complex than mere livelihood. He was a born promoter and also an inventor. He was raising the minimum stake with which to promote an invention in which he had unbounded faith—even though hosts of advisers had told him that the times were bad for him—the wars were over, everything was peaceful. For this young man's invention was a repeating pistol, a revolver, as it came to be known. "Dr. Coult" was a thin disguise for Samuel Colt. He had picked up the knowledge of the gas and the technique of handling it from the chief chemist at his father's Massachusetts silk mill, and with his flair for showmanship, turned it to account.

The money raised with laughing gas was used to have models made of the repeating pistol and rifle, and to obtain patents. With a group of backers, the Patent Arms Manufacturing Co., of Paterson, N. J., was organized. The failure and discontinuance of the short-lived venture was at least partly due to the fact that its business organizers did not pay sufficient attention or give enough responsibility to the inventor, who had well-formed ideas of how his product should be exploited.

To cut back to the beginning of this story, Sam Colt was the most authentic of all whittling boys, for he literally whittled the complete first model of his pistol on shipboard, as a young seaman returning home from India.

He had been born near Hartford in 1814, but his father, Christopher, a man of abilities, later established a silk mill at Ware, Massachusetts. Sam was the youngest child. Early in his boyhood his mother died. The stepmother who succeeded her farmed out the children—at least some of them. Little Sam, about nine, was sent to work at chores on a farm at Glastonbury, Connecticut. A year or so later he returned to Ware and worked in the silk mill. Here he learned something of mechanics and the smattering of chemistry that led to the gas experiments and later to his knowledge of explosives.

He went to sea on the brig *Corvo* at about twelve. On this voyage, while in Calcutta, Sam saw a repeating pistol. It was the invention of Elisha Collier, of Boston, who had found no encouragement for his gadget at home around 1813 (it's hard to guess why) and had taken it to England where it was put into manufacture. It had the rotating cylinder basic to revolvers, but Colt saw that it was far too complicated in its mechanism. He had been interested in pistols since early childhood. On the voyage home, pondering Collier's gun, he whittled the model which contained his truly distinctive feature, the pawl mechanism (a pawl is a projection, set in relation to the teeth of a cog wheel to permit it to turn in one direction only) for rotating and locking the cylinder by the action of the cocking of the hammer. The fact that a model thus could be made of wood attests the simplicity of its conception. He burned the holes in his cylinder with a hot wire.

At home, the elder Colt admired the ingenuity of the gun but was one of the many to deprecate its practical or commercial value. All the same, he supported Sam to the extent of financing the making of the first working models of both the revolver and repeating rifle by Anson Chase, a gunsmith. The interlude of the laughing gas, and then the abortive Paterson manufacturing venture followed. The one important thing was, Colt salvaged his patent rights from the Paterson wreckage.

A few Colt revolvers had got into the hands of Texas rangers and made a reputation. The generally prevailing peace, which was supposed to be his great business deterrent, was ended by the Mexican War, in 1846. There was a demand for Colt's revolvers. General Zachary Taylor himself called for them. The Texas men wanted them. And there were none. Colt didn't even have one himself. Nor was there any place to make them. Accepting a government order on the basis of faith in possibilities, almost like Whitney in 1798, Colt prepared a new model and arranged with Eli Whitney, Jr. to make them for him at Whitneyville. Meanwhile, he studied the methods of that long-famous armory, making his future plans.

From the time Colt opened up his plant in Hartford, in 1847, there were no more major setbacks. He held the management of the enterprise in his own inspired hands, and he made possibly the wisest single move of his career. He hired as his plant manager, Elisha King Root. It took a high bid to fetch him, but it was worth it.

E. K. Root had the reputation of being the best mechanic in New England. He was to the Colt enterprise what Samuel Slater had been to Almy & Brown, and what Paul Moody had been to the Waltham and Lowell Mills.

There is a story that in 1829, on the pond at Ware, Sam Colt drenched many of the best citizens of the town by the miscalculated effects of an explosion set off on a raft as a Fourth of July stunt. E. K. Root, some years older, is said to have been in the crowd and to have defended Colt from their anger. Young Sam may or may not have discussed his revolver and other mechanical subjects with Root, from whom he is said to have learned how to make sketches embodying his ideas.

Whether this pleasingly romantic encounter occurred or not, Colt certainly knew of Root and his worth. Root, born in 1808 in Ludlow, Massachusetts, was the son of a euphoniously named pair, Darius and Dorcas Root. He grew up in what Joseph Wickham Roe has called, speaking of Eli Whitney, "that best school of mechanics, the New England hill farm." At an early age he took a job handling a lathe in an axe factory, in Collinsville, Connecticut. He remained with the Collins firm for seventeen years, rising fast to the rank of foreman, and in that time he changed the Collins enterprise from a small hand shop to a major factory on the newly developed production concepts Whitney, and North, and the clockmakers had set under way.

In combination with the talents and vision of Colt, he

was an immediate success in the new field of arms making.
When Colt died, at only forty-eight, E. K. Root became
President of the firm. He contributed incalculably, more
even than Colt himself, to the numerous inventions and
conceptions by which the Hartford arms plant advanced
the Whitney method of production. In addition to the fur-
thering of the interchangeable parts principle, the Colt
plant evolved the modern assembly line. No wonder it was
for Mark Twain the obvious place for the time-travelling
Connecticut Yankee to learn his trade. Under Root were
developed some of the skilled men who went out and
brought into existence the great machine-tool industry in its
full modern sense.

In the scope of this book, that is the substance of Sam
Colt's career. Actually he is the chronological terminal point
to our story, for with the Colt Arms plant, as specifically as
any such matter can be localized, the basic transition from
the old hand craft days, and from the emergent era of industrial evolution, can be said to have become complete.
What we understand as industry today now existed. The
rest is a story of expansion in which the individual inventor's role is never again quite the same as in the relatively primitive days of industrial manufacture.

Samuel Colt's personal life saw its share of tragedies and
sensations. His sister, Sarah Ann, committed suicide by taking arsenic at the age of twenty-one. In 1841, his oldest
brother, John, committed one of the celebrated murders of
the mid-century, killing one Samuel Adams in a row over
accounts and trying to ship away the dismembered and
salted body in a packing case. The trial was sensational. In
his cell, a few hours before execution, John Colt was married to Caroline Henshawe, his supposed mistress and
mother of his child. Then he is said to have slain himself
with a knife, during the distraction from a highly suspicious
fire that broke out in the prison. The question was raised
and never settled as to whether the corpse was in fact John
Colt, or whether he was smuggled away from prison in the
cloak of his bride. Moreover, Samuel Colt's latest and most

thorough biographer asserts that Caroline Henshawe was, in fact, Sam Colt's wife and that the child was his, and that the wedding in the cell was an expedient adopted with John's collusion to dispose conveniently of a secret marriage which Colt felt to be a social handicap to his expected career.

Colt established beyond a doubt that he made the best revolvers and the most of them. Others were fast to enter the field. In the beginning, he was vexed by the usual harassments of the inventor. A man named Mighill Nutting, from Maine, dogged him for a long while with a revolver which he claimed to be superior to Colt's and prior by patent right. Adam Humbarger, an Ohioan, made repeating guns that involved Colt, quite without foundation, in piracy charges. We know of Collier's gun, and recall that Simeon North had made a repeating rifle in 1825.

Colt did much to develop the percussion cap, without which there could have been no revolver, and also the tin-foil waterproof cartridge. There are many claimants to the original percussion cap and lock. One of these was Joshua Shaw, of Philadelphia. He had come from England, in 1817. A friend of Benjamin West (under whom Fulton had studied painting), Shaw brought to the Pennsylvania Hospital the great expatriate's picture "Christ Healing the Sick."

Colt further took up the work on submarine mines about where Fulton had let it drop, and developed this kind of weapon substantially. He was associated with Samuel Morse in the telegraph enterprise and experimented with the first underwater electric cable, helping to prepare the way for Cyrus Field's great exploit with the Atlantic cable.

At least three other New England men are major figures in the munitions industry, but their work was carried out chiefly past the range of this book. Christian Sharps manufactured at Hartford his new invention, the breech-loading rifle. Berkley B. Hotchkiss, of Sharon, Connecticut, and his older brother, Andrew, developed the modern rifle-cannon projectile, including various types of percussion fuses.

Sylvanus Sawyer, of Fitchburg, Massachusetts, had a highly diversified talent, springing from a family appropriately identified with the earliest sawmills in the country. Sawyer's numerous and varied inventions, begun in his 'teens, include a reed organ, a steam engine, a screw propeller, several machines used in the making of rattan chairs, rifled cannon and shells for the same, together with new and improved fuses.

Yet the heart of this story has been Eli Whitney. With his coming, the long era of the gunsmith was ended, those individual gunmakers who survived had become technological fossils. With Colt and Root, what Whitney had pioneered came to flower as a new order. The way was prepared for the age of Henry Ford, the lustre of whose name really belongs in part to Whitney and Colt. But so fast are these processes that Aldous Huxley's satirical use, in his futuristic horror-Utopia of *Brave New World,* of the phrase "Great Ford" in place of "Great God," already seems vaguely quaint and dated.

CHAPTER 12

WHAT TIME IS IT?

Then comes a Yankee Clockmaker,
and he sells clocks warranted to run
from July to Eternity, stoppages included, and I must say they do run
as long as—as long as wooden
clocks commonly do, that's a fact.

—T. C. HALIBURTON

ONE OF the stories about the Arkansas Traveller relates
how he was passing a farm and saw a man standing beside
a pear tree holding up a shoat and letting the animal eat
the fruit from the branches. The Traveller stopped and
said, "It's going to take a long time for that hog to get fed
that way." And the farmer answered, "Shucks, what's time
to a hog?"

That could never have been a New England story. Time
to a Yankee was an important consideration. Possibly these
New Englanders were the first frenetically time-conscious
people, in the evolution that has led to our own stop-watch
psychology. The Puritan tradition helped to engender this
time sense, for it saw time, in relation to energy, as a commodity and conceived the wasting of it to be as much a sin
as the wasting of any substance. And where the wasting of
time was a sin, the measuring of time was necessarily vital

as a gauge of a man's relative worth or worthlessness, morally and practically.

Thus, although clocks were invented a long time before Yankees were, the clock was naturally destined to be a factor in Yankee life. And when the Yankee became a legendary personage in American folklore, the clock he manufactured, at first by meticulously arduous handicraft, and then in mass production, evolved in the popular mind as the symbol of his amusing idiosyncrasies, with the figure of the Yankee peddler, sharp trading, wooden nutmegs, "soft sawder" and all that we have already encountered in the person of the fabulous Sam Slick.

The history of clockmaking in Connecticut is not so much a chronicle of things made as it is a story of methods. Some new types of clocks were introduced, along with specific mechanical improvements in the movements, but it is in the field of methods that Eli Terry's wooden clocks are descended from Eli Whitney's guns and ultimately related to Henry Ford's automobiles.

The earliest clockmaker made, at the most, three or four at a time (at first only when "spoken for" but later on speculation, meaning literally on the hope of finding a buyer), then he would put his stock in a wagon, or simply in the capacious saddlebags on his horse, and seek his market as close at home as luck might warrant or as far afield as necessity might require.

Another of the great clockmakers, Chauncey Jerome, has sketched for us the portrait of Eli Terry, the master of wooden clocks, at the beginning of his career, exchanging his product, as often a not, for salt pork and carrying this booty back home in the same saddlebags that had fetched forth the merchandise.

The desire to nullify time and the need to measure it go hand in hand, as do the desire to nullify space and the urge to "beget motion," for it is inevitable that where time is much in the consciousness through mechanisms to measure it, we will find the question, "What time is it?" leading, in philosophical minds, to the question, "What is time?" and thus the mechanical and transcendental genius burgeoning simultaneously in New England can be said to have a link. (Though I think the clockmaking Yankee would have been disconcerted and bewildered at the sage Emerson's dictum, "Time dissipates to shining ether the solid angularity of facts.")

Behind all the fabric of folklore and quaintness that has been woven around the Yankee peddler and the clocks he dealt in, lies the actuality of the Connecticut clock industry. There were more clockmakers in that state, and elsewhere in New England and the eastern seaboard, than can be accounted for other than in the long catalogues in the books devoted to early American clocks, for collectors. There are several such books that do a comprehensive job. The merits of the artist-craftsman as such are not in our scope. We are concerned with the few figures who took a meticulous handcraft and made it into an industry by inventiveness in the field of method. In other words, we are interested in them as *manufacturers* who changed *the means of making* the product more than they changed the actual product itself.

The classic work on the subject of this country's early industries is *A History of American Manufactures,* by J. Leander Bishop. Two short statements from it emphasize the meaning of the changes in method with regard to the clock business. Remember that we began with the individual workman turning out a few clocks by hand. Bishop reports on the year 1802: "The manufacture of clocks by water power, for a wholesale trade, was this year commenced at Plymouth, Conn., by Eli Terry; an enterprise regarded by many, as a rash adventure." Eighteen years later, in 1820, we find that: "Six establishments in Litchfield County, Conn., made 11,450 brass and wooden clocks, valued at $75,400. . . ." By the decade of the 1840's Connecticut manufacturers were producing more than a million dollars worth of clocks per year, and were just beginning the development of their export business.

What of Eli Terry, the reputed prototype of Sam Slick?

"The manufacture of clocks by water power," cited above, means their manufacture by machinery, in quantity, instead of by hand.

Terry was born in 1772 in East Windsor, Connecticut. He learned the handcraft of clockmaking from one of its great practitioners, Daniel Burnap, and also from one or another of the brothers Cheney. We have already heard of these Cheneys, in connection with John Fitch, the steamboat man, who was trying to learn clockmaking from the Cheneys about ten years before Terry was born.

Terry began his independent clockmaking in Plymouth, Litchfield County, and it was there, around 1802, that he started to evolve the methods that developed into machine manufacturing. At first these amounted to little more than the employment of a few young men at the specialized tasks of cutting wheels and teeth with saws and jackknives. (This has nothing to do with the exaggerated tradition about clocks made by whittling. The knife was simply one of the many small tools used in shaping complicated wooden parts.)

About 1807, he housed his operations in a larger mill to begin an actual industrial type of manufacture. It was here, a year later, in Chauncey Jerome's account, that "the first five hundred clocks ever made by machinery in the country were started at one time by Mr. Terry . . . a larger number than had ever been begun at one time in the world."

According to Henry Terry, one of Eli's sons, these are conservative figures. Henry Terry states that in 1808 his father contracted to make four thousand clocks. "It took a considerable part of the first year to fit up the machinery, most of the second year to finish the first thousand clocks, and the third to complete the remaining three thousand."

This is much like the sequence of events in Eli Whitney's famous first contract for arms for the United States government about ten years earlier. Several writers about Terry have suggested that Eli Whitney gave helpful suggestions to Terry on the subject of production methods, by the duplication of interchangeable parts. It is quite possible, for there is no doubt the clockmaker had opportunities to know the gunmaker.

The local wiseacres mocked at Terry's ambitious commitments, predicting that he would never live to finish so many clocks, and that even if he did, he would never find markets for them.

Most of his production devices were simple and basic, consisting of various types of "arbors" and "mandrels," the former being turning axles or beams, and the latter devices for holding in place the parts being cut and shaped. These were the prototypes of lathes and jigs (jigs are pattern shapes to guide cutting; your key serves as a jig when you have your key duplicated in the little copying lathe for that purpose), and Whitney and others were their pioneers much more truly than Terry, whose contribution was their adaptation to clockmaking. Another new tool of the period was the circular saw. We know from Jerome that Terry had one of these in his enlarged factory of 1816 where he produced his patent shelf clock. It was the first such saw in the area and a notable novelty.

The standard wooden wall clock was Terry's first product. Around 1814 he invented his famous short clock, or shelf clock, a much more compact mechanism, with ingenious suspension of the weights, by pulleys, within the case on either side of the movement. Such modification was necessary because the shelf clock could not use the convenient, long weight cords (which preceded springs as the motive power) possible in the wall clock, or the long "grandfather" type. The popular, fast-selling model of this clock is described for us by Jerome. It was called the Pillar Scroll Top Case:

> The pillars were about twenty-one inches long, three-quarters of an inch at the base, and three-eighths at the top—resting on a square base, and the top finished by a handsome cap. It had a large dial eleven inches square, and tablet below the dial seven by eleven inches. This style of clock was liked very much and was made in large quantities and

for several years. Mr. Terry sold a right to manufacture them to Seth Thomas, for $1,000, which
was thought to be a great sum. At first, Terry and
Thomas made each about 6,000 clocks per year,
but afterwards increased to ten or twelve thousand.
They were sold for $15 apiece when first manu-
factured. I think that these two men cleared about
$100,000 apiece, up to the year 1825.

All such clocks, except where otherwise specified, struck
the hour and were held in much greater esteem than mere
silent "timepieces."

Terry carried the wooden clock industry as far as it could
go, radically altering the whole concept of clock production. The future after Terry lay not so much in different
methods as in different materials. The wooden clock was
obsolete almost at the very time Terry perfected its manufacture. It was supplanted by the mass-produced brass
clock with a speed just about as notable as that with which
Terry had changed the basic ways of clockmaking.

Terry's mechanical inventiveness was considerable. The
details of his alterations in clock mechanisms are far too
technical to be pursued here, but we can take a few lines
from Henry Terry's sketch of his father's life, written in
1853, describing the essentials of Terry's invention, the
wooden shelf clock.

The improvements made by Mr. Terry, at this time
and subsequently, marked distinctly a new era in
clock making, and laid the foundation for a lucrative business, by which many have gained their thousands, however willing or unwilling they may be to
acknowledge it. Some of the important improvements which should have been secured by this patent, are in use to this day, and cannot be dispensed
with in the making of low-priced clocks, nor indeed
with any convenient mantle clock. The mode or
method of escapement universally adopted at this
time in all common shelf clocks was his plan or

invention. The construction of the clock so as to allow the carrying of the weights each side of the movement or wheels of the clock, to the top of the case, bringing the pendulum, crown-wheel and verge in front, the dial-wheels between the plates, making the pendulum accessible by removing the dial only, were his arrangement and invention. These things cannot now be dispensed with, even in the clocks driven by a spring, as the motive power, much less in those carried by weights. Millions of them have been made, the precise model of the one made by him, 1814. No clock either in this or any foreign country, was ever made previous to this time with the weights carried each side of the movement the whole length of the case; the dial wheels inside the plates, the pendulum, crown-wheel, verge or pallet together in front of the other wheels. This mode of escapement is one of great value still, and will probably never be abandoned, so long as low-priced clocks are needed.

Eli Terry withdrew from the manufacture of clocks around 1833, having made a considerable fortune, on which he lived the rest of his life, although making other investments and continuing until the end his experiments with clock mechanisms, including those on the large scale of steeple clocks. He was held in great esteem by his contemporaries, being called "a natural philosopher, and almost an Eli Whitney in mechanical ingenuity." His sons, and a brother, and nephew, continued in the clock business. The family name took root in that part of Plymouth which became known as Terryville.

In addition to selling rights of manufacture, Terry at one time sold one of his factories to Seth Thomas and Silas Hoadley, both employees of his and subsequently famous names in Connecticut clockmaking. Neither was an inventor, per se, of new clocks or methods.

It was Joseph Ives, of Bristol, Connecticut, who gave the

first impetus to this country's metal clock industry. In 1818, and for some years afterward, he made a metal clock with brass wheels and iron plates, but it was of grandfather proportions, big and heavy. In 1822, he made the first metal shelf clock, embellished by a mirror, which became known as his Looking-Glass Clock. His famous brass eight-day clock was designed in 1832, and the firm of C. & L. C. Ives, of Bristol, was organized to produce it.

"Uncle Joe Ives," as he was known affectionately around Bristol, had a long and variegated career in the clock business, complicated by frequent financial disasters. He patented numerous mechanical inventions and improvements in clock movements, but they were not fundamental and were superseded. His greatest contribution is to be found in a link with another growing American enterprise, the Connecticut brass industry.

Joseph Ives was not the first to use rolled brass in clocks, but he was the first to do so in this country. It is obvious that if he had not done so, someone else would have, and in short order—nevertheless, Ives it was. The brass used in clockmaking prior to this was cast brass, rough of surface, requiring filing and polishing before parts could be made from it. The development of rolled, sheet brass eliminated this necessity and brought with it another essential operation—die stamping. Wheels and other parts could be stamped from rolled brass faster than any machine process could turn and shape wooden parts.

It was not Joseph Ives who made the most of this industrial potential, but Chauncey Jerome, whom we have met already as a source of our knowledge of Eli Terry's operations. Jerome had a rags-to-riches career, narrowly missing going back again to rags. His flourishing business failed, late in his career, as the result of crooked manipulations among his associates, according to Jerome's charge. He held that P. T. Barnum, the great showman, was one of the moving spirits in the skulduggery wrought against him.

Jerome was a skilled mechanic, and like Terry contributed original mechanical innovations in clock design. But again like Terry, it is as a method man, and as an *inventor of merchandise,* that he becomes important. He has left us one of the rare first-hand accounts of the clock business. Let's look quickly over the life of this archetypal Yankee, with some assistance in his own words from his autobiography, published in 1860.

It has the elaborate, descriptive title characteristic of the 19th century: *History of the American Clock Business for the Past Sixty Years and Life of Chauncey Jerome, written by himself.* And as an added rider, below: *Barnum's Connection with the Yankee Clock Business.*

The author, in the frontispiece, is shown with a domed, bald forehead. He has a large nose, a wide, straight mouth, a strong chin and a general expression of determination. He looks like a New England deacon.

The preface discloses the melancholy occasion for the book. It is an *apologia* for his career, a defense of his business misfortunes—and he hopes it may show a little profit. "It has been a long and laborious undertaking for me in my old age to write such a work as this . . . in presenting it to the public it is with the hope that it will meet with some favor, and that I shall derive some pecuniary benefit therefrom."

He is proud of his more than forty-five years in the clock business. "Its whole history is familiar to me, and I cannot write my life without having much to say about Yankee clocks. Neither can there be a history of that business written without alluding to myself.

". . . I am no author, but claim a title which I consider nobler, that of a 'Mechanic.' Being possessed of a remarkable memory, I am able to give a minute account and even the date of every important transaction of my whole life, and distinctly remember events which took place when I was but a child, three-and-a-half years old, and how I celebrated my fourth birthday."

Armed with these powers, Jerome tells a harrowing story

of childhood. He was born in Canaan, Connecticut, on June 10th, 1793, the son of a blacksmith and maker of wrought nails.

Young Chauncey had cursory education, at the most three months of the year. From the moment he could hold a hoe he was set at farm labor and he joined his father at hammering nails from the age of nine.

His father died in October, 1804, of "black colic," and soon after, Chauncey had to seek his fortune, as "stern necessity compelled me. . . . Never shall I forget the Monday morning that I took my little bundle of clothes, and with a bursting heart bid my poor mother goodbye."

He paints a Dickensian picture of himself, at about eleven years old, working as a farm hand and weeping in the fields. "I have many times worked all day in the woods, chopping down trees, with my shoes filled with snow; never had a pair of boots till I was more than twenty years old. Once in two weeks I was allowed to go to church." He tells of being terrified, like many others, by an eclipse of the sun on June 16, 1806, while he was working in the fields and found the day unaccountably turning to night. (Twain's Connecticut Yankee exploited a 6th-century eclipse to save himself from death at the stake.)

At fifteen, Jerome became a carpenter's apprentice. The terms of such arrangements were harsh, and the abuses sometimes were great, as we saw John Fitch experience them. Chauncey had no special troubles, but arranged with his master to have four months during the winter to seek other activity by which to clothe himself. He went to Waterbury and got a job from one Lewis Stebbins, a singing master who carried on other enterprises. Young Jerome found himself making dials for old-fashioned long clocks.

This was Chauncey's first encounter with a business that had long attracted him. At the age of fourteen he had wished he might be apprenticed to Eli Terry, but the knowing ones around him said there were no prospects for a young lad in such a line, as too many clocks were being made anyway. He heard the tavern men ridiculing Terry's grandiose production schemes, and remarks with natural satisfaction: "What would those good old men have thought . . . if they had known that the little urchin who was so eagerly listening to their conversation would live to make 200,000 metal clocks in one year, and many millions in his life?"

Over the next few years, Jerome worked at the trade of carpentry, with occasional seasons of making clock cases, which was close to becoming an industry unto itself. He served for a time with a regiment of Connecticut State troops, during the war of 1812. In New Haven, in 1815, he married Salome, daughter of Captain Theophilus Smith, "one of the last of the Puritanical families there was in the town."

These were hard years in the young United States. Chauncey and his wife had settled for a time in Farmington, Connecticut. "1815, the year after the war, was probably the hardest one there has been for the last one hundred years, for a young man to begin for himself. Pork was sold for thirteen dollars per hundred, flour at thirteen dollars per barrel; molasses was sold for seventy-five cents per gallon, and brown sugar at thirty-four cents per pound. I remember buying some cotton cloth for a common shirt, for which I paid one dollar a yard, no better than can now be bought for ten cents. . . . The times were awful hard and but little business done at anything. It would almost frighten a man to see a five dollar bill, they were so very scarce. . . . I worked at my trade and had the job of finishing the inside of a three-story house, having twenty-seven doors and a white oak matched floor to make, and did the whole for eighty-five dollars. The same work could not now be done as I did it for less than five hundred dollars."

That meteorological freak, the year 1816, was known all over New England as "eighteen-hundred-and-froze-to-death." It was the year without a summer. Snow fell in July and August, ruining crops and causing great famine and hardship. Jerome, almost in despair, was about to give up and go southward, to try his luck in Baltimore, when his destiny beckoned (as I'm sure it seemed to him) and he got a job in Plymouth, Connecticut, helping Eli Terry to fit out the new factory he was opening to manufacture his patent shelf clock.

After working for Terry through the winter of '16-'17, he went into business for himself in a small way, buying some parts, mahogany, veneers, and other necessaries. There was a developing "jobbers" business, in the clock field, involving such operations all or in part as assembling clocks, casing them, or manufacturing cases.

When Jerome moved to Bristol, in 1821, the complicated transactions involved are highly revealing of that period in the American economy. "I sold my house and lot, which I had almost worshipped, to Mr. Terry; it was worth six hundred dollars. He paid me one hundred wooden clock movements, with the dials, tablets, glass and weights. I went over to Bristol to see a man by the name of George Mitchell, who owned a large two-story house, with a barn and seventeen acres of good land in the south part of the town, which he said he would sell and take his payment in clocks. I asked him how many of the Terry Patent Clocks he would sell it for; he said two hundred and fourteen. I told him I would give it, and closed the bargain at once. I finished up the one hundred parts which I had got from Mr. Terry, exchanged cases with him for more, obtained some credit, and in this way made out the quantity for Mitchell."

From 1825 until 1837, the latter being the great depression year that virtually ruined the clock and all other businesses, Chauncey operated a company in Bristol known as Jeromes and Darrow. The plural is due to the partnership of his brother, Noble. They were making a product which Chauncey had contrived, to compete with Terry's shelf clock. Jerome called his the Bronze Looking-Glass Clock. "This was the richest looking and best clock that had ever been made for the price. They could be got up for one dollar less than the Scroll Top [Terry's], yet sold for two dollars more," (presumably somewhere in the neighborhood of fifteen to seventeen dollars).

Jerome's biggest venture was launched after the rough year of 1837, and began the new clock era in earnest. He put on the market a one-day brass clock. Chauncey had conceived it, but his brother Noble "worked up" the movement. It's a pity we don't know the story of Noble's life and how he learned the clock trade. With regard to all these ventures, I see the shape of what our own day calls industrial design, which literally is the inventing of merchandise, the creating of a style or model of a basic product for competitive advantage, in terms both of pricing and customer-appeal.

The brass-clock business which Joseph Ives had created was strictly for the eight-day clock. The brass one-day clock was a new idea, and there were other new features added, including the zinc dial, which became standard. Jerome could sell these for around one-and-a-half to two dollars. He could outprice and outproduce both the wooden one-day clock (thirteen to fifteen dollars) and the brass eight-day (at about twenty dollars). This astonishing development in cheap mass production was carried even further, a few years later. "The last thing that I invented, which has proved to be of great usefulness, was the one-day timepiece [meaning that it did not strike the hours] that can be sold for seventy-five cents, and a fair profit at that."

Jerome gives us a partial account of his manufacturing procedures which is sufficient to show us the changes wrought in a few years from the day of the clock produced by one man's handwork on a custom-trade basis.

I will describe the manner in which the O-G case is made . . . [O-G is a standard designation in the trade, referring to the shape of the molding around the case] . . . which will give some idea with what facility the whole thing is put through. Common merchantable pine lumber is used for the body of the case. The first workman draws a board of the stuff on a frame and by a moving circular saw cuts it in proper lengths for the sides and top. The knotty portions of it are sawed in lengths suitable for boxing the clocks when finished, and but little need be wasted. The good pieces are then taken to another saw and split up in proper widths, which are then passed through the planing machine. Then another workman puts them through the O-G cutter which forms the shape of the front of the case. The next process is the glueing on of the veneers—the workman spreads the glue on one piece at a time and then puts on the veneer of rosewood or mahogany. A dozen of the pieces are placed together in handscrews until the glue is properly hardened. The O-G shapes of the piece fit into each other when they are screwed together. When the glue is sufficiently dry, the next thing is to make the veneer smooth and fit for varnishing. We have what is called a sandpaper wheel, made of pine plank, its edge formed in an O-G shape, and sandpaper glued to it. When the wheel is revolved rapidly, the pieces are passed over it and in this way smoothed very fast. They are then ready to varnish, and it usually takes about ten days to put on the several coats of varnish, and polish them ready for mitering, which completes the pieces ready for glueing in shape of the case. The sides of the case are made much cheaper. I used to have the stuff for 10,000 of these cases in the works at one time. With the great facility, the labor costs less than twenty cents apiece for this kind of case, and with the stock they cost less than fifty cents. A cabinetmaker could not make one for less than five dollars. This proves and shows what can be done by system. The dials are cut out of large sheets of zinc, the holes punched by machine, and then put into the paint room, where they are painted by a short and easy process. The letters and figures are then printed on. I had a private room for the purpose, and a man who could print twelve or fifteen thousand in a day. The whole dial cost me less than five cents. The tablets were printed in the same manner, the colors put on afterwards by girls, and the whole work on these beautiful tablets cost less than one-and-a-half cents; the cost of glass and work was about four cents. Everybody knows that all of the parts must be made very cheap or an O-G clock could not be sold for one-and-a-half or two dollars. The weights cost about thirteen cents per clock, the cost of boxing them about ten cents, and the first cost of the movement for a one-day brass clock is less than fifty cents. I will here say a little about the process of making the wheels. It will no doubt astonish a great many to know how rapidly they can be made. I will venture to say, that I can pick out three men who will take the brass in the sheet, press out and level under the drop, there cut the teeth, and make all of the wheels to five hundred clocks in one day; there are from eight to ten of these wheels in every clock, and in an eight-day clock, more. This will look to some like a great story, but is one of the wonders of the clock business. If some of the parts of a clock were not made for almost nothing, they could not be sold so cheap when finished.

In the above monstrous paragraph is seen the particular genius of Chauncey Jerome, projected of course upon the pioneer work in wooden clocks of Eli Terry, all representing aspects of the birth of the industrial revolution. This invention of a *way* far transcends in importance the several inventions of detailed parts of clock mechanisms which are to the credit of Terry and Jerome.

Jerome's cheap, brass clock opened up a vast, new field to the burgeoning industry—the export market. Export of wooden clocks was utterly impossible. A sea voyage always warped the wooden parts; climate being the chief enemy of the wooden clock in any case. A long wet spell could cause the clock works to swell up and stop.

The export trade was begun in 1842, when Jerome shipped to England the first consignment of cheap brass clocks, under the loving chaperonage of Chauncey, Jr. and a young man with the pleasing name of Epaphroditus Peck.

This shipment threw British customs officials into a state of shock and rewarded Jerome, for the first couple of rounds, with one of the weirdest markets a merchant ever had. Clocks at such low prices were unheard of. At Liverpool, the load was confiscated by the Customs on a charge of undervaluation, the assumption being that this was an attempt to evade duties.

Such malefaction was punished by seizing the undervalued goods at their declared value plus ten per cent. When goods *were* undervalued this would represent a loss, hence a penalty. But Jerome was in the position of having his entire shipment confiscated at a ten per cent profit. He sent over a larger consignment and phlegmatically endured the same penalty. When a third boatload, the largest yet, showed up, the British government washed its hands of American brass clocks and opened the doors.

After a brief period of customer suspicion, the clocks looking like too much for the money, the business caught hold. It became world wide. Within a few years, Jerome's brass clocks were reported from as far afield as St. Helena, the Sandwich Islands, Egypt, and Jerusalem.

The culmination of his corporate ventures was the Jerome Manufacturing Co., organized in New Haven, 1850. In a little more than five years, the business failed as a result of financial machinations, presumably set under way in Jerome's absence. He named Phineas T. Barnum as the chief malefactor.

Barnum seemed to like dabbling as an investor (and apparently a managerial kibitzer) in the clock business. He was involved with the Terrys for a while as Terry & Barnum. The troubles resulted from a complicated sale of assets of Terry & Barnum to the Jerome Manufacturing Co. Jerome's cries of pain were countered by cries of rape from Barnum who claimed to have been swindled and rendered bankrupt by wily clockmakers. Nevertheless, Jerome was broke and Barnum was in business.

The New York *Daily Tribune* carried a story on March 24th, 1860:

> THE GREAT SHOWMAN—P. T. Barnum, "the great American showman," as he loves to hear himself called, who furnishes more amusement for a quarter of a dollar than any other man in America, is, we are happy to announce, himself again. He has disposed of the last of those villainous clock notes, re-established his credit up on a cash basis, and once more comes forward to cater for the public amusement at the American museum. Today, between the acts of the play, Mr. Barnum will appear upon his own stage, in his own costly character of the Yankee Clockmaker, for which he qualified himself, with the most reckless disregard of expense, and will "give a brief history of his adventures as a clockmaker, showing how the clock ran down, and how it was wound up; shadowing forth in the same the future of the museum." Of course, Barnum's benefit will be a bumper.

Poor Jerome was left to write his *History of the American Clock Business* with its modest hope of "pecuniary benefit."

Barnum, like Jerome, was a Connecticut Yankee. He may be said to have invented the modern techniques of ballyhoo, publicity stunts, and advertising. He was born in Bethel, on July 5th, 1810, and possibly the only natural publicity tie-up he ever muffed in his life was his failure to be born one day earlier so as to capitalize on the Fourth.

His father practiced the diverse trades of tailor, tavern-keeper, and farmer. Phineas was inducted into some of the mysteries of each of them, and also received a brief schooling in that tolerably harsh New England regimen in which "the ferule was the assistant schoolmaster."

Even as a child he was a great trader and swapper, with

a natural knack for turning any opportunity into profit. On holidays and at fairs he peddled homemade molasses candy, ginger bread, cookies, and cherry rum. He boasts in his joshing way that he was becoming as rich as Croesus until his father, observing these talents, "kindly permitted me to purchase my own clothing."

He liked to attribute his success as a universal promoter to "a settled aversion to manual labor." But an undoubted native genius has also to be taken into account, with further weight given to an early training in the swapping and selling techniques gained from working in a Connecticut country store.

The incredible gusto, curiosity, trading appetite, and speculative instinct of this man created the tradition of the American circus, brought Jenny Lind to these shores, built the fabulous museum of freaks, novelties and wonders which was a showplace of New York for years, and hatched some great amiable hoaxes and frauds for those buyers who would not beware. Josh Billings remarked, "Mankind luv to be cheated, but they want to hav it dun by an artist." Phineas T. Barnum was that artist. He probably put more genius and effort into inventiveness productive of nothing except money than any other Yankee who ever lived.

He could enjoy being victimized himself (within reason) as in his account of how a fellow Yankee "took him" with the offer of a bona fide cherry-colored cat. Barnum paid handsomely for it, on a guaranteed basis, sight unseen. The cat was black.

He drummed up trade for the museum by scores of clever dodges and devices which he describes in his *Struggles and Triumphs,* by some of the most extensive newspaper advertising to have been seen in his time, and by the first use of the kind of lighting now associated with a Hollywood film première at Grauman's Chinese, anticipating The Great White Way.

> Powerful Drummond lights were placed at the top
> of the Museum, which, in the darkest night, threw
> a flood of light up and down Broadway, from the

> Battery to Niblo's, that would enable one to read a newspaper in the street. These were the first Drummond lights ever seen in New York, and they made people talk, and so advertise my Museum.

Also he relied on the powerful advertising of word-of-mouth from satisfied customers. Though he loved a hoax or swindle, for its own sake, he made sure that it gave some basic type of customer satisfaction in terms of entertainment. "I took care to see that they not only received the full worth of their money, but were more than satisfied." They went away agape, goggling, and talking.

It was inevitable that this showman would turn any fiasco such as his clock industry investments into entertainment capital.

Turning back from this digression on Yankee showmanship (before Barnum's time, the famous evangelist Lorenzo—"Crazy"—Dow would sometimes end up his sermons by hawking homemade remedies), the story of Connecticut clocks which we have been examining is a little like the classic "dumb show," a revealing prelude to things that were to come in America's industrial drama. Jerome's cheap shelf clocks were followed in due time by that characteristic Yankee product, Ingersoll's dollar watch, but there was nothing about the concept basically different in idea from what Terry had begun in wood and Jerome had carried out in brass. Waltham, Massachusetts, became the seat of cheap watch production.

Since brass was so important to the clockmakers, this is the best place for an added note about Connecticut's brass industry, too large a history in itself for treatment here, but needing a bit more said about it because various uses of brass called forth inventiveness of a number of kinds.

Waterbury was the initial center of the brass industry, which took its rise from buttons. The making of these began as a typical household industry. Pewter and brass were the commonest materials. They had to be polished, and also the eye, for sewing the button to the garment, had to be finished by hand. It was cast as a solid, flat, circular projection from the button and the hole had to be pierced in it.

Around 1790 three brothers, Henry, Silas and Samuel Grilley, came from Boston, where they had learned the tricks of button making from an Englishman, and settled in Waterbury, Connecticut. Some ten years later they invented the idea of fixing a little loop of wire in the mold, to become set in the metal, instead of the old tedious way of making the button eye.

Then two other brothers, Abel and Levi Porter, came from Southington and set up partnership with the Grilleys, suggesting that the latter were laboring under some disadvantages, for the new business was called Abel Porter & Co. It was under Abel Porter's vigorous leadership that sheet brass was rolled, cut and stamped for buttons. He is supposed to have been the first to roll brass in this country. The significance of this step, far beyond its application to buttons, will be remembered in the importance of wheels stamped out of sheet brass to Jerome's mass-produced clocks.

For buttons or clock wheels, this stamping was done with another of the tools basic to modern industry—the die. Dies are shapes for cutting or imprinting materials in a desired manner. A cookie cutter is a die, and so is the little mold for imprinting maple leaves, or Indian heads, on pats of butter. The great dies and hydraulic presses of twentieth-century industry can virtually shape an auto body with one stroke. Their ancestors were Abel Porter's button dies and Chauncey Jerome's clock-wheel dies.

Of course this is a principle basically different from the turning and shaping of forms by the lathe method, which also found application in the brass industry. Sometime after 1820, W. H. Scovill, again in Waterbury, had developed the factory system thoroughly in the working of brass. In 1851, an employee of the Scovill plant, W. H. Hayden, invented a lathe method of making brass kettles by spinning and turning blanks of sheet metal against a shaping tool.

Another of the important uses of brass was the pin industry. The pin is an ancient household implement, probably suggested to primitive man by the thorn. The Greek and Roman world made pins of bronze. Being handmade, they remained relatively expensive throughout European history. Just as the phrase "not worth his salt" is revealing of the historical value of that commodity, so is the other phrase, "pin money," significant of the one-time budgetary allotment to the housewife for this need.

Heads of pins used to be made separately. Attaching them was awkward and their security was unreliable. In the late 18th century it was said that eighteen distinct operations involving as many as seven workmen went into the making of a pin. Modern ingenuity greater than mine would be required to figure out the complexities of such methods.

The colonies relied on England for pins. A paper of them was important enough to be itemized in the estates of deceased persons. A dollar a package was the price around 1812, at a time when the purchasing power of a dollar was fantastic by our standards.

American manufacture of brass pins, on any significant scale, awaited the invention of the first pin-making machine, by J. I. Howe, of New York, in 1831. Howe improved his processes over a long period of time, and within ten years had a machine to make solid-headed pins. Close on his heels, the firm of Slocum and Jillson, in Poughkeepsie, and the Fowler Brothers, of Northford, Connecticut, had pin machines of their own.

The machine-made pin left the problem of packaging them as a more tedious and costly thing than the making of them. Howe rose to this need and clinched the leadership in the industry by inventing a machine to stick pins in papers.

Brass has led us apart from the primary concern of this chapter with the clock industry. In considering this first half of the 19th century in which so much that this book examines took place, I want to come back to some brave, valiant reflections of the aging, weary and bankrupt Chauncey Jerome. All men tend to think that the age in which they live is that age of wonders that did not occur before and surely never can come again. And they always are at least partly right. As it seemed to Jerome:

"I cannot now believe that there will ever be in the same space of future time so many improvements and inventions as those of the past half century—one of the most important in the history of the world. Everyday things with us now would have appeared to our forefathers as incredible."

CHAPTER 13

BRIDGE-BUILDERS

There is no country of the world
which is more in need of good and
permanent Bridges than the United
States of America. Extended along
an immense line of coast on which
abound rivers, creeks and swamps, it
is impossible that any physical union
of the country can really take place
until the labours of the architect
and mechanic shall have more perfectly done away the inconvenience
arising from the intervention of the
waters.

—THOMAS POPE, 1811

THE FULL like of Benjamin Franklin is hardly to be found
among our inventors, considering his extraordinary faculty
for mixing mechanical creativeness with scientific study and
experiment, and at the same time performing one of the
key political roles in the shaping of the United States, at
home and abroad.

Yet there are at least some likenesses to Franklin in a
man whom I shall first let a fellow inventor, Eli Whitney,
describe for us. Whitney lodged at the same tavern with
him, in 1802, on one of his trips to Washington connected

with the musket business. Consider the portrait before seeking the identity:

> I should judge from his appearance that he is nearly
> 70 years of age . . . He is about five feet 10
> inches high—his hair three fourth white—black
> eyes—a large bulbous nose—a large mouth drawn
> down at the corners with flabby lips—with more
> than half decayed, horrid looking teeth—his com-
> plection of a brick colour—his face & nose covered
> with carbuncles & spots of a darker hue than the
> general colour of his skin—his dress rather mean
> & his whole appearance very slovenly—his hands
> so convulsed that while his expansive lips almost
> encompassed a wine glass, he could hardly get the
> contents of it into his head without spilling it. . . .
> In short he is a mere loathsome carcase, which has
> withstood the ravages & rackings of brutal intem-
> perance for an uncommon length of time & from
> which (were it exposed on the barren heath of
> Africa) the Hyena & Jackals would turn away with
> disgust.
>
> He observed that he had dined with Mr. Jefferson
> yesterday & the Day before—& I make no doubt he
> is a 'bosome friend' of the President . . . [Appar-
> ently Whitney did not approve politically and philo-
> sophically of the President who had been always so
> perceptive of his genius.] . . . Tho' some of the
> democrats will swallow common carrion with a good
> rellish, I think most of them will loathe the putrid
> rattle snake which has died from the venom of his
> own bite. . . .

And so Eli Whitney, a genius of mechanics and a man of
stable character, but limited philosophically by his Puritan-
Congregational nurturing, sketched for a friend the person
of one of America's political, philosophical, and mechanical geniuses, Thomas Paine. Already because of the views
embodied in *The Age of Reason* and his connection with

the French Revolution (disillusioning as that had been for Paine) the face of a once admiring public had been set against him. Only a few of the great men left from our own Revolution, such as Jefferson, who knew their man for what he was and more or less openly shared his Deism, still acknowledged him. Even Washington had somewhat shied away. The tide of opinion was to run against Paine up to Theodore Roosevelt's famous dismissal of him as "a dirty little atheist" until the last decade or so, which has seen a recovery of his reputation. Ironically the Communists have been the latest to jeopardize him by taking him up, over his own dead body. His late 19th-century definitive biographer, the Virginia-born Unitarian clergyman, Moncure D. Conway, was a rare exception to the general attitude.

Now to return to Whitney's letter to his friend:

> You have doubtless heard of the arrival of the notorious Tom Paine in this country—[So Whitney had begun the letter.] Being informed, previous to my arrival here, that he was in this neighborhood I had some curiosity to see him . . . on entering the room [of the public house]—to my great surprise I found that T. Paine was there & a lodger in the house & in less than five minutes we were seated opposite each other at table—

> I was not disappointed in my expectation of his appearance—I found him the same filthy old sot that he has ever been represented—

No—not "ever," as Whitney should have known, but only since the relative post-Revolutionary security and complacency had obscured in the memories of some what Franklin had called "the prodigious effects" of the *Crisis* papers and *Common Sense,* and since the French Revolution had alarmed many with its implications (justifiably enough, for that matter), and since a wave of Puritan orthodoxy had begun to sweep the country in the wake of the liberal Deism that had reached highwater mark at the time of the War for Independence. I am not now pleading the case of either

Deism or the form of orthodoxy following after it, but am simply remarking the context in which public opinion reversed itself toward Paine. If he had survived into the ensuing era of Unitarian transcendentalism in New England, he would have found friends again, in Emerson, Thoreau, and others. The man whom disease and age (not debauchery) had made so repulsive when Whitney saw him, had been not only a literary but a social lion in 1785, when Congress was sitting in New York. He was, of course, the friend of Franklin and had often exchanged ideas with him, and was a member of the Philosophical Society.

In the matter of steamboats, Fitch had consulted him in New Jersey; Rumsey in England; and Fulton, in France. Paine's actual concepts of a steamboat and the engine to drive it, if undeveloped, were all the same more advanced than those of any others, for he proposed the application of the turbine principle which, with either steam, water, hot air, or gas as impeller was to be a major mode of transmitting power. (Though the great time of the turbine had not yet come, the idea of it was far older than Paine.)

The democratic political visions of Fulton and his notions of ending war by the horrors of the submarine, together with his first enthralment and then disillusionment with Napoleon (the same experience that Beethoven had, and Tolstoy's Pierre Bezuhov) all must reflect in part some influences from Paine. Joel Barlow was a great friend of Paine, and it was in Barlow's house that Fulton lived in France.

This was an age of religious and philosophical naïveté, although it thought itself an age of sophistication. Liberalism in politics, the new surges of scientific enquiry, had inspired in Paine and others (Comte to follow) the concept of the Religion of Humanity—a noble sounding thing, on the face of it, which had the unhappy, and for some of its exponents the unforeseen, result of passing subtly into a form of the worship of Man by himself and the belief in Man's possible and even imminent self-perfectibility. This notion, which continued to develop throughout the 19th century, was not to find its greatest and most shocking dis-

illusionment until our century with the coming of modern
Communism and Fascism and the doctrines of man frankly
promulgated by them.

Paine, the Quaker whose fate it was to be denied even a
place in a Quaker burial ground, wanted to redeem gunpowder and convert it to humanitarianism, as our age hopes
to convert atomic energy to peaceful use rather than hydro-
gen bombs. Paine saw gunpowder as a substance with enormous power relative to its bulk and weight. He proposed a
gunpowder motor—again related to the turbine—urging
Jefferson, when President, to test a turbine type of wheel to
receive its impulse from small discharges of powder, as
from blank pistols. He appears to have missed the concept
of using the powder for a reaction turbine—which is the
simple pinwheel.

> When I consider the wisdom of nature I must think
> that she endowed matter with this extraordinary
> property for other purposes than that of destruction
> . . . If the power which an ounce of gunpowder
> contains could be detailed out as steam or water
> can be it would be a most commodious natural
> power.

This, however, is the wilder flight of Paine's inventiveness. He devised a smokeless candle, going to Franklin's
house at one time where the two of them experimented
with it. How it worked is far from clear to me and I had
best let Paine describe it himself, in what I find a greatly
confusing letter to Franklin:

> Dec. 31, 1785.—Dear Sir,—I send you the Can-
> dles I have been making;—In a little time after they
> are lighted the smoke and flame separate, the one
> issuing from one end of the Candle, and the other
> from the other end. I supposed this to be because
> a quantity of air enters into the Candle between
> the Tallow and the flame, and in its passage down-
> wards take the smoke with it; for if you allow a
> quantity of air up the Candle, the current will be

changed, and the smoke reascends, and in passing this the flame makes a small flash and a little noise.

But to express the Idea I mean, of the smoke descending more clearly it is this,—that the air enters the Candle in the very place where the melted tallow is getting into the state of flame, and takes it down before the change is completed . . .

Paine further invented for his own use a machine for planing boards, a crane, and an improved, reinforced carriage wheel, with an inner, concentric rim. For Paine's patent applications for the latter, his friend Robert Fulton did the necessary drawings.

His greatest invention, however, and the one symbolically nearest to his heart, was his iron bridge, which preoccupied him through many years, in England, France, and America. He further took out patents on a variety of arches, vaulted roofs, and ceilings.

The pamphleteer who had earned his living as a stay-maker and had labored for the political and intellectual liberty of his countrymen, turned to the conception of great stays of iron that should span rivers to unite people both literally and figuratively.

Paine once wrote of the War for Independence that it had "energized invention and lessened the catalogue of impossibilities." It was characteristic of him, after the Revolution, to design an iron bridge of a single arch for the Schuylkill River, calling for five hundred and twenty tons of iron, "to be distributed into thirteen ribs, in commemoration of the Thirteen United States." (This was never built, at least partly because of the inadequacies of American iron production at the time.)

Paine's letters to various people throughout many years contain mention of different bridge models he had built from time to time and cast in metal. Several bridges were built in England on his designs. The great British engineer Stephenson, builder of the famous early locomotive, "The Rocket," said of one of Paine's bridges in England that it "will probably remain unrivalled . . . as regards its proportions and the small quantity of materials employed in its construction." Charles Wilson Peale exhibited a number of the models in his Philadelphia museum.

As Paine wrote to Franklin, when sending some models to him, the chief concept was to make spans of a strength to extend from shore to shore, across fairly large rivers, avoiding the use of piers, as commonly used in Europe, because of the danger to them from ice during the American winters. He argued, in reference to the Schuylkill, that his designs were more economical as well as stronger than piers, which latter, if they held against the onslaughts of ice, might cause major diversion of the channels and flow of the river. All his bridges were based on mathematical calculations of weight and stress and qualify in the modern sense as works of engineering as well as invention. In his contributions to the discussion about a Constitution for the United States he was given to using analogies based on bridge structures. The vision of the bridge became in his mind a symbol to link not merely the banks of rivers, but nation with nation.

In 1790, Lafayette entrusted to Paine for presentation to George Washington, the key of the fallen Bastille. The Revolution in France was in its first flush of success and idealism. The Terror had not yet set in. Lafayette could still believe that there was an appropriate kinship between the French and American Revolutions, in making this gesture to his old commander.

In Paine's letter to Washington (written from London) accompanying the key, he speaks of his bridges, with which Washington was familiar, and adds a personal gift of his own.

> In the partition in the Box, which contains the Key of the Bastille, I have put up half a dozen Razors, manufactured from Cast-steel made at the Works where the Bridge was constructed, which I request you to accept as a little token from a very grateful heart.

The warmest picture of Paine the inventor was sketched by his friend Mme. Bonneville, describing a time when he was staying at the Paris home of herself and her husband. He had brought with him from America a wooden bridge model and spent much time making its replica, with improvements, in lead. Upon this he used to bang ferociously with a sledgehammer, exulting in this demonstration of its strength. The Bonnevilles were once roused by this pounding in the middle of the night and exhorted by Paine to witness again the model's powers of resistance. As the robe-enveloped host and hostess looked on—with mixed feelings, I should imagine—Paine cried out, "Nothing in the world is so fine as my bridge!" But, then, suddenly aware of Mme. Bonneville, his gallantry came to the fore and he added, "Except a woman!"

I have given so much attention to Paine because there is in him, as in Franklin, an outstanding measure of the combination of gifts and interests which in their greater or lesser degrees were common enough to bring distinction to the time. Also, Paine's rehabilitated reputation as a patriot and literary man has obscured his authentic inventive genius. Walt Whitman was one of those who realized the truth that underlay years of slander, and once said that, "Paine was double-damnably lied about."

There is no better way to capture the melancholy circumstances of this great man's death than to cap Eli Whitney's expressions of personal revulsion, with which I introduced Paine, with a sympathetic and angry cartoon by John Wesley Jarvis, done at the time of Paine's death, in 1809. Moncure Conway described it so succinctly that I simply cite his lengthy footnote:

> Paine is seen dead, his pillow "Common Sense," his hand holding a manuscript, "A rap on the knuckles for John Mason." On his arm is the label, "Answer to Bishop Watson." Under him is written: "A man who devoted his whole life to the attainment of two objects—rights of man and freedom of conscience—had his vote denied when living, and was denied

a grave when dead!" The Catholic Father O'Brian (a notorious drunkard), with very red nose, kneels over Paine exclaiming, "Oh you ugly drunken beast!" The Rev. John Mason (Presbyterian) stamps on Paine, exclaiming, "Ah, Tom! Tom! thou'lt get thy frying in hell; they'll roast thee like a herring.

> "They'll put thee in the furnace hot,
> And on thee bar the door:
> How the devils all will laugh
> To hear thee burst and roar!"

The Rev. Dr. Livingston kicks at Paine's head, exclaiming, "How are the mighty fallen, Right fol-de-riddle-lol!" Bishop Hobart kicks the feet, singing:

> "Right fol-de-rol, let's dance and sing,
> Tom is dead, God save the king—
> The infidel now low doth lie—
> Sing Hallelujah—hallelujah!"

A Quaker turns away with a shovel, saying, "I'll not bury thee."

Shades of Dean Swift!

As we cast a look at the New England bridge builders, we see that Paine was impressively far ahead. The wooden bridge prevailed, to become almost a New England trademark, long after Paine's bold experiments with iron.

First we must consider roads. Bridges do not cross rivers until roads have led a considerable number of people to them who desire to get across. There is a long time, in the evolution of a road, when a ferry is thoroughly adequate to the needs—indeed the modern ferryboat is still a large factor in American road travel along with the fabulous modern bridges.

Vehicles precede roads—there is no chicken-or-egg uncertainty about that. Each step of the way, from ox-cart to Roman chariot to Concord coach to automobile has led men to improve their roads relative to the estimated potential of their improved wheel vehicles. Twice in the 19th century the apparent (or real) promise of other modes of travel, temporarily set back the progress of roads—the coming of the canal, and the coming of the railroad.

Earliest colonial land travel—a matter of horse or foot—was slow and hard indeed, as in the testimony of Madam Knight's famous journey from Boston to New York, by horseback, early in the 1700's. It was hard riding, through long stretches of dense, unpopulated forest, getting drenched and muddy fording streams, crossing rivers on rotten and shaky makeshift bridges, lodging by night as chance dictated in dubious hovels among hosts of a character less than reassuring.

The building of the high-wheeled, spring-suspended stagecoaches forced improvements of roads and the turnpike companies came into existence. Most were private enterprises, but generally bore some relationship to the towns or provinces if only through grants of the right of way. For these they had to guarantee the maintenance of reasonably good road surfaces. Turnpikes get their name from the turnstiles, where tolls were collected. Attempts by some travellers to avoid these by looping out around the toll gates created what were called "shunpikes." The schedule of tolls on a turnpike varied from the commercial coaches to private wagons, horsemen, pedestrians, and hooved cattle being driven down the pike.

Building the turnpikes required many men and a lot of tools—especially the shovel, pick-axe, and crowbar. A number of the men we've met, the Wilkinsons, the Orrs, and others like them made the needed equipment. The shovel factories of Robert Orr and Oliver Ames served the turnpike needs, as well as those of the farms.

The immense value of the turnpike development is expressed by a Vermont Congressman, in 1823:

In that part of the country where I live, when I first went into it, when we had to travel the roads with a cart or wagon loaded with six or eight hundredweight, we had to employ half a dozen men to hang on one side or the other, to keep the cart from turning over; but since we have constructed our turnpike roads, one man can drive his team with a load of two or three tons on his wagon . . . the farms and wild lands which they go through or lead to are worth double as much as ever they would have been without having these roads to travel upon.

The American stagecoach found its own true personality in 1826 when two Massachusetts men, Lewis Downing and J. Stephen Abbot, began to make the famous Concord coach in Concord, New Hampshire. Abbot-Downing coaches were far lighter and yet much stronger than any others ever made. They added supreme quality of materials and workmanship to improved design. Custom color jobs and picture door panels were among their features. Out of Concord streamed the American stagecoaches inseparably a part of the tradition and legend of the West.

The old main turnpike roads, unlike the twisting subordinate ones, tried their best to drive a bee-line from hither to yon. As a ballad put it,

> The old time roads, they used to run
> Right over all the hills and rises . . .

But the thing that could bring turnpikes up short was rivers.

The first of the really notable bridges designed to tie together the growing road systems was built by Colonel Enoch Hall, across the Connecticut River near Bellows Falls, Vermont, in 1784. It was built in defiance of skeptics, scoffers, and prophets of doom (Franklin's "croakers"). The abundant native white pine was its material, a rocky projection midway in the river anchored its central pier. It was a 365-foot bridge, fifty feet above the water, evoking the amazed admiration of Timothy Dwight, afterwards President of Yale, and other travellers.

A little over two years later, the somewhat more elegant Charles River bridge, connecting Boston and Charlestown, was built. It was lower but longer, and of different construction, being 1503 feet in span, resting upon seventy-five piers. Both of these bridges represented the determination of the newly freed nation to bind itself together.

The nostalgia of our latter day owes a debt to Timothy Palmer, of Newburyport, one of the greatest early bridge builders. He was a good engineer and built some remarkable spans of truss, and trussed-arch, design. But his unique inspiration was the time when he thought of protecting a wooden bridge from the harsh New England weather by building a roof over it and walls around it. The New England covered bridge was thus invented—sometime before 1821—and happily it survives still. If you drive through many of them, especially the very oldest, with an observant eye, you will see a great variety of simple engineering principles in the different types of trusses, with or without arches, that support them.

Several other New England men contributed to bridges. Theodore Burr, born in Torrington, Connecticut, patented a trussed arch. Father and son, Caleb and Thomas Pratt, of Boston, developed trusses combining wood and iron, which marked the transition from the coach and wagon bridge to the railroad bridge. So did the lattice truss with iron tension rods, developed by William Howe, of Spencer, Massachusetts. (This was quite a family; his brother Tyler invented bedsprings, and their nephew was Elias Howe, of the sewing machine.)

These New England bridge men may have owed some of the concepts of their trusses to the intricate structure of the beautiful, soaring church steeples of the region. A good deal of basic engineering skill went into them, too. Sometime around 1814, while the young nation was still engaged in a kind of stalemate war, a crowd of gawpers might have been seen gathered on the New Haven common. The Center Church had been abuilding there, all through the time of conflict and stress, since 1812, under the direction of the New Haven architect, Ithiel Town. Conceivably young Chauncey Jerome, later a great maker of clocks but then in a Connecticut regiment, might have been looking on with the New Haven girl he was courting. Conceivably Eli Whitney might have dropped by from his outlying arms factory to see the interesting engineering attempt. Nothing could have kept Ezra Stiles away, had he been alive. His successor, President Timothy Dwight, who had so much admired Bushnell's ingenuity, quite possibly strolled over from the adjacent Yale College to watch.

Inside the hollow square brick tower a beautiful steeple had been built. Now it was to be raised, straight up the center of the tower it was to cap, and to have supporting members thrust under it. I wish we had a diagram of the "ingenious windlass and tackle" by which the job was done. All was finished in a little more than two hours, while the throng, no doubt cheering at the crucial moments, listened to the groaning and creaking of ropes and pulleys and watched the rise, foot by foot.

The youthful architect, Ithiel Town, was largely self-educated and had studied his craft under Boston's great Asher Benjamin, trainer of a generation of American architects. (An attempt at a similar feat by a pupil of Town, in Danbury some years after, ended in spectacular disaster when a rope broke.) Near his Center Church, Town shortly built the markedly contrasting Trinity Church.

He was one of the greatest of the bridge builders, whose designs, like those of Howe and Platt, carried over into the railroad era. In 1823, Town built the first pure truss bridge near the arms plant at Whitneyville. Eli, to whose convenience it contributed, must have watched its construction with interest. Years later, this bridge was moved upstream a quarter of a mile, in one piece, to a new site, Eli Whitney, Jr. supervising the operation. Its timber and wooden-pin structure lasted in use until 1891.

These were the early American bridge engineers who

would be succeeded, in later days, by the Roeblings of Brooklyn Bridge, and after them the builders of those magnificent esthetic-engineering flights, the George Washington Bridge, the Delaware River Memorial, and the Golden Gate.

CHAPTER 14

TWO MEN OBSESSED

If you meet a man who has on an
India rubber cap, stock, coat, vest,
and shoes, with an India rubber
money purse *without a cent of
money in it,* that is he.

IN NEW HAVEN, as the 18th gave way to the 19th century, there was a certain Amasa Goodyear, of a distinguished old family of the town. Amasa was with one of the great West Indies trading houses, but was of an inventive, active turn of mind and anxious to set up for himself in other lines of work. Around 1807 he saw a chance to buy a share of the patent rights in a process for making pearl buttons. It looked like a good thing and he took it. Then, in time-honored fashion, he moved to Naugatuck, Connecticut for water power, setting up a small and versatile manufactory on the stream, as adjunct to a farm, in good New England tradition of the period. In addition to the first machine-made pearl buttons, he manufactured scythes, spoons, and even clocks. Just how these things assorted together heaven knows. He further invented the first steel manure- and hay forks, to which he found so much dogged resistance (as Thaddeus Fairbanks found for his iron plow in Vermont, a few years later) that for a while he had to give them away, until experience of their merits created a demand. This was only one of a number of agricultural implements of his invention.

Amasa's son Charles, who had been born in the New Haven days, grew up with the mingled experience from early youth of working on the farm and in the shops. There were thoughts of his entering the ministry, but the pressures of his father's affairs and his own involvment in them sidetracked these studies before they got started. Even so, he remained devoutly religious, a singularly gentle, patient, loving spirit, and felt that the work upon which he later launched was a true "call" from God.

Charles was more interested in articles than in machines. A legend (almost less interesting than the later "accidental" reality) has it that as a boy he peeled off a thin coat of India rubber from a bottle and speculated as to whether a fabric might not be made from it. This exotic product was becoming more and more familiar and finding a variety of uses. It was widely known as "Gum elastic" but had come to be called "rubber" because its earliest recorded use (other than as balls to play with) by white men who fetched it from South America, was as an eraser. The "India" crept in as a joint reference to the South American Indians who gathered it and to the West Indies which became a trading channel for it. Its original name was Caoutchouc (pronounced something like koochook). The first rubber shoes ever seen in New England were brought into Boston in 1820, as a great curiosity. Yankees were intrigued and were not slow to take the raw material, often brought to New England ports just for ballast, and try to make shoes themselves.

Charles Goodyear was not to become stuck up with gum elastic for some years, yet. In his teens he worked for a hardware firm in Philadelphia. At twenty-one he was back in Connecticut in business with his father. He married Clarissa Beecher, who was letting herself in for more than she knew. In 1826 he went back to Philadelphia and with many products manufactured by his father opened the first hardware store stocked completely with American-made articles. On a business trip to New York, in these days, depressed by carousing that he witnessed there, he wrote his wife: "I have quit smoking, chewing, and drinking . . . I invite you to forbid in our house anything stronger than wines and cordials."

When he was thirty years old, he had a severe decline in health. At the same time, and perhaps partly because of it, the hardware firm failed and passed out of his hands. It had overextended its operations. Later the same business was to prove profitable in other hands. But Charles owed money, was hounded by creditors, and in the course of the next ten painful years was often in debtors' prison—an institution about which we think little in the history of our own country, chiefly associating it with Dickens' novels. Like Mrs. Micawber, poor Clarissa Goodyear frequently left the infants with her oldest daughter and went to visit Charles in prison.

Around 1834, during his difficult times, Charles was in New York and bought a "life-saver" from the store of the Roxbury India Rubber Co. I don't know what he felt to be his urgent need for it. He probably looked back upon the purchase as the work of his own inscrutable destiny. Charles tinkered with his life-saver and came back to the Roxbury India Rubber store, some time later, to try to sell them an improvement in the tube. They were impressed by his ingenuity and took him to their bosoms, but at the same time took him into the back room and poured out their woes.

The India Rubber trade, they confided to him, was the next thing to being dead. In the previous year they had been shaken to the foundations by having $20,000 worth of their merchandise returned to them, melted, decomposing, and stinking so mightily that it had to be buried. Frantic efforts to improve the formulae so far had been fruitless and the worst of it was, each new experiment required a full summer and winter of testing before you could know whether it worked or not. The plagued India rubber either melted and ran in the summer or petrified in the winter.

The great Daniel Webster was given an India rubber coat
and hat. In winter the coat froze rigid and he let it stand
alone, on his porch, like a scarecrow, with the hat upon it.
On the other hand, body heat was enough to melt suspenders, and of course you couldn't take any rubber product
near the fire. The only mystery was that for some unknown
reason, rubber shoes made by the Amazon Indians, by their
own primitive processes, stood up much better than the
American made ones.

Scores of people were experimenting with the rubber
problem. A great many doctors, sensing the contributions
that rubber could make to their profession, had interested
themselves in it. As for Charles, he had become a kind of
evangelist. He recognized this as God's chosen work for
him. Nothing would stop him.

Since these were the years when creditors constantly
hounded him, he did much of his work during his periodic
sojourns in prison. Luckily his raw materials were relatively cheap (few people wanted the stuff) and he needed
no tools beyond pots and pans and his hands. He said,
"Fortunately the substance is one with which, in experimenting, fingers are better than any other mechanical
power." So, like a baker, he kneaded hundreds of pounds
of gum elastic with his hands, batch after batch, spreading
it out with a rolling pin on a slab of marble.

There were several occasions on which he thought he had
achieved success, only to be disappointed due to the necessity of a long wait to confirm the results. His first false
lead was when he mixed magnesia with the gum, obtaining
the attractive novelty of a white rubber, apparently much
more stable—but decomposition was merely slowed.

Back in New Haven, in one phase of the endless pere-
grinations of these years, the whole Goodyear family found
itself living in a rubber factory. His wife and daughters
worked, and they also employed some young women to live
with the family and dabble in rubber. Patches of thin
rolled rubber were to be encountered all over the house,
spread on the window panes, the table tops, vases, or din-

ner plates to dry out. His eldest daughter was quite close to him in the enterprise and it became her boast that she made with her own hands the first pair of overshoes of vulcanized rubber.

Charles was forced to seek moneymaking ventures. Among his efforts was an unsinkable lifeboat (that lifesaver motif again), having tin air tubes running along its hull.

He went back to New York for a while, his daughter accompanying him. They lived in a wretched hotel attic. He walked three miles daily to Pike's Mill, in Greenwich Village, where he had obtained shop privileges, and he generally carried armloads of equipment with him. His brother-in-law and other friends or relatives were tapped for funds as much as possible and he continually pled to them his certainty of ultimate success.

When they visited his room, where he was once found ill and nearly dead from fumes, it was a mess of kettles, pans, pots of white lead, rubber, shellac, and miscellaneous chemicals. Goodyear had become hopelessly smeared with the gum and chemical stains. It was in these days that he clothed himself from head to toe in his experimental rubber, like the old man clothed all in leather of the nursery rhyme. That was when someone gave the famous description of how he might be recognized: "If you meet a man who has on an India rubber cap, stock, coat, vest, and shoes, with an India rubber money purse *without a cent of money in it*, that is he."

The discovery of the sought-for secret came in 1839. After the promising effects of nitric acid had disappointed him, he had been experimenting with sulphur and the heat of the sun. This led to the great mailbag fiasco. Believing that the "tanning" effect of the sulphur had solved his problem, he took a government order for rubber mailbags. They were heavy, and went to pieces at the handles about the time they were delivered. The sulphur curing affected only the outer surface.

Following this, which had driven off the last of those

who had borne with him except for his wife and children, he was boiling rubber and sulphur on the kitchen stove, trying to make the curing process permeate it. A blob fell on the hot stove top and hardened. It was what came to be called "vulcanized."

Here is a primary example of one important aspect of invention. This was an accident—yes, but it was an *accident in a context*. It was no accident that sulphur was in the rubber, no accident that heat was being applied, and above all, no accident that Goodyear was able to recognize what had happened immediately. To be able to recognize the happy accident is one of the basic necessities in invention.

His work was not finished. How much sulphur? How much dry heat? How long for the process? These things had to be worked out experimentally. But Charles had it, he genuinely had it. It was not a great deal later that his brother Nelson, following after him, found the right combinations and processes for the valuable hard rubbers, anticipations of the plastic age.

Ironies have a way of being persistent. The boy who had cried "Wolf!" was not believed when the wolf did come. Poor Goodyear, not at all through fault of his own, had failed just so many times that now when he really had succeeded nobody wanted to hear any more about rubber, nobody was prepared to consider that this might be anything but one more familiar fiasco. In success, he was at the extreme of bankruptcy. He tells it himself, in the third person:

> The pawning or selling some relic of better days or some article of necessity was a frequent expedient. His library had long since disappeared, but shortly after the discovery of this process, he collected and sold at auction the schoolbooks of his children, which brought him the trifling sum of five dollars; small as the amount was, it enabled him to proceed. At this step he did not hesitate. The occasion, and the certainty of success, warranted

the measure which, in other circumstances, would have been sacrilege.

For five years more he wandered in poverty around New England, working out the process, begging facilities, seeking a backer, travelling by foot in all weathers, exhausted. It wasn't until 1844 that he got a patent.

When, abruptly, the reality of what Goodyear had accomplished did impress itself upon people, the encroachments began, and Charles found himself involved in legal struggles almost as harassing as his days of trial and error. His rights were challenged and pirated on fine points.

He had the best legal mind of his day on his side, luckily. The final showdown on priority and patent rights took place in 1852 before the U. S. Circuit Court, at Trenton, New Jersey (a situation reminiscent of Whitney's hearing before a U. S. Court that had resulted in Judge Johnson's great decision). Daniel Webster, who was then Secretary of State, spoke for the tired, ill man who still had reaped little from his work. Of this statesman-lawyer, Van Wyck Brooks says, "His politics, his economic doctrines were those of any sound New Hampshire farmer who owned a dam and a mill and turned his dollars over to the Boston bankers."

Mr. Webster was in good form at this trial:

. . . is Charles Goodyear the discoverer of this invention of vulcanized rubber? Is he the first man upon whose mind the idea ever flashed, or to whose intelligence the fact ever was disclosed, that by carrying heat to a certain height it would cease to render plastic the India Rubber and begin to harden and metallize it? Is there a man in the world who found out that fact before Charles Goodyear? Who is he? Where is he? On what continent does he live? Who has heard of him? What books treat of him? What man among all the men on earth has seen him, known him, or named him? Yet it is certain that this discovery has been made. It is certain that it exists. It is certain that it is now a matter of common knowledge all over the civilized world. It is certain that ten or twelve years ago it was not knowledge. It is certain that this curious result has grown into knowledge by somebody's discovery and invention. And who is that somebody? . . . If Charles Goodyear did not make this discovery, who did make it? Who did make it? . . . We want to know the name, and the habitation, and the location of the man upon the face of this globe, who invented vulcanized rubber, if it be not he, who now sits before us.

That was the year that Daniel Webster died, his flag flying and his light burning, as he said. His dying words were, "I still live." Goodyear's was the last great case that he pled with that rolling eloquence which Benét has enshrined in a litigation won against the Devil. And Daniel Webster won that case for Charles Goodyear, whose status as sole inventor of vulcanized rubber was permanently established in the high courts of the land.

What were the fruits? One of the mightiest industries ever to spring from one man's efforts was launched—an industry to the accumulating of untold billions of dollars. But when Goodyear died in 1860, knowing the scope of his success, seeing already a large industry at work, holding sixty patents, he was satisfied that he had fulfilled the purpose God had marked out for him. He felt no bitterness that it was chiefly others who were making the money.

The career of Elias Howe had many striking similarities, as well as a number of marked contrasts, to that of Charles Goodyear. Howe was born in 1819, in Massachusetts, not far from the birthplace of Eli Whitney. His father was a farmer and small time miller who never enjoyed prosperity. In his 'teens, Elias left the farm and went to seek work in the mill town of Lowell. There he served an apprenticeship as a mechanic in a shop for textile machinery. Moving on at least twice more, he came to rest for a while in the employ of a Boston machinist named Ari Davis.

Goodyear's obsession with rubber seemed to have stemmed from the chance purchase of a life-saver. Similarly, Howe's obsession began with his accidental overhearing of Davis' advice to a mechanic to invent a sewing machine if he wanted to make some money. Howe appeared to have recognized his destiny instantly. He quit his job, borrowed a little money, and also accepted such pittances as his wife could make from hand sewing, to dedicate all his energies to the great idea. This was about 1841.

He knew almost as little of what had been done in this line before him as Fitch had known about steamboats. Thimmonier, a Frenchman, had made a practical machine, with the eye in the point of the needle, in 1830. Angry tailors and seamstresses, in the pattern so often repeated in Europe, had smashed his machines in fear of being thrown out of work and Thimmonier had been afraid to push his invention.

As early as 1790, Thomas Saint, in England, took out patents for a machine especially intended to sew leather, but it was not a success. In Vienna, later, Josef Madersperger tried much the same thing with no better results.

In America, in 1834, Walter Hunt of New York City patented a machine, but for a long while he did nothing serious in the field, becoming sidetracked by interest in a popular, promising, and infinitely simpler invention of his, which he called a safety pin.

So, when Elias went to work, the idea of a sewing machine was scarcely new. Still, no one had broken through to the supposed potential market with a proven, practical, economical machine.

Howe's hardships through the next few years are a match for Goodyear's. His wife and child felt the pinch. They all lived for a time in a shop on his father's farm. That burnt down. Mrs. Howe earned what she could toward their support. A loyal friend named George Fisher, who had lent him the first money and continued to lend more until his ultimate limit at around two thousand dollars, also had the Howe family occupying his attic in Cambridge for a while.

Elias kept watching the motions of his wife's hands, as she sewed, and experimented fruitlessly in the blind alley of imitative motion. Even though he had worked at looms himself, in his time, it remained for a chance glimpse of a weaver, through a window, to liberate him from preoccupation with the human hand and turn him toward an adaptation and variation of the shuttle. He emerged with a crude machine that combined a shuttle motion with a needle motion and produced a lock stitch.

Now, although he had a machine that worked and could be demonstrated, he was appalled at the indifference when he tried to interest people in it. Tailors snorted in contempt. It was clumsy. Howe and Fisher staged a contest in which he far outsewed, with a better quality of stitching, the efforts of five expert seamstresses. His feat was acknowledged, but no real results came of it because the machine was too expensive. It cost Howe about three hundred dollars to make one. In his very success, in 1845, Howe had to table the whole enterprise and take another job.

The following year, his brother went to England and took along the sewing machine, to see if he could get English patents and any interest in it over there. A London corset maker named William Thomas bought the model below its cost, insisting on the right to have it duplicated, too. He promised to patent it in Elias' name, but when the brother had returned to America, patented it in his own and was the first man to begin to reap a profit from it. Later he had the gall to offer to hire Elias for three pounds a week, if he would come to England and work at improvements on it. Howe, hoping for the best, and desperate, took his wife and child to London. He worked there for a while under Thomas' exploitation until he could stand his insolence no longer and left him. He borrowed money, partly by pawning his American patent papers, to send his wife and child home. As soon as he could, he followed them, working his passage as a cook.

Soon after his return to America, his wife died, worn out and discouraged. The few possessions he owned, shipped on another boat, were lost at sea. Suddenly there was a burst of publicity relating to sewing machines. But it was not Howe's invention, but Hunt's, with improvements by a newcomer named Isaac Singer, that was claiming the public attention. The market, at last, was ready.

Now, when Howe was crushed, George W. Bliss came forward to help him. He had seen Howe's competition against the seamstresses, some years before, and had been impressed. He had the means and the worldly skill to fight the financial and legal battles involved. A long litigation, comparable to Goodyear's, ensued. Howe won it. His patents were recognized as fundamental to all successful sewing machines. Every manufacturer had to pay him royalties. He manufactured his own machines as well. Almost at once Howe was a rich man, soon a millionaire.

Howe, Singer and several others dominated a brisk and expanding market. Singer brought both inventive (he introduced the treadle to free both hands of the operator, and other improvements) and merchandising skills to the business which caused his name, rather than Howe's, to become the American household word associated with sewing machines.

Howe died at forty-eight. After all his struggles with his inventive *idée fixe,* and his abrupt wealth, so narrowly missed by his patient and loyal wife, he refused to renew his patents at their expiration, saying that he had made enough money from them and did not wish to earn any more from the labor of others.

CHAPTER 15

NAVIGATION AND COMMUNICATION

"Of what use is it, Mr. Faraday?"
"Of what use is a new-born child?"

ONE DAY in the mid-century, the sleek haughty clipper ship *Flying Cloud,* subject of many a popular lithograph, sailed into San Francisco harbor, to run up a record. She was nineteen days ahead of a rival that had sailed from New York with her. The *Flying Cloud* had made it around the Horn, from ocean to ocean, port to port, in eighty-nine days—a mark unbeaten in sail, notwithstanding her crew was surly and her rigging damaged in a storm.

She was one of the masterpieces of Donald McKay, a "Bluenose" (Nova Scotian) who had turned Yankee, as if hearkening to Sam Slick's celebration of Yankee speed and enterprise. It is certain that he had, in Slick's phrase, the ambition to "nullify time and space." His ships were yearning ships, and showed it in their sleekness and narrowness, their daring load of canvas, their long, challenging bowsprits, their raked masts.

His fastest was the *Lightning,* built for the Australian run and whipped to capacity by Skipper "Bully" Forbes (every driving skipper in those days was "Bully"), whose war-cry was "Melbourne or Hell in sixty days." He may have made both.

McKay may possibly have been the greatest, but

America had many builders of clippers, working from the yards of New England to those of New York, and those of Fell's Point, in Baltimore. "Yankee" became the generic term for all these clippers and their crews. But they picked up some other labels, too. The Australian clippers and the China clippers were so-called after their runs. Some of the latter were called tea clippers, because of their cargo.

All of their cargoes tended toward the exotic: rum, opium, slaves (illicit by the clipper days), tea, ivory, spices, and many other products of the Orient. There certainly was an "ivory, apes, and peacocks" aura about some of their ladings. The California gold-rush boomed the passenger trade.

What were the clippers and who invented them? What they were can be told, but it is almost as unprofitable to ask who invented them, as to ask who invented the Gothic cathedral. The clipper emerged, or evolved, out of the temperament of a people. You can say that French naval architects anticipated some of its characteristics and built the fastest warships of the late 18th century. But the Yankee built the clipper. From early in the 19th century the rakish characteristics had shown up first in small craft, and gradually developed in many yards under many hands. The piling on of canvas became a kind of dare.

"Cod's head and mackerel tail" was the description applied to the conventional, blunt-nosed schooner. Its hull and its prow bellied out. Though clippers varied, the characteristic that distinguished their hulls was that at waterline they were concave, not convex, at both bow and stern. Today we would call them streamlined.

These beautiful, inherently glamorous ships, flourished in pride over a short span. They extended the life of the sailing-ship era by a couple of decades, but they were the flower of its decadence. During the transition, the first great clumsy sea-going paddle-wheel vessels, and the first of the graceless iron steamers, had rings run around them by the fleet clippers. But it was like the spanking team and

carriage passing the clattering one-cylinder car with derisive shouts of "get a horse!" The awkward, noisy, smelly
new thing had destiny's right of way in each case. The
steamship retired the clipper.

The clippers as a generic type were the anonymous product of collective Yankee inventiveness. The years of their
evolution were the heyday of Yankee trading with the
world at large, but especially with the Far East. Yankee
captains and seamen wandered the ports of China and
Burma, Malaya, Java, and India. And in these years Chinese and Burmese, Malayans, Javanese and Indians might
be seen on the streets and docks of Boston, Portsmouth,
Salem, and New Bedford. Strange tongues were heard in
New England's ports. Her staid merchants sometimes
sported Chinese robes. Strange objects of art and ornament
graced private mansions, Yankee homes and museums.
Money from this world-flung trade built private mansions,
endowed colleges and academies and hospitals, founded
banks, and represented much of the capital that established
industries, such as the great textile mills.

There was one man in New England who had served
these skippers well, and who had helped to make sure, and
safe, and speedy the global navigation of waters. His name
was Nathaniel Bowditch. He was born and did much of his
work in Salem. About a hundred years after that port's
brief and overemphasized association with witches, Bowditch associated it with the enlightened discipline of mathematics.

As a young man he went to sea, took the long Pacific
voyages, and rose rapidly to be a captain. In the tedious
shipboard hours he studied mathematics, astronomy, and
navigation. Legends sprang up about his fabulous skill,
culminating in the tale of his bringing his ship, the
Putnam, straight into its dock at Salem in a blank fog, or
as some have it, a snowstorm, on his return from his last
voyage. All his hands, down to cook, learned navigation,
and all became captains.

Moore's *Navigation,* an English work, was the standard handbook on the subject, when this young man first put to sea. Bowditch turned his mathematical talents to a close scrutiny of this and found more than 8,000 errors, many of them on matters of such importance that they had undoubtedly led to major miscalculations and shipwreck.

What began as corrections to Moore emerged finally as a classic in its own right, Bowditch's *New American Practical Navigator,* first published in 1802. Bowditch saw it through ten editions in his lifetime. Revisions have continued ever since, and Bowditch still is issued by the United States Hydrographic Office.

Bowditch forsook the sea at about the age of thirty to take his mathematical abilities into the new and apparently promising field which men were beginning to call insurance—first fire insurance and later life insurance, to both of which he made great contributions. He was much in demand. Harvard wanted him. Jefferson personally courted him, but in vain, for the University of Virginia, and the military academy at West Point wanted him.

The peppery, diminutive, lively man could scarcely be popular with everybody—he was much too successful and gifted. A foe described him as "the little Mr. Bowditch puffed up by the flattery of his mathematical studies and destitute of every degree of literature or manners." All the same, he had produced one of the two most profoundly influential books of all New England, neither of them exactly "literary," the other of which was the great dictionary of the Connecticut man, Noah Webster, which saw the beginnings of an American language with its own characteristic spellings of English words.

In contrast to hostile views, the son of the German mathematical genius, Karl Friedrich Gauss, whose father sent him with letters to visit Bowditch, found the latter: "A vigorous and cheerful man with a very pleasant family."

Bowditch's second great work was his translation and elaborate annotation of that post-Newtonian masterwork, the *Celestial Mechanics* of the Frenchman Laplace. The Salem youth had early taught himself Latin, that he might read Newton's *Principia,* and French that he might study Laplace. He did more than simply bring the latter's work to the United States in accessible form—in so doing he opened up continental mathematics to Americans for the first time. Laplace himself, shortly before his death, said, "M. Bowditch comprehends my work, for he has not only detected my errors, but he has also shown me how I came to fall into them." Bowditch, whose insurance career had made him moderately wealthy, published Laplace in English at his own expense—some $20,000.

During the same period there was an unusual man on Nantucket, perhaps too versatile by far for his own good in the Leonardian sense of dissipating his energies in more fields than he could hope to develop fully. Walter Folger was kin to Benjamin Franklin through the latter's mother, Abiah Folger. This Nantucket clan was numerous and lively. One of its several sea captains, Timothy, had talked about the Gulf Stream with Franklin.

Walter had some of Benjamin Franklin's diverse abilities, though on a far more constricted scale. But he is the only other inventor of whom I know who shared his kinsman's extraordinary personal disinterestedness toward the fruits of invention. Walter Folger gave away inventions without hesitation, believing with Franklin that profits and patents yielded more grief than benefit.

The museum of the Historical Association on the Island still contains Folger's fabulous astronomical clock. It gives seconds, minutes, hours, days, months, years, leap years and centuries. Also phases of the moon, rising and setting of sun and moon and their courses, and the hours of high tide (for Nantucket). He devised many scientific instruments and made metallurgical experiments. He was himself an able mathematician, surveyor, and navigator. In the cotton industry he was an early user of power looms. His interests and activities extended themselves into law and politics.

While industrialization and transportation were making their steady headway, the element urgently needed to accompany them was a comparable advancement in communication. The greater part of the story of modern communication falls outside the scope of this book, in a new era and a changed context of invention. But the man who gave a special impetus to its development, without being its sole inventor or being a man "but for whom" we would not have had it, was the Massachusetts-born portrait painter, Samuel Finley Breese Morse. (Incidentally he painted one of the best known portraits of his contemporary, Eli Whitney.)

Wheatstone and others, in England, were working on the principles of the electro-magnetic telegraph, and perfected it fast enough to preëmpt the British patent field. One of America's great electrical pioneers, Joseph Henry of Albany, who did extensive work with electro-magnetics, made a workable telegraphic device (but didn't do much about it) around 1830, several years before Morse made his famous shipboard sketches, on the way home from Europe, ostensibly inspired by a demonstration of electro-magnetic parlor magic.

It is this casual, circumstantial process of invention by one who was neither scientist nor mechanic, yet who invaded with epochal results what was soon to become a highly technical field, that lends a fascination and characteristic Yankee touch to the story of Morse.

It is true that Morse had dabbled in science, particularly electricity. He studied at Yale, where its great scientific arbiter, Benjamin Silliman, had aroused his interest in matters electrical. But art was his chosen province. He practiced in his early years as a wandering portraitist—peddler-like—charging fifteen dollars, a high price on that circuit, for a portrait. With the help of the wife he met and married during these travels, he was soon a fashionable artist, painting Presidents, and such worthies as Whitney. Washington Allston had been his master, in art.

As inventor, the significant thing about Morse was the

leap he made in ideas. A famous anecdote tells of a gentleman regarding Michael Faraday's quivering electrical needle and asking, "But of what use is it, Mr. Faraday?" To which Faraday replied, "Of what use is a new-born child?"

Countless people besides Morse looked with casual interest at parlor demonstrations of the powers of electromagnetism—mere wire-wound miniature horseshoes picking up nails and tacks, and dropping them again, as a wire was attached, or removed from, a battery. To all but one of these spectators this was merely, in a telling expression of the day, a "scientific toy." The mind of Morse made an instant and mysterious leap and saw it as communication. This insight was the heart of Morse's invention.

The most important unaided step that he made after this was the invention of the relay, to renew the weak electrical impulse which could not travel more than some forty-five feet without a boost. Even with this important advance, it took the collaboration of the imaginative young mechanical genius, Alfred Vail, to perfect the telegraph mechanism. It took, also, the money and political influence which Vail's father could supply—and even so years of patience and persistence before the telegraph was a working reality. (A corrupt Postmaster General, Johnson, fought it ruthlessly by politics and sabotage, fearing its rivalry to his postal-express network.) It was the telegraph's immense value in swift message transmission at a Presidential nominating convention in Baltimore, in 1844, that broke down the barriers of resistance or indifference to it.

But for all Vail's indispensable help, the imaginative artist had yet one more purely creative accomplishment to contribute to the process. The alphabetical problem was a great stumbling block in the recording of messages. Morse was inspired, abruptly, with the concept of the dot-and-dash code, based on the greatest incidence of appearance of letters of the alphabet. He worked it out rapidly and the Morse International code remains in use to this day—notwithstanding the modern teletype—unchanged basically from the way Morse first wrote it out.

Edison, Bell, Gray, DeForest, Armstrong, and others were to follow. But Morse, the nontechnical, imaginative creator, had given unique impetus to the era of modern communication. But apart from all the other channels of modern technical research and study there are now the great institutional laboratories of Bell, Dumont, General Electric, Westinghouse, and the like, pursuing in systematic, organized plans, the processes of invention and advancement in collective endeavor. Individuals can contribute—and do—but a science-dabbling portrait painter such as Morse could scarcely get his foot in the door today, any more than an eccentric tinkering mechanic-silversmith such as Fitch, or a visionary painter such as Fulton, could approach the drawing boards where the atomic-powered submarine *Nautilus,* bearing the same name as Fulton's submarine, was developed.

CHAPTER 16

FOR VOLUNTEERS

Now there are diversities of gifts
. . . And there are diversities of
operations, but it is the same God
which worketh all in all.

ST. PAUL, *Corinthians* 1: 11

THE TITLE of this chapter is simply fair warning that we've reached the end of the story, as such. But now that we've reviewed some of the human and dramatic aspects of the genius for invention that flourished so markedly in the colonial and post-colonial years of New England, I'd like to test some reflections about just what we mean by the word "invention" and its relatives. What manner of action does the verb "invent" denote? What is an "invention"? What is an "inventor"?

In the history of our language, "invention" has had a wide range of meanings. It has meant to "come upon" or "discover by chance" just as much as to "devise" or "contrive" deliberately. It has meant to plan, and also to plot. It has meant to "make up," in the sense of creating a fiction, whether as art, calumny, or boast. It has been used as meaning to introduce something, bring something into use, or to found or establish an institution, or to initiate a practice in terms of social custom.

A 16th-century writer observes that: "Daedalus . . . firste inuented the art of Carpentrie with these instruments folowyng, the Sawe, Chippe axe, and Plumline."

"Invent" has been used to mean finding out how to do something else, with the infinitive of some other verb, as in Hall's *Chronicles of Edward IV:* "When as kyng Edward sought, invented and studied dayly and howerly to bring hym selfe to quietnesse."

Church history speaks of "The Invention of the Cross," meaning the reputed finding of the true cross by Helena, mother of the Emperor Constantine, in A.D. 326.

"Invention" has been used to mean finding the solution of a problem. Thomas Burton, in *The Anatomy of Melancholy,* tells that "Pythagoras offered an hundred Oxen for the invention of a Geometrical Probleme."

As for "inventor," the word has been used to speak of explorers in the geographical sense as well as explorers in the laboratory or machine shop. A modern man would not call Columbus the inventor of America, but our language has known such usage. The modern vocabulary tends to separate the words "invent" and "discover" but we will find it difficult to understand the spirit and events of the period in New England history which has occupied most of our attention if we do not realize how much the terms "invent" and "discover" are used synonymously. Also we have found an "invention" to be as often a process or method as it is an object or artifact.

Francis Bacon, in *The New Atlantis,* gives a catalogue of inventors that serves to illustrate the ancient range in the use of the word:

> There we have the statue of your Columbus, that discovered the West Indies: also the Inventor of Ships: your monk that was the Inventor of Ordnance and Gunpowder: the Inventor of Music: the Inventor of Letters: the Inventor of Printing: the Inventor of observations by astronomy: the Inventor of Works in Metal: the Inventor of Glass: the Inventor of Silk of the Worm: the Inventor of Wines:

the Inventor of Corn and Bread: the Inventor of Sugars.

Inventiveness may be called a state of mind, just as much as a specific faculty or ability. How did this state of mind called inventiveness come to flourish so conspicuously in early New England? I believe that it was part of a larger, more inclusive state of mind, an *élan* or tone, prevailing at the time.

Of course, as we've seen, the inventive upsurge was not confined to New England, on these shores, nor to the New World in general. It was stirring in the whole of Western society. Lewis Mumford attributes the progress in mechanics in part to the rise of natural philosophy that both came with, and produced, the Renaissance. Men began to scrutinize the natural world more than they meditated on a mystical world—not altogether a beneficial shift. As Mumford says: "Mechanical invention, even more than science, was the answer to a dwindling faith and a faltering life-impulse . . . the application of power to motion, and the application of motion to production, and of production to money-making, and so the further increase of power—this was the worthiest object that a mechanical habit of mind and a mechanical mode of action put before men."

We've seen that Franklin, in his prospectus for the American Philosophical Society, dedicated it to all inquiries tending "to increase the power of man over matter."

So there was, in the 18th century, an already well-developed philosophy to inspire the mechanical tinkerer. It was a long-range *Zeitgeist,* and we encounter it even in the simplest and least-lettered of the mechanic-innovators, such as John Fitch. This went right on into the 19th century. Many of our inventors were men who, more or less consciously, thought of the Universe as a stupendous machine. John Ericsson, the builder of the *Monitor,* called God "the Great Mechanician." He believed in God to the extent that he did not believe matter could take forms not imposed by some Will, but the product of that Will seemed to him expressed in mechanical concepts.

With such currents abroad, we have in New England the special added impetus from the fact that so many people had come there for an idea. People who do anything whatever for an idea are rare enough. New England had a heavy concentration of them.

Invention is a part of the social process of evolution in the same way that mutation is a part of the biological process of evolution. Biology, the instrumentality of God, brought into being and endowed *homo sapiens;* he, by the development of his endowments, made himself into *homo faber,* man the maker.

In all the connotations and denotations that "invention" and its related family of words ever have had or will have, there remains the fact that invention is a manifestation of creativity. Where man's creativity is flourishing, invention in its technical and mechanical aspects will flourish also, always in some reasonable proportion to the level of society. The true spirit of the inventor-creator is embraced in "Behold, I make all things new," and "Behold, I tell you a new thing."

The inventor-creator is the one with the capacity for seeing anything as if he were seeing it for the first time; indeed, as if it had never been seen before by anyone. This is true of the poet, the architect, the painter, the inventor of a steam-engine, or of Dr. Einstein. All share the priceless sense of wonder, of newness. It is impossible for the creative-inventive mind to be *blasé,* to see something as the usual, as "the same old thing."

The creator-inventor is able to ask himself the magnificently wise foolish questions from which the merely smart or merely educated man shrinks, saying, "Any ass knows that!" Any fool knows what a door is, or a window, or a roof, or a wall, but a Frank Lloyd Wright, as a young architect, was able to ask himself in earnest, "What is a door? A window? A roof? A wall?" The consequence is that a door, a window, a roof, a wall have never been quite the same again.

The creator-inventor must have the gift of turning from a familiar road onto a new one. The stream of error digs a deep channel for itself until at last a canyon is created. But sometimes a new conception, determined boldly to develop another way, can avoid such canyons.

The great Leonardo and many others floundered with the problem of flight because they were committed to the concept that man must somehow duplicate the wing-flapping flight of birds. The problem was solved only when it was seen that except for some common aerodynamic laws involved, the flight of birds and man's mechanical flight were totally different in kind. Such a fixation on animal motion of various kinds consistently inhibited early mechanical experimenters.

Both the French nobleman Jouffroy and the Yankee tinkerer Ormsbee fiddled with web-footed steamboats as if they were no more than mechanical waterfowl.

The modern machine age is full of robots, such as the dial phone and the automatic washer-dryer. But for centuries the creative mind (and even today the popular mind) pictured the robot in android terms, trying to create literal mechanical men. Why design a Bendix in the shape of the Irish washerwoman?

Considerable mechanical ingenuity was balked and frustrated in the attempt to make a machine that would duplicate the motions of a needle in a woman's hand. Elias Howe created the successful sewing machine when he accepted the concept that a new kind of sewing movement was necessary to a mechanical operation.

One of the most curious examples of this anthropocentric approach to a mechanism is an old drawing of an impulse turbine invented in 1629 by one Branca. The picture shows a fire kindled around the chest of a hollow iron bust. From a tube in the lips of this male figure a jet of hot air, or steam, is directed upon the vanes of a turbine wheel to actuate the machine. This mighty blowhard has a ring set in his scalp for hoisting by block and tackle.

The Mayas, a people of genius in some respects, never mastered either the wheel or the arch. Mumford observes that circular motion, so characteristic of machinery, is little seen in nature. He believes the wheel might have sprung from observing the rolling of a log, and remarks that this motion may have been seen for thousands of years "before some neolithic inventor performed the stunning act of dissociation that made possible the cart." By "dissociation" he simply means the ability to see something happen in one circumstance and apply it in another, as in the legend of Davy Watt and the steam kettle. Thus Marc Isambard Brunel invented the tunneling shield by observing the natural equipment of *Teredo navalis,* the shipworm, borrowing a constructive principle from an old enemy of man.

The upsurge in the arts of mechanical invention, and in technical skill and knowledge that we have traced are a part of what Van Wyck Brooks has celebrated as *The Flowering of New England.* He examined it in its literary-artistic-philosophic aspects. This book touches that flowering in the field of the so-called useful or applied arts. Yet we have seen over and over that these areas cannot be separated entirely, being part of a common phenomenon.

I said a moment ago that when creativity of any kind is flourishing, mechanical invention tends to accompany it; when creativity is languishing, mechanical arts tend to languish with it. Most human phenomena occur in cyclic or undulant patterns, and this is notably true of the upsurge, diminishment, and resurge of human creativity. Toynbee's historical method addresses itself particularly to this fact.

My point is that there is a tone, an *élan,* a morale out of which creativity gushes. Attic Greece and the Italian Renaissance are simply two of the more spectacular of such instances. We may not associate either of them primarily with mechanical experiment and insight, yet they abounded in both, relative to the context of mechanical awakening. The significant fact about such times is that everything happens at once, in all fields, and happens with an immense degree of overlap as far as the activities of individuals are concerned.

Artist-artisan-architect often are inextricably fused. The degree of genius may be greatly variable, but Leonardo as painter-inventor and Robert Fulton or Samuel F. B. Morse as painter-inventors are similar phenomena. Cellini and Paul Revere have something in common as both artists in silver and practical mechanic-artisans. Michelangelo paints, sculptures, builds a dome for St. Peter's, and writes sonnets. Benjamin Franklin is journalist, philosopher, statesman, mechanic, and theoretical scientist. Thomas Paine writes political tracts and designs iron bridges.

Invention as a process of social evolution is seen in the coincidental welling-up in several minds of the same new concept. We see Darwin and Wallace separately and concurrently developing their concepts of evolution; Bell and Gray making remarkably similar telephones, and we face the fact that none of the major inventions or ideas are one-man propositions. Bernard Shaw speaks of his age as being "visibly pregnant" with certain ideas. There is such a pregnancy of mechanical inventions visible at times.

A review of the history of invention shows no indispensable men but for whom we would not have our modern technology. The creative-inventive-evolutionary process finds its instruments in one place and another, generally with some to spare, and is not dependent upon the chance of the birth of certain individuals. Yet this does not detract from the greatness of those who *are* its instruments. If this is mysticism we shall have to make the most of it, for such is the evidence in the proliferation of ideas. There is a saying about "accidents looking for a place to happen." We could speak of "inventions looking for someone to invent them."

Another aspect of overlapping is the composite invention, to which several minds have contributed consciously. This is the pattern to which invention, today, and since the industrial age, has conformed. We are relatively less conscious of individual invention today, with a few exceptions. This is partly because an invention stood out more conspicuously in the pre-industrial era, but chiefly it is because of the vast complex of today's industrial laboratory organization. We tend toward conscious team-work invention, sometimes involving all the resources and energies of a plant, a foundation, or a government project. Relative anonymity cloaks most of this, except for such occasional glaring lights of publicity as that focussed—safely after the work was done—upon the great team that conceived, calculated, and engineered the atomic bomb.

We also see emerging from the inventor the more complex type we call the engineer. The empirical inventor has an idea and tries something, tinkering it until he gets it to work, often "wasting" much time, energy and material in the process. The early steamboat builders, from Fitch to Fulton, are prime examples. Subsequently, a theory or principle may be deduced from what the experimenter has done. Fulton and Eli Whitney are men who began as practical experimenters but ended as something close to what we recognize as engineers.

Contrariwise, the true type of engineer-inventor, or scientist-inventor, knows to begin with the potential in some theoretical principle. As he seeks to apply it, the very knowledge of principles helps to keep him from some of the time-wasting blundering of the empirical inventor.

Most of the early steam-engine inventors knew nothing of the thermodynamics involved. Watt, who was not the first to make a steam engine, was the first to study the theory as well as the mechanics, thus becoming a true engineer. Basically, "engine" means the result of ingenuity, and "engineer" means one who knows how to produce results with his ingenuity.

All these things lead us to consider what might be called the genealogy of invention. The old saw says that "necessity is the mother of invention." This is not quite so. I suggest that necessity might be considered the *father. Cre-*

ativity is the mother of invention, for it conceives, gestates, and produces it. Without this latent fertility no invention occurs, be the necessity what it may. Events from the scale of the decline of civilizations to the abandonment of New England hill towns demonstrate this. But where the creativity is latent, necessity may, and often does, serve as the fertilizing agent.

We should be on guard against rigidly deterministic theories about invention. A few such theories involving New England contain partial truths but do not, alone or together, represent the whole truth. There is the "bleak New England" explanation. This is that the terrain was not agriculturally rewarding and thus geographic-economic necessity forced the Yankee to become inventive. That is perfectly true. But did this *make* him inventive? Did it endow him with the mysterious gift? I think not. If the latent creativity had not been there nothing would have happened, in spite of the need.

There is a politico-economic theory, arguing that the attempt of the mother country to suppress the autonomous industrial development of the colonies, to compel them to buy British-made goods at exorbitant prices, forced the colonies to become inventive. This, too, is quite true and worth knowing—it is a factor in the story of Yankee invention—but it too does not explain the creative ability to invent.

More useful than these specific theories about the prodding supplied by circumstances is Toynbee's concept of challenge-and-response, which fits a larger conceptual frame than that of immediate necessity. The challenge will awaken the response where the response is latent. Yet history shows us many challenges that have awakened no response, along with those which have called forth superb responses.

In Paul's words, "there are diversities of gifts" and "there are diversities of operations . . ." The chronicles of invention contain melancholy instances of men given only a fragmentary endowment, or of men working "before their time," which common phrase means only that the context of economic and technological development was not yet ready to absorb that which the inventor's conception had made possible. The electric motor was invented before there was any economic means to produce electric power to operate it. Ironically, this was because the principle of the motor was perceived long before it was realized that the same principle, in reverse action, was the dynamo which could produce the necessary power. Thomas Davenport and Orange Smalley, and Wareham Chase, created working electric motors prematurely, in the valleys of Vermont, rich in the waterpower which could have set their inventions humming, had they perceived the connective relationship.

By a ruthless fact of life, the inventive gift is apt to die aborning if it is not combined with a reasonable measure of the promotional-managerial-business gift. This endowment often is what separates the fulfilled inventor from the frustrated tinkerer. Some men, notably Eli Whitney and Samuel Colt, had an organizing skill commensurate with their genius. But the mix varies, from the type of Whitney and Colt through those whose careers were continually harassed by their managerial ineptitude, to obscure men whose work came utterly to nothing from lack of the ability to develop, sell, and make a place for it.

The creative gift rarely displays itself just once. Even in instances in which a man is known to us for one famous invention, a close look generally shows a life-long record of experimenting and contriving.

The inventive gift is capricious in its choice of those to play host to it. It may touch a single individual, beginning and dying with him so far as any evident continuity is concerned. Yet now and then we find a family of inventors. The Whitney family and the Stevens family are notable cases.

For whatever reason, there are few women inventors, even in the realm of household arts. I cannot find a really conspicuous exception to cite. The likeliest cases are those of Hannah Wilkinson Slater, who is credited with inventing cotton sewing thread, and Hannah Lord Montague, of Troy, who invented the detachable shirt collar to lighten the burden of her blacksmith husband's laundry. In both cases men, the Slater-Wilkinson family in one, and the imaginative Reverend Ebenezer Brown in the other, took up the idea for manufacture and promotion.

On the other hand, Ellen Butterick, the wife of a Massachusetts tailor, invented the standard thin-paper pattern and took an active part in developing the enormous business that grew up from it. This was a kind of footnote to Howe's sewing machine.

I suppose, too, that the later Lydia E. Pinkham has some sort of claim to being both inventor and promoter—especially with regard to the invention of advanced techniques in salesmanship and advertising copywriting.

Yet it was Elias Howe who mechanized the woman's art of sewing, and Newcomen and Watt who harnessed the steam from the spout of her kitchen kettle (though the specific legend of Watt and the kettle belongs with Washington and the cherry tree). But woman's status in society inevitably inhibited her in roles of this sort (and may often have robbed her of credit). There is no doubt that women are contributing to the team-work mode of invention in modern science and industry, from such a case as Madame Curie to Lisa Meitner in the atomic bomb project, and that increasing numbers of women are working at the nation's drawing boards and in the laboratories.

The inventor is the one who keeps the room ready for anything that may come into it. He is at times a waiter. There is a passive, as well as an active, role involved. Inventiveness is not just an initiative to go out and search, or to tinker. There must also be the capacity to seize that which presents itself uninvited at the threshold. The ability to recognize the significant accident is basic to invention. This is what put Goodyear on the track after agonizing false starts. The ability to spot "the little difference" may be more important, cumulatively, than "the big idea." The *idée fixe* inventor, of which Goodyear is an archetype, is a minority.

The spontaneous generation of an idea is a factor in mechanical invention as in all other creative processes. A concept which had not been present in the mind before simply appears. If the mind is unready or unreceptive, nothing happens (though possibly no authentic concept ever presents itself to such a mind). But if the mind is alert, the concept will set in motion the chain of events which we commonly think of as the processes of invention. Yet it is also true that in the active creative mind, the initial processes of logical reasoning may stimulate and arouse the unconscious resources. There is a real interaction.

The great 19th-century mathematician, Karl Friedrich Gauss, spoke of how, for years, he had been working on the proof of a theorem: "At last, two days ago, I succeeded, not by dint of painful effort, but so to speak by the grace of God. As a sudden flash of light, the enigma was solved. For my part, I am not in a position to point to the thread which joins what I knew previously to what I have succeeded in doing."

In the whole range of the creative, whether in art or in science or mechanics, some of the process is waiting. The experimental function is an important one. Edison's point about having found out "five thousand things that won't work" is valid. But intuitive knowledge and perception may be more basic. Laboratory experiment of a direct nature did not precede the formula $E = mc^2$, rather this creative concept was subjected to later tests and verification. Initially it had to be awaited.

The creators on the highest level, in invention and all other fields, are the master waiters, who have prepared the room, and who recognize the concept when it comes. When it does come, the parable of the sower is the best possible comment on the question of what, if anything, will result from the creative idea.

A SELECTED BIBLIOGRAPHY

BISHOP, J. Leander, *A History of American Manufactures, 1608–1860*. 2 vols. Philadelphia. 1861–64.

BOTKIN, Ben, *A Treasury of New England Folklore*. New York. 1947.

BOYD, Thomas, *Poor John Fitch*. New York. 1935.

BROOKS, Van Wyck, *The Flowering of New England, 1815–1865*. New York. 1936.

BURLINGAME, Roger, *March of the Iron Men*. New York. 1938.

CONWAY, Moncure D., *The Life of Thomas Paine*. New York. 1892.

EDWARDS, William B., *The Story of Colt's Revolver*. Harrisburg. 1953.

FLEXNER, James Thomas, *Steamboats Come True; American Inventors in Action*. New York. 1944.

FORBES, Esther, *Paul Revere and the World He Lived In*. Boston. 1942.

FORBES, Esther, *Rainbow on the Road*. Boston. 1954.

FRANKLIN, Benjamin, *Autobiography*. 1791–1868.

HOWE, Henry, *Memoirs of the Most Eminent American Mechanics*. New York. 1844.

JEROME, Chauncey, *History of the American Clock Business*. New Haven. 1860.

KIRBY, R. S., *Inventors and Engineers of Old New Haven*. New Haven. 1939.

LATHROP, W. G., *The Brass Industry in the United States*. Mount Carmel, Conn. 1926.

MIRSKY, J. & Nevins, A., *The World of Eli Whitney*. New York. 1952.

MONTMASSON, J. M., *Invention and the Unconscious*. New York. 1932.

MORISON, Samuel Eliot, *Builders of the Bay Colony*. Boston. 1930.

MUMFORD, Lewis, *Technics and Civilization*. New York. 1934.

PARSONS, William Barclay, *Robert Fulton and the Submarine*. New York. 1922.

ROE, Joseph Wickham, *English and American Tool Builders.* New Haven. 1916.

STILES, Ezra, *The Literary Diary of Ezra Stiles,* ed. F. B. Dexter. 3 vols. New York. 1901.

STRUIK, Dirk J., *Yankee Science in the Making.* Boston. 1948.

TAUSSIG, F. W., *Inventors and Money Makers.* New York. 1915.

THOMPSON, Holland, *The Age of Invention.* New Haven. 1921.

TURNBULL, A. D., *John Stevens; An American Record.* New York. 1928.

USHER, Abbott Payson, *A History of Mechanical Inventions.* Revised Edition. Boston. 1954.

VAN DOREN, Carl, *Benjamin Franklin.* New York. 1938.

WHITE, George S., *Memoir of Samuel Slater, the Father of American Manufactures.* Philadelphia. 1836.

CLARK, V. S., *History of Manufactures in the United States, 1607–1860.* Washington. 1916.

INDEX